ANNUAL EDITIONS

Physical Anthropology
02/03

Eleventh Edition

EDITOR
Elvio Angeloni
Pasadena City College

Elvio Angeloni received his B.A. from UCLA in 1963, his M.A. in anthropology from UCLA in 1965, and his M.A. in communicaiton arts from Loyola Marymount University in 1976. He has produced several films, including *Little Warrior*, winner of the Cinemedia VI Best Bicentennial Theme, and *Broken Bottles*, shown on PBS. He also served as an academic adviser on the instructional television series, Faces of Culture.

McGraw-Hill/Dushkin
530 Old Whitfield Street, Guilford, Connecticut 06437

Visit us on the Internet
http://www.dushkin.com

Credits

1. **Natural Selection**
   Unit photo—Courtesy of New York Library Picture Collection.
2. **Primates**
   Unit photo—United Nations photo by George Love.
3. **Sex and Society**
   Unit photo—© National Geographic Society, Washington, DC.
4. **Fossil Evidence**
   Unit photo—American Museum of Natural History photo.
5. **Late Hominid Evolution**
   Unit photo—AP/World Wide photo by Jean Clottes.
6. **Human Diversity**
   Unit photo—United Nations photo by Doranne Jacobson.
7. **Living With the Past**
   Unit photo—United Nations photo by Nagata/jr.

Copyright

Cataloging in Publication Data
Main entry under title: Annual Editions: Physical Anthropology. 2002/2003.
1. Physical anthropology—Periodicals. I. Angeloni, Elvio, *comp.* II. Title: Physical anthropology.
ISBN 0–07–250630–X   573'.05   ISSN 1074–1844

Eleventh Edition

Cover image © 2002 by PhotoDisc, Inc.
Printed in the United States of America   234567890BAHBAH5432   Printed on Recycled Paper

Editors/Advisory Board

Members of the Advisory Board are instrumental in the final selection of articles for each edition of ANNUAL EDITIONS. Their review of articles for content, level, currentness, and appropriateness provides critical direction to the editor and staff. We think that you will find their careful consideration well reflected in this volume.

To the Reader

In publishing ANNUAL EDITIONS we recognize the enormous role played by the magazines, newspapers, and journals of the public press in providing current, first-rate educational information in a broad spectrum of interest areas. Many of these articles are appropriate for students, researchers, and professionals seeking accurate, current material to help bridge the gap between principles and theories and the real world. These articles, however, become more useful for study when those of lasting value are carefully collected, organized, indexed, and reproduced in a low-cost format, which provides easy and permanent access when the material is needed. That is the role played by ANNUAL EDITIONS.

This eleventh edition of *Annual Editions: Physical Anthropology* contains a variety of articles pertaining to human evolution. The writings were selected for their timeliness, relevance to issues not easily treated in the standard physical anthropology textbook, and clarity of presentation.

Whereas textbooks tend to reflect the consensus within the field, *Annual Editions: Physical Anthropology 02/03* provides a forum for the controversial. We do this in order to convey to the student the sense that the study of human development is an evolving entity in which each discovery encourages further research and each added piece of the puzzle raises new questions about the total picture.

Our final criterion for selecting articles is their readability. All too often, the excitement of a new discovery or a fresh idea is deadened by the weight of a ponderous presentation. We seek to avoid that by incorporating essays that are written with enthusiasm and with the desire to communicate some very special ideas to the general public in the liveliest way possible.

Included in this volume are a number of features designed to be useful for students, researchers, and professionals in the field of anthropology. While the articles are arranged along the lines of broadly unifying subject areas, the *topic guide* can be used to establish specific reading assignments tailored to the needs of a particular course of study. Other useful features include the *table of contents* abstracts, which summarize each article and present key concepts in bold italics, and a comprehensive *index*. In addition, each unit is preceded by an overview that provides a background for informed reading of the articles, emphasizes critical issues, and presents *key points to consider* in the form of questions. Also included are *World Wide Web* sites, coordinated to follow the volume's units, which can be used to further explore the topics.

In contrast to the usual textbook, which by its nature cannot be easily revised, this book will be continually updated in each yearly edition to reflect the dynamic, changing character of its subject. Those of us who are involved in producing *Annual Editions: Physical Anthropology 02/03* wish to make the next edition as useful and effective as possible. Your criticism and advice are always welcomed. Please complete and return the postage-paid *article rating form* on the last page of the book and let us know your opinions. Any anthology can be improved, and this one will continue to be.

Elvio Angeloni
Editor

Contents

UNIT 1
Natural Selection

Four articles examine the link between genetics and the process of natural selection.

UNIT 2
Primates

Ten selections examine some of the social relationships in the primate world and how they mirror human society.

The concepts in bold italics are developed in the article. For further expansion, please refer to the Topic Guide and the Index.

UNIT 3
Sex and Society

Eight articles discuss the relationship between the sexes and the evolution of a so-cial structure.

The concepts in bold italics are developed in the article. For further expansion, please refer to the Topic Guide and the Index.

UNIT 4
The Fossil Evidence

Four selections discuss some of the fossil evidence for hominid evolution.

The concepts in bold italics are developed in the article. For further expansion, please refer to the Topic Guide and the Index.

UNIT 5
Late Hominid Evolution

Nine articles examine archaeological evidence of human evolution.

Unit Overview

The concepts in bold italics are developed in the article. For further expansion, please refer to the Topic Guide and the Index.

UNIT 6
Human Diversity

Four articles examine human racial evolution and diversity.

UNIT 7
Living With the Past

Four articles discuss evolutionary theory and the impact of genetic heritage on our present and our future.

The concepts in bold italics are developed in the article. For further expansion, please refer to the Topic Guide and the Index.

The concepts in bold italics are developed in the article. For further expansion, please refer to the Topic Guide and the Index.

Topic Guide

This topic guide suggests how the selections in this book relate to the subjects covered in your course. You may want to use the topics listed on these pages to search the Web more easily.

On the following pages a number of Web sites have been gathered specifically for this book. They are arranged to reflect the units of this *Annual Edition*. You can link to these sites by going to the DUSHKIN ONLINE support site at *http://www.dushkin.com/online/*.

ALL THE ARTICLES THAT RELATE TO EACH TOPIC ARE LISTED BELOW THE BOLD-FACED TERM.

Aggression
5. Machiavellian Monkeys
6. What Are Friends For?
10. Dim Forest, Bright Chimps
11. To Catch a Colobus
12. Coping With Crowding
13. Aping Language
15. These Are Real Swinging Primates
22. Apes of Wrath
35. Archaeologists Rediscover Cannibals

Anatomy
21. What's Love Got to Do With It?
25. A New Human Ancestor?
27. *Erectus* Rising
29. The Scavenging of "Peking Man"
30. Old Masters
32. The Gift of Gab
33. The Dating Game
34. Who Were the Neandertals?
35. Archaeologists Rediscover Cannibals
36. The Lost Man
40. Profile of an Anthropologist: No Bone Unturned

Archaeology
27. *Erectus* Rising
30. Old Masters
31. Secrets of the Cave's Art
33. The Dating Game
35. Archaeologists Rediscover Cannibals
36. The Lost Man
40. Profile of an Anthropologist: No Bone Unturned

Asian civilization
29. The Scavenging of "Peking Man"

Australopithecines
23. Early Hominid Fossils From Africa
25. A New Human Ancestor?
26. Scavenger Hunt

Bipedalism
21. What's Love Got to Do With It?
23. Early Hominid Fossils From Africa
25. A New Human Ancestor?
26. Scavenger Hunt

Blood groups
37. Black, White, Other
38. Racial Odyssey

Burials
35. Archaeologists Rediscover Cannibals

Catastrophism
1. The Growth of Evolutionary Science

Chain of being
1. The Growth of Evolutionary Science

Communication
32. The Gift of Gab

Cro-Magnons
30. Old Masters
33. The Dating Game

Crowding
12. Coping With Crowding

Culture
9. The Cultures of Chimpanzees

Darwin, Charles
42. Dr. Darwin

Disease
3. Curse and Blessing of the Ghetto
4. The Saltshaker's Curse
38. Racial Odyssey
41. The Viral Superhighway
42. Dr. Darwin

DNA
3. Curse and Blessing of the Ghetto
37. Black, White, Other

Dominance hierarchy
6. What Are Friends For?
15. These Are Real Swinging Primates
21. What's Love Got to Do With It?
22. Apes of Wrath

Ethnicity
36. The Lost Man

Evolution
1. The Growth of Evolutionary Science
33. The Dating Game

Evolutionary perspective
1. The Growth of Evolutionary Science
42. Dr. Darwin

Family systems
19. A Woman's Curse?

Forensic anthropology
40. Profile of an Anthropologist: No Bone Unturned

Fossils
23. Early Hominid Fossils From Africa

World Wide Web Sites

The following World Wide Web sites have been carefully researched and selected to support the articles found in this reader. The easiest way to access these selected sites is to go to our DUSHKIN ONLINE support site at *http://www.dushkin.com/online/*.

AE: Physical Anthropology 02/03

The following sites were available at the time of publication. Visit our Web site—we update DUSHKIN ONLINE regularly to reflect any changes.

General Sources

American Anthropological Association (AAA)
http://www.ameranthassn.org/index.htm

Maintained by the AAA, this site provides links to AAA's publications (including tables of contents of recent issues, style guides, and others) and to other anthropology sites.

Anthromorphemics
http://www.anth.ucsb.edu/glossary/index2.html

A glossary of anthropological terms is available at this Web site.

Anthropology in the News
http://www.tamu.edu/anthropology/news.html

Texas A&M provides data on news articles that relate to anthropology, including biopsychology and sociocultural anthropology news.

Anthropology on the Internet
http://www.as.ua.edu/ant/libguide.htm

This Web site provides addresses and tips on acquiring links to regional studies, maps, anthropology tutorials, and other data.

Anthropology 1101 Human Origins Website
http://www.geocities.com/Athens/Acropolis/5579/TA.html

Exploring this site, which is provided by the University of Minnesota, will lead to a wealth of information about our ancient ancestors and other topics of interest to physical anthropologists.

Anthropology Resources on the Internet
http://www.socsciresearch.com/r7.html

Links to Internet resources of anthropological relevance, including Web servers in different fields, are available here. *The Education Index* rated it "one of the best education-related sites on the Web."

Anthropology Resources Page
http://www.usd.edu/anth/

Many topics can be accessed from this University of South Dakota site. South Dakota archaeology, American Indian issues, and paleopathology resources are just a few examples.

Library of Congress
http://www.loc.gov

Examine this extensive Web site to learn about resource tools, library services/resources, exhibitions, and databases in many different subfields of anthropology.

The New York Times
http://www.nytimes.com

Browsing through the archives of the *New York Times* will provide a wide array of articles and information related to the different subfields of anthropology.

The PaleoAnthro Lists Home Page
http://www.pitt.edu/~mattf/PalAntList.html

Spend time at this site and the related PaleoChat site, at *http://www.pitt.edu/~mattf/PaleoChat.html,* to exchange information related to physical anthropology.

UNIT 1: Natural Selection

Charles Darwin on Human Origins
http://www.literature.org/Works/Charles-Darwin/

This Web site contains the text of Charles Darwin's classic writing, *The Origin of Species,* which presents his scientific theory of natural selection.

Enter Evolution: Theory and History
http://www.ucmp.berkeley.edu/history/evolution.html

Find information related to Charles Darwin and other important scientists at this Web site. It addresses preludes to evolution, natural selection, and more. Topics cover systematics, dinosaur discoveries, and vertebrate flight.

Fossil Hominids FAQ
http://www.talkorigins.org/faqs/fossil-hominids.html

Some links to materials related to hominid species and hominid fossils are provided on this site. The purpose of the site is to refute creationist claims that there is no evidence for human evolution.

Harvard Dept. of MCB—Biology Links
http://mcb.harvard.edu/BioLinks.html

This site features sources on evolution and links to anthropology departments and laboratories, taxonomy, paleontology, natural history, journals, books, museums, meetings, and many other related areas.

UNIT 2: Primates

African Primates at Home
http://www.indiana.edu/~primate/primates.html

Don't miss this unusual and compelling site describing African primates on their home turf. "See" and "Hear" features provide samples of vocalizations and beautiful photographs of various types of primates.

Chimpanzee and Great Ape Language Resources—Anthropology
http://www.brown.edu/Departments/Anthropology/apelang.html

This series of Web sites on primates includes the Primate home page and the Gorilla home page. It provides links to the entire text of Darwin's *Origin of Species* and more.

Electronic Zoo/NetVet-Primate Page
http://netvet.wustl.edu/primates.htm

This site touches on every kind of primate from A to Z and related information. The long list includes Darwinian theories and the *Descent of Man,* the Ebola virus, fossil hominids, the nonhuman Primate Genetics Lab, the Simian Retrovirus Laboratory, and zoonotic diseases, with many links in between.

Jane Goodall Research Center
http://www.usc.edu/dept/elab/anth/goodall.html

The Jane Goodall Research Center, a program of the University of Southern California's Anthropology Department, is a repository for data gathered over more than 30 years at Gombe National Park, Tanzania. Search this site for information about primate research.

UNIT 3: Sex and Society

American Anthropologist

http://www.aaanet.org/aa/index.htm

Check out this site—the home page of *American Anthropologist*—for general information about anthropology as well as articles relating to such topics as biological research.

American Scientist

http://www.amsci.org/amsci/amsci.html

Investigating this site will help students of physical anthropology to explore issues related to sex and society.

Bonobo Sex and Society

http://songweaver.com/info/bonobos.html

Accessed through Carnegie Mellon University, this site includes a *Scientific American* article discussing a primate's behavior that challenges traditional assumptions about male supremacy in human evolution.

UNIT 4: The Fossil Evidence

The African Emergence and Early Asian Dispersals of the Genus *Homo*

http://www.sigmaxi.org/amsci/subject/EvoBio.html

Explore this site and click on this title to learn about what the Rift Valley in East Africa has to tell us about early hominid species. An excellent bibliography is included.

Anthropology, Archaeology, and American Indian Sites on the Internet

http://dizzy.library.arizona.edu/users/jlcox/first.html

This Web page points out a number of Internet sites of interest to different kinds of anthropologists, including physical and biological anthropologists. Visit this page for links to electronic journals and more.

Long Foreground: Human Prehistory

http://www.wsu.edu:8001/vwsu/gened/learn-modules/top_longfor/lfopen-index.html

This Washington State University site presents a learning module covering three major topics in human evolution: Overview, Hominid Species Timeline, and Human Physical Characteristics. It also provides a helpful glossary of terms and links to other Web sites.

UNIT 5: Late Hominid Evolution

Archaeology Links (NC)

http://www.arch.dcr.state.nc.us/links.htm#stuff/

North Carolina Archaeology provides this site, which has many links to physical anthropologists' sites such as the paleolithic painted cave at Vallon-Pont-d'Arc (Ardeche).

Human Prehistory

http://users.hol.gr/~dilos/prehis.htm

The evolution of the human species, beginning with the *Australopithecus* and continuing with *Homo habilis, Homo erectus,* and *Homo sapiens* is examined on this site. Also included are data on the people who lived in the Palaeolithic and Neolithic Age and are the immediate ancestors of modern man.

UNIT 6: Human Diversity

Cult Archaeology Topics

http://www.usd.edu/anth/cultarch/culttopics.html

This fun site provides information on interesting pseudoscientific theories that have attracted scholarly attention. The Lost Tribes and the Moundbuilder Myth and Cryptozoology: Bigfoot and Nessie are among the many myths debunked here.

Hominid Evolution Survey

http://www.geocities.com/SoHo/Atrium/1381/index.html

This survey of the Hominid family categorizes known hominids by genus and species. Beginning with the oldest known species, data includes locations and environments, physical characteristics, technology, social behaviors, charts and citations.

Human Genome Project Information

http://www.ornl.gov/TechResources/Human_Genome/home.html

Obtain answers about the U.S. Human Genome Project from this site, which details progress, goals, support groups, ethical, legal, and social issues, and genetics information.

OMIM Home Page-Online Mendelian Inheritance in Man

http://www3.ncbi.nlm.nih.gov/omim/

This database from the National Center for Biotechnology Information is a catalog of human genes and genetic disorders. It contains text, pictures, and reference information of great interest to students of physical anthropology.

Patterns of Human Variability: The Concept of Race

http://www.as.ua.edu/ant/bindon/ant101/lectures/race/race1.htm

This site provides a handy, at-a-glance reference to the prevailing concepts of race and the causes of human variability since ancient times. It can serve as a starting point for research and understanding into the concept of race.

UNIT 7: Living With the Past

Ancestral Passions

http://www.canoe.ca/JamBooksReviewsA/ancestral_morell.html

This review of Virginia Morell's book, *Ancestral Passions,* a biography of the famously dysfunctional Leakey family, will likely spur you to the bookstore in order to learn more about the history of paleontology and the thrill and trials of the hunt for human origins. It is this evolutionary detective story that is the book's true drama. Jump over to *http://url.co.nz/african_trip/tanzania.html* to read an individual's account of a recent trip "In the Cradle of Humankind."

Forensic Science Reference Page

http://www.lab.fws.gov

Look over this site from the U.S. Fish and Wildlife Forensics Lab to explore topics related to forensic anthropology.

Zeno's Forensic Page

http://forensic.to/forensic.html

A complete list of resources on forensics is presented on this Web site. It includes general information sources, DNA/serology sources and databases, forensic medicine anthropology sites, and related areas.

We highly recommend that you review our Web site for expanded information and our other product lines. We are continually updating and adding links to our Web site in order to offer you the most usable and useful information that will support and expand the value of your Annual Editions. You can reach us at: *http://www.dushkin.com/annualeditions/*.

UNIT 1
Natural Selection

Unit Selections

1. **The Growth of Evolutionary Science**, Douglas J. Futuyma
2. **Darwin's Influence on Modern Thought**, Ernst Mayr
3. **Curse and Blessing of the Ghetto**, Jared Diamond
4. **The Saltshaker's Curse**, Jared Diamond

Key Points to Consider

- In nature, how is it that design can occur without a designer, orderliness without purpose?

- What is "natural selection"? How does Gregor Mendel's work relate to Charles Darwin's theory?

- In what ways has Charles Darwin influenced modern thought?

- Why is Tay-Sachs disease so common among Eastern European Jews?

- What is the "saltshaker's curse," and why are some people more affected by it than others?

- What do genes actually do and how predictive are they of human social behavior?

 **Links: www.dushkin.com/online/**
These sites are annotated in the World Wide Web pages.

Charles Darwin on Human Origins
http://www.literature.org/Works/Charles-Darwin/
Enter Evolution: Theory and History
http://www.ucmp.berkeley.edu/history/evolution.html
Fossil Hominids FAQ
http://www.talkorigins.org/faqs/fossil-hominids.html
Harvard Dept. of MCB—Biology Links
http://mcb.harvard.edu/BioLinks.html

As we reflect upon where science has taken us over the past 100 years, it should come as no surprise that the field of genetics has swept us along a path of insight into the human condition as well as heightened controversy as to how to handle this potentially dangerous knowledge of ourselves.

Certainly, Gregor Mendel, in the late nineteenth century, could not have anticipated that his study of pea plants would ultimately lead to the better understanding of over 3,000 genetically caused diseases, such as sickle-cell anemia, Huntington's chorea, and Tay-Sachs. Nor could he have foreseen the present-day controversies over such matters as surrogate motherhood, cloning, and genetic engineering.

The significance of Mendel's work, of course, was his discovery that hereditary traits are conveyed by particular units that we now call "genes," a then-revolutionary notion that has been followed by a better understanding of how and why such units change. It is knowledge of the process of "mutation," or alteration of the chemical structure of the gene, that is now providing us with the potential to control the genetic fate of individuals.

The other side of the evolutionary coin, as discussed in the unit's first two articles, "The Growth of Evolutionary Science" and "Darwin's Influence on Modern Thought," is natural selection, a concept provided by Charles Darwin and Alfred Wallace. Natural selection refers to the "weeding out" of unfavorable mutations and the perpetuation of favorable ones. The reproductive aspects of this process have also become a matter of continuing investigation.

It seems that as we gain a better understanding of both of these processes, mutation and natural selection, and grasp their relevance to human beings, we draw nearer to that time when we may even control the evolutionary direction of our species. Knowledge itself, of course, is neutral—its potential for good or ill being determined by those who happen to be in a position to use it. Consider the possibility of eliminating some of the harmful hereditary traits discussed in "Curse and Blessing of the Ghetto" and "The Saltshaker's Curse," both by Jared Diamond. While it is true that many deleterious genes do get weeded out of the population by means of natural selection, there are other harmful ones, Diamond points out, that may actually have a good side to them and will therefore be perpetuated. It may be, for example, that some men are dying from a genetically caused overabundance of iron in their blood systems in a trade-off that allows some women to absorb sufficient amounts of the element to guarantee their own survival. The question of whether we should eliminate such a gene would seem to depend on which sex we decide should reap the benefit.

The issue of just what is a beneficial application of scientific knowledge is a matter for debate. Who will have the final word as to how these technological breakthroughs will be employed in the future? Even with the best of intentions, how can we be cer-

tain of the long-range consequences of our actions in such a complicated field? Note, for example, the sweeping effects of ecological change upon the viruses of the world, which in turn seem to be paving the way for new waves of human epidemics. Generally speaking, there is an element of purpose and design in our machinations.

Yet, even with this clearly in mind, the whole process seems to be escalating out of human control. It seems that the whole world has become an experimental laboratory in which we know not what we do until we have already done it.

As we read the essays in this unit and contemplate the significance of genetic diseases for human evolution, we can hope that a better understanding of congenital diseases will lead to a reduction of human suffering. At the same time, we must remain aware that someone, at some time, may actually use the same knowledge to increase rather than reduce the misery that exists in the world.

The Growth of Evolutionary Science

Douglas J. Futuyma

Today, the theory of evolution is an accepted fact for everyone but a fundamentalist minority, whose objections are based not on reasoning but on doctrinaire adherence to religious principles.

—James D. Watson, 1965*

In 1615, Galileo was summoned before the Inquisition in Rome. The guardians of the faith had found that his "proposition that the sun is the center [of the solar system] and does not revolve about the earth is foolish, absurd, false in theology, and heretical, because expressly contrary to Holy Scripture." In the next century, John Wesley declared that "before the sin of Adam there were no agitations within the bowels of the earth, no violent convulsions, no concussions of the earth, no earthquakes, but all was unmoved as the pillars of heaven." Until the seventeenth century, fossils were interpreted as "stones of a peculiar sort, hidden by the Author of Nature for his own pleasure." Later they were seen as remnants of the Biblical deluge. In the middle of the eighteenth century, the great French naturalist Buffon speculated on the possibility of cosmic and organic evolution and was forced by the clergy to recant: "I abandon everything in my book respecting the formation of the earth, and generally all of which may be contrary to the narrative of Moses." For had not St. Augustine written, "Nothing is to be accepted save on the authority of Scripture, since greater is that authority than all the powers of the human mind"?

When Darwin published *The Origin of Species*, it was predictably met by a chorus of theological protest. Darwin's theory, said Bishop Wilberforce, "contradicts the revealed relations of creation to its Creator." "If the Darwinian theory is true," wrote another clergyman, "Genesis is a lie, the whole framework of the book of life falls to pieces, and the revelation of God to man, as we Christians know it, is a delusion and a snare." When *The Descent of Man* appeared, Pope Pius IX was moved to write that Darwinism is "a system which is so repugnant at once to history, to the tradition of all peoples, to exact science, to observed facts, and even to Reason herself, [that it] would seem to need no refutation, did not alienation from God and the leaning toward materialism, due to depravity, eagerly seek a support in all this tissue of fables."[1] Twentieth-century creationism continues this battle of medieval theology against science.

One of the most pervasive concepts in medieval and post-medieval thought was the "great chain of being," or *scala naturae*.[2] Minerals, plants, and animals, according to his concept, formed a gradation, from the lowliest and most material to the most complex and spiritual, ending in man, who links the animal series to the world of intelligence and spirit. This "scale of nature" was the manifestation of God's infinite benevolence. In his goodness, he had conferred existence on all beings of which he could conceive, and so created a complete chain of being, in which there were no gaps. All his creatures must have been created at once, and none could ever cease to exist, for then the perfection of his divine plan would have been violated. Alexander Pope expressed the concept best:

Vast chain of being! which from God
    began,
Natures aethereal, human, angel, man,
Beast, bird, fish, insect, what no eye
    can see,
No glass can reach; from Infinite to
    thee,
From thee to nothing.—On superior
    pow'rs
Were we to press, inferior might on
    ours;
Or in the full creation leave a void,
Where, one step broken, the great
    scale's destroy'd;
From Nature's chain whatever link
    you strike,
Tenth, or ten thousandth, breaks the
    chain alike.

Coexisting with this notion that all of which God could conceive existed so as to complete his creation was the idea that all things existed for man. As the philosopher Francis Bacon put it, "Man, if we look to final causes, may be regarded as the centre of the world... for the whole world works together in the service of man… all things seem to be going about man's business and not their own."

"Final causes" was another fundamental concept of medieval and post-medieval thought. Aristotle had distinguished final causes from efficient causes, and the Western world saw no reason to doubt the reality of both. The "efficient cause" of an event is the mechanism responsible for its occurrence: the cause of a ball's movement on a pool table, for example, is the impact of the cue or another ball. The "final cause," however, is the goal, or purpose for its occurrence: the pool ball moves because I wish it to go into the corner pocket. In post-medieval thought there was a final cause—a purpose—for everything; but purpose implies intention, or foreknowledge, by an intellect. Thus the existence of the world, and of all the creatures in it, had a purpose; and that purpose was God's design. This was self-evident, since it was possible to look about the world and see the palpable evidence of God's design everywhere. The heavenly bodies moved in harmonious orbits, evincing the intelligence and harmony of the divine mind; the adaptations of animals and plants to their habitats likewise reflected the devine intelligence, which had fitted all creatures perfectly for their roles in the harmonious economy of nature.

Before the rise of science, then, the causes of events were sought not in natural mechanisms but in the purposes they were meant to serve, and order in nature was evidence of divine intelligence. Since St. Ambrose had declared that "Moses opened his mouth and poured forth what God had said to him," the Bible was seen as the literal word of God, and according to St. Thomas Aquinas, "Nothing was made by God, after the six days of creation, absolutely new." Taking Genesis literally, Archbishop Ussher was able to calculate that the earth was created in 4004 B.C. The earth and the heavens were immutable, changeless. As John Ray put it in 1701 in *The Wisdom of God Manifested in the Works of the Creation*, all living and nonliving things were "created by God at first, and by Him conserved to this Day in the same State and Condition in which they were first made."[3]

The evolutionary challenge to this view began in astronomy. Tycho Brahe found that the heavens were not immutable when a new star appeared in the constellation Cassiopeia in 1572. Copernicus displaced the earth from the center of the universe, and Galileo found that the perfect heavenly bodies weren't so perfect: the sun had spots that changed from time to time, and the moon had craters that strongly implied alterations of its surface. Galileo, and after him Buffon, Kant, and many others, concluded that change was natural to all things.

A flood of mechanistic thinking ensued. Descartes, Kant, and Buffon concluded that the causes of natural phenomena should be sought in natural laws. By 1755, Kant was arguing that the laws of matter in motion discovered by Newton and other physicists were sufficient to explain natural order. Gravitation, for example, could aggregate chaotically dispersed matter into stars and planets. These would join with one another until the only ones left were those that cycled in orbits far enough from each other to resist gravitational collapse. Thus order might arise from natural processes rather than from the direct intervention of a supernatural mind. The "argument from design"—the claim that natural order is evidence of a designer—had been directly challenged. So had the universal belief in final causes. If the arrangement of the planets could arise merely by the laws of Newtonian physics, if the planets could be born, as Buffon suggested, by a collision between a comet and the sun, then they did not exist for any purpose. They merely came into being through impersonal physical forces.

From the mutability of the heavens, it was a short step to the mutability of the earth, for which the evidence was far more direct. Earthquakes and volcanoes showed how unstable terra firma really is. Sedimentary rocks showed that materials eroded from mountains could be compacted over the ages. Fossils of marine shells on mountain-tops proved that the land must once have been under the sea. As early as 1718, the Abbé Moro and the French academician Bernard de Fontenelle had concluded that the Biblical deluge could not explain the fossil-

ized oyster beds and tropical plants that were found in France. And what of the great, unbroken chain of being if the rocks were full of extinct species?

To explain the facts of geology, some authors—the "catastrophists"—supposed that the earth had gone through a series of great floods and other catastrophes that successively extinguished different groups of animals. Only this, they felt, could account for the discovery that higher and lower geological strata had different fossils. Buffon, however, held that to explain nature we should look to the natural causes we see operating around us: the gradual action of erosion and the slow buildup of land during volcanic eruptions. Buffon thus proposed what came to be the foundation of geology, and indeed of all science, the principle of uniformitarianism, which holds that the same causes that operate now have always operated. By 1795, the Scottish geologist James Hutton had suggested that "in examining things present we have data from which to reason with regard to what has been." His conclusion was that since "rest exists not anywhere," and the forces that change the face of the earth move with ponderous slowness, the mountains and canyons of the world must have come into existence over countless aeons.

If the entire nonliving world was in constant turmoil, could it not be that living things themselves changed? Buffon came close to saying so. He realized that the earth had seen the extinction of countless species, and supposed that those that perished had been the weaker ones. He recognized that domestication and the forces of the environment could modify the variability of many species. And he even mused, in 1766, that species might have developed from common ancestors:

If it were admitted that the ass is of the family of the horse, and different from the horse only because it has varied from the original form, one could equally well say that the ape is of the family of man, that he is a degenerate man, that man and ape have a common origin; that, in fact, all the families among plants as well as animals have come from a single stock, and that all animals are descended from a single animal, from which have sprung in the course of time, as a result of process or of degeneration, all the other races of animals. For if it were once shown that we are justified in establishing these families; if it were granted among animals and plants there has been (I do not say several species) but even a single one, which has been produced in the course of direct descent from another species... then there would no longer be any limit to the power of nature, and we should not be wrong in supposing that, with sufficient time, she has been able from a single being to derive all the other organized beings.[4]

This, however, was too heretical a thought; and in any case, Buffon thought the weight of evidence was against common descent. No new species had been observed to arise within recorded history, Buffon wrote; the sterility of hybrids between species appeared an impossible barrier to such a conclusion; and if species had emerged gradually, there should have been innumerable intermediate variations between the horse and ass, or any other species. So Buffon concluded: "But this [idea of a common ancestor] is by no means a proper representation of nature. We are assured by the authority of revelation that all animals have participated equally in the grace of direct Creation and that the first pair of every species issued fully formed from the hands of the Creator."

Buffon's friend and protégé, Jean Baptiste de Monet, the Chevalier de Lamarck, was the first scientist to take the big step. It is not clear what led Lamarck to his uncompromising belief in evolution; perhaps it was his studies of fossil molluscs, which he came to believe were the ancestors of similar species living today. Whatever the explanation, from 1800 on he developed the notion that fossils were not evidence of extinct species but of ones that had gradually been transformed into living species. To be sure, he wrote, "an enormous time and wide variation in successive conditions must doubtless have been required to enable nature to bring the organization of animals to that degree of complexity and development in which we see it at its perfection"; but "time has no limits and can be drawn upon to any extent."

Lamarck believed that various lineages of animals and plants arose by a continual process of spontaneous generation from inanimate matter, and were transformed from very simple to more complex forms by an innate natural tendency toward complexity caused by "powers conferred by the supreme author of all things." Various specialized adaptations of species are consequences of the fact that animals must always change in response to the needs imposed on them by a continually changing environment. When the needs of a species change, so does its behavior. The animal then uses certain organs more frequently than before, and these organs, in turn, become more highly developed by such use, or else "by virtue of the operations of their own inner senses." The classic example of Lamarckism is the giraffe: by straining upward for foliage, it was thought, the animal had acquired a longer neck, which was then inherited by its off-spring.

In the nineteenth century it was widely believed that "acquired" characteristics—alterations brought about by use or disuse, or by the direct influence of the environment—could be inherited. Thus it was perfectly reasonable for Lamarck to base his theory of evolutionary change partly on this idea. Indeed, Darwin also allowed for this possibility, and the inheritance of acquired characteristics was not finally proved impossible until the 1890s.

Lamarck's ideas had a wide influence; but in the end did not convince many scientists of the reality of evolution. In France, Georges Cuvier, the foremost paleontologist and anatomist of his time, was an influential opponent of evolution. He rejected Lamarck's notion of the spontaneous generation of life, found it inconceivable that changes in behavior could produce the exquisite adaptations that almost every species shows, and emphasized that in both the fossil record and among living animals there were numerous "gaps" rather than intermediate forms between species. In England, the philosophy of "natural theology" held sway in science, and the best-known naturalists continued to believe firmly that the features of animals and plants were evidence of God's design. These devout Christians included the foremost geologist of the day, Charles Lyell, whose *Principles of Geology* established uniformitarianism once and for all as a guiding principle. But Lyell was such a thorough uniformitarian that he believed in a steady-state world, a world that was always in balance between forces such as erosion and mountain building, and so was forever the same. There was no room for evolution, with its concept of steady change, in Lyell's world view, though he nonetheless had an enormous impact on evolutionary thought, through his influence on Charles Darwin.

Darwin (1809–1882) himself, unquestionably one of the greatest scientists of all time, came only slowly to an evolutionary position. The son of a successful physician, he showed little interest in the life of the mind in his early years. After unsuccessfully studying medicine at Edinburgh, he was sent to Cambridge to prepare for the ministry, but he had only a half-hearted interest in his studies and spent most of his time hunting, collecting beetles, and becoming an accomplished amateur naturalist. Though he received his B.A. in 1831, his future was quite uncertain until, in December of that year, he was enlisted as a naturalist aboard *H.M.S. Beagle*, with his father's very reluctant agreement. For five years (from December 27, 1831, to October 2, 1836) the *Beagle* carried him about the world, chiefly along the coast of South America, which it was the *Beagle's* mission to survey. For five years Darwin collected geological and biological specimens, made geological observations, absorbed Lyell's *Principles of Geology*, took voluminous notes, and speculated about everything from geology to anthropology. He sent such massive collections of specimens back to England that by the time he returned he had already gained a substantial reputation as a naturalist.

Shortly after his return, Darwin married and settled into an estate at Down where he remained, hardly traveling even to London, for the rest of his life.

Despite continual ill health, he pursued an extraordinary range of biological studies: classifying barnacles, breeding pigeons, experimenting with plant growth, and much more. He wrote no fewer than sixteen books and many papers, read voraciously, corresponded extensively with everyone, from pigeon breeders to the most eminent scientists, whose ideas or information might bear on his theories, and kept detailed notes on an amazing variety of subjects. Few people have written authoritatively on so many different topics: his books include not only *The Voyage of the Beagle, The Origin of Species*, and *The Descent of Man*, but also *The Structure and Distribution of Coral Reefs* (containing a novel theory of the formation of coral atolls which is still regarded as correct), *A Monograph on the Sub-class Cirripedia* (the definitive study of barnacle classification), *The Various Contrivances by Which Orchids are Fertilised by Insects, The Variation of Animals and Plants Under Domestication* (an exhaustive summary of information on variation, so crucial to his evolutionary theory), *The Effects of Cross and Self Fertilisation in the Vegetable Kingdom* (an analysis of sexual reproduction and the sterility of hybrids between species), *The Expression of the Emotions in Man and Animals* (on the evolution of human behavior from animal behavior), and *The Formation of Vegetable Mould Through the Action of Worms*. There is every reason to believe that almost all these books bear, in one way or another, on the principles and ideas that were inherent in Darwin's theory of evolution. The worm book, for example, is devoted to showing how great the impact of a seemingly trivial process like worm burrowing may be on ecology and geology if it persists for a long time. The idea of such cumulative slight effects is, of course, inherent in Darwin's view of evolution: successive slight modifications of a species, if continued long enough, can transform it radically.

When Darwin embarked on his voyage, he was a devout Christian who did not doubt the literal truth of the Bible, and did not believe in evolution any more than did Lyell and the other English scientists he had met or whose books he had read. By the time he re-turned to England in 1836 he had made numerous observations that would later convince him of evolution. It seems likely, however, that the idea itself did not occur to him until the spring of 1837, when the ornithologist John Gould, who was working on some of Darwin's collections, pointed out to him that each of the Galápagos Islands, off the coast of Ecuador, had a different kind of mockingbird. It was quite unclear whether they were different varieties of the same species, or different species. From this, Darwin quickly realized that species are not the discrete, clear-cut entities everyone seemed to imagine. The possibility of transformation entered his mind, and it applied to more than the mockingbirds: "When comparing… the birds from the separate islands of the Galápagos archipelago, both with one another and with those from the American mainland, I was much struck how entirely vague and arbitrary is the distinction between species and varieties."

In July 1837 he began his first notebook on the "Transmutation of Species." He later said that the Galápagos species and the similarity between South American fossils and living species were at the origin of all his views.

During the voyage of the *Beagle* I had been deeply impressed by discovering in the Pampean formation great fossil animals covered with armour like that on the existing armadillos; secondly, by the manner in which closely allied animals replace one another in proceeding southward over the continent; and thirdly, by the South American character of most of the productions of the Galápagos archipelago, and more especially by the manner in which they differ slightly on each island of the group; none of these islands appearing to be very ancient in a geological sense. It was evident that such facts as these, as well as many others, could be explained on the supposition that species gradually become modified; and the subject has haunted me.

The first great step in Darwin's thought was the realization that evolution had occurred. The second was his brilliant insight into the possible cause of evolutionary change. Lamarck's theory of "felt needs" had not been convincing. A better one was required. It came on September 18, 1838, when after grappling with the problem for fifteen months, "I happened to read for amusement Malthus on Population, and being well prepared to appreciate the struggle for existence which everywhere goes on from long-continued observation of the habits of animals and plants, it at once struck me that under these circumstances favorable variations would tend to be preserved, and unfavorable ones to be destroyed. The result of this would be the formation of new species. Here, then, I had at last got a theory by which to work."

Malthus, an economist, had developed the pessimistic thesis that the exponential growth of human populations must inevitably lead to famine, unless it were checked by war, disease, or "moral restraint." This emphasis on exponential population growth was apparently the catalyst for Darwin, who then realized that since most natural populations of animals and plants remain fairly stable in numbers, many more individuals are born than survive. Because individuals vary in their characteristics, the struggle to survive must favor some variant individuals over others. These survivors would then pass on their characteristics to future generations. Repetition of this process generation after generation would gradually transform the species.

Darwin clearly knew that he could not afford to publish a rash speculation on so important a subject without developing the best possible case. The world of science was not hospitable to speculation, and besides, Darwin was dealing with a highly volatile issue. Not only was he affirming that evolution had occurred, he was proposing a purely material explanation for it, one that demolished the argument from design in a single thrust. Instead of publishing his theory, he patiently amassed a mountain of evidence, and finally, in 1844, collected his thoughts in an essay on natural selection. But he still didn't publish. Not until 1856, almost twenty years after he became an evolutionist, did he begin what he planned to be a massive work on the subject, tentatively titled *Natural Selection*.

Then, in June 1858, the unthinkable happened. Alfred Russel Wallace (1823–

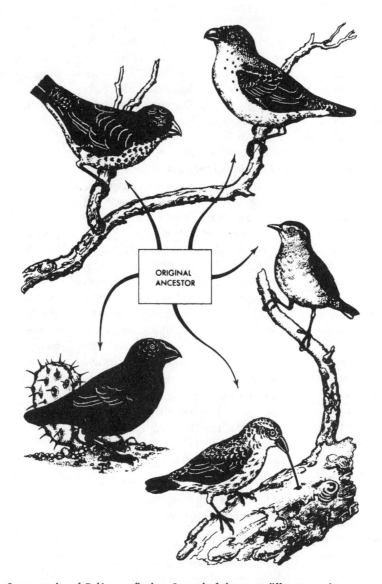

Figure 1. *Some species of Galápagos finches. Several of the most different species are represented here; intermediate species also exist. Clockwise from lower left are a male ground-finch (the plumage of the female resembles that of the tree-finches); the vegetarian tree-finch; the insectivorous tree-finch; the warbler-finch; and the woodpecker-finch, which uses a cactus spine to extricate insects from crevices. The slight differences among these species, and among species in other groups of Galápagos animals such as giant tortoises, were one of the observations that led Darwin to formulate his hypothesis of evolution.* (From D. Lack, Darwin's Finches [Oxford: Oxford University Press, 1944].)

1913), a young naturalist who had traveled in the Amazon Basin and in the Malay Archipelago, had also become interested in evolution. Like Darwin, he was struck by the fact that "the most closely allied species are found in the same locality or in closely adjoining localities and… therefore the natural sequence of the species by affinity is also geographical." In the throes of a malarial fever in Malaya, Wallace conceived of the same idea of natural selection as Darwin had, and sent Darwin a manuscript "On the Tendency of Varieties to Depart Indefinitely from the Original Type."

Darwin's friends Charles Lyell and Joseph Hooker, a botanist, rushed in to help Darwin establish the priority of his ideas, and on July 1, 1858, they presented to the Linnean Society of London both Wallace's paper and extracts from Darwin's 1844 essay. Darwin abandoned his big book on natural selection and condensed the argument into a 490-page "abstract" that was published on November 24, 1859, under the title *The Origin of Species by Means of Natural Selection; or, the Preservation of Favored Races in the Struggle for Life.* Because it was an abstract, he had to leave out many of the de-

tailed observations and references to the literature that he had amassed, but these were later provided in his other books, many of which are voluminous expansions on the contents of *The Origin of Species.*

The first five chapters of the *Origin* lay out the theory that Darwin had conceived. He shows that both domesticated and wild species are variable, that much of that variation is hereditary, and that breeders, by conscious selection of desirable varieties, can develop breeds of pigeons, dogs, and other forms that are more different from each other than species or even families of wild animals and

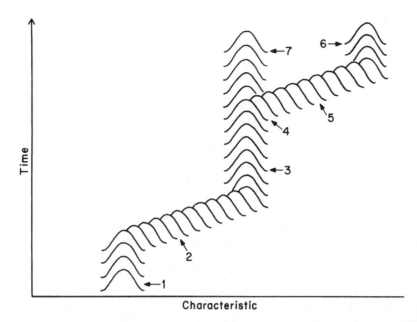

Figure 2. *Processes of evolutionary change. A characteristic that is variable (1) often shows a bell-shaped distribution--individuals vary on either side of the average. Evolutionary change (2) consists of a shift in successive generations, after which the characteristic may reach a new equilibrium (3). When the species splits into two different species (4), one of the species may undergo further evolutionary change (5) and reach a new equilibrium (6). The other may remain unchanged (7) or not. Each population usually remains variable throughout this process, but the average is shifted, ordinarily by natural selection.*

plants are from each other. The differences between related species then are no more than an exaggerated form of the kinds of variations one can find in a single species; indeed, it is often extremely difficult to tell if natural populations are distinct species or merely well-marked varieties.

Darwin then shows that in nature there is competition, predation, and a struggle for life.

Owing to this struggle, variations, however slight and from whatever cause proceeding, if they be in any degree profitable to the individuals of a species, in their infinitely complex relations to other organic beings and to their physical conditions of life, will tend to the preservation of such individuals, and will generally be inherited by the offspring. The offspring, also, will thus have a better chance of surviving, for, of the many individuals of any species which are periodically born, but a small number can survive. I have called this principle, by which each slight variation, if useful, is preserved, by the term natural selection, in or-

der to mark its relation to man's power of selection.

Darwin goes on to give examples of how even slight variations promote survival, and argues that when populations are exposed to different conditions, different variations will be favored, so that the descendants of a species become diversified in structure, and each ancestral species can give rise to several new ones. Although "it is probable that each form remains for long periods unaltered," successive evolutionary modifications will ultimately alter the different species so greatly that they will be classified as different genera, families, or orders.

Competition between species will impel them to become more different, for "the more diversified the descendants from any one species become in structure, constitution and habits, by so much will they be better enabled to seize on many and widely diversified places in the polity of nature, and so be enabled to increase in numbers." Thus different adaptations arise, and "the ultimate result is that each creature tends to become more and more improved in relation to its conditions. This improvement inevitably leads to the greater advancement of the

organization of the greater number of living beings throughout the world." But lowly organisms continue to persist, for "natural selection, or the survival of the fittest, does not necessarily include progressive development—it only takes advantage of such variations as arise and are beneficial to each creature under its complex relations of life." Probably no organism has reached a peak of perfection, and many lowly forms of life continue to exist, for "in some cases variations or individual differences of a favorable nature may never have arisen for natural selection to act on or accumulate. In no case, probably, has time sufficed for the utmost possible amount of development. In some few cases there has been what we must call retrogression of organization. But the main cause lies in the fact that under very simple conditions of life a high organization would be of no service...."

In the rest of *The Origin of Species*, Darwin considers all the objections that might be raised against his theory; discusses the evolution of a great array of phenomena—hybrid sterility, the slave-making instinct of ants, the similarity of vertebrate embryos; and presents an enor-

7

mous body of evidence for evolution. He draws his evidence from comparative anatomy, embryology, behavior, geographic variation, the geographic distribution of species, the study of rudimentary organs, atavistic variations ("throwbacks"), and the geological record to show how all of biology provides testimony that species have descended with modification from common ancestors.

Darwin's triumph was in synthesizing ideas and information in ways that no one had quite imagined before. From Lyell and the geologists he learned uniformitarianism: the cause of past events must be found in natural forces that operate today; and these, in the vastness of time, can accomplish great change. From Malthus and the nineteenth-century economists he learned of competition and the struggle for existence. From his work on barnacles, his travels, and his knowledge of domesticated varieties he learned that species do not have immutable essences but are variable in all their properties and blend into one another gradually. From his familiarity with the works of Whewell, Herschel, and other philosophers of science he developed a powerful method of pursuing science, the "hypothetico-deductive" method, which consists of formulating a hypothesis or speculation, deducing the logical predictions that must follow from the hypothesis, and then testing the hypothesis by seeing whether or not the predictions are verified. This was by no means the prevalent philosophy of science in Darwin's time.[5]

Darwin brought biology out of the Middle Ages. For divine design and unknowable supernatural forces he substituted natural material causes that could be studied by the methods of science. Instead of catastrophes unknown to physical science he invoked forces that could be studied in anyone's laboratory or garden. He replaced a young, static world by one in which there had been constant change for countless aeons. He established that life had a history, and this proved the essential view that differentiated evolutionary thought from all that had gone before.

For the British naturalist John Ray, writing in 1701, organisms had no history—they were the same at that moment, and lived in the same places, doing the same things, as when they were first created. For Darwin, organisms spoke of historical change. If there has indeed been such a history, then fossils in the oldest rocks must differ from those in younger rocks: trilobites, dinosaurs, and mammoths will not be mixed together but will appear in some temporal sequence. If species come from common ancestors, they will have the same characteristics, modified for different functions: the same bones used by bats for flying will be used by horses for running. If species come from ancestors that lived in different environments, they will carry the evidence of their history with them in the form of similar patterns of embryonic development and in vestigial, rudimentary organs that no longer serve any function. If species have a history, their geographical distribution will reflect it: oceanic islands won't have elephants because they wouldn't have been able to get there.

Once the earth and its living inhabitants are seen as the products of historical change, the theological philosophy embodied in the great chain of being ceases to make sense; the plenitude, or fullness, of the world becomes not an eternal manifestation of God's bountiful creativity but an illusion. For most of earth's history, most of the present species have not existed; and many of those that did exist do so no longer. But the scientific challenge to medieval philosophy goes even deeper. If evolution has occurred, and if it has proceeded from the natural causes that Darwin envisioned, then the adaptations of organisms to their environment, the intricate construction of the bird's wing and the orchid's flower, are evidence not of divine design but of the struggle for existence. Moreover, and this may be the deepest implication of all, Darwin brought to biology, as his predecessors had brought to astronomy and geology, the sufficiency of efficient causes. No longer was there any reason to look for final causes or goals. To the questions "What purpose does this species serve? Why did God make tapeworms?" the answer is "To no purpose." Tapeworms were not put here to serve a purpose, nor were planets, nor plants, nor people. They came into existence not by design but by the action of impersonal natural laws.

By providing materialistic, mechanistic explanations, instead of miraculous ones, for the characteristics of plants and animals, Darwin brought biology out of the realm of theology and into the realm of science. For miraculous spiritual forces fall outside the province of science; all of science is the study of material causation.

Of course, *The Origin of Species* didn't convince everyone immediately. Evolution and its material cause, natural selection, evoked strong protests from ecclesiastical circles, and even from scientists.[6] The eminent geologist Adam Sedgwick, for example, wrote in 1860 that species must come into existence by creation,

a power I cannot imitate or comprehend; but in which I can believe, by a legitimate conclusion of sound reason drawn from the laws and harmonies of Nature. For I can see in all around me a design and purpose, and a mutual adaptation of parts which I *can* comprehend, and which prove that there is exterior to, and above, the mere phenomena of Nature a great prescient and designing cause.... The pretended physical philosophy of modern days strips man of all his moral attributes, or holds them of no account in the estimate of his origin and place in the created world. A cold atheistical materialism is the tendency of the so-called material philosophy of the present day.

Among the more scientific objections were those posed by the French paleontologist François Pictet, and they were echoed by many others. Since Darwin supposes that species change gradually over the course of thousands of generations, then, asked Pictet, "Why don't we find these gradations in the fossil record... and why, instead of collecting thousands of identical individuals, do we not find more intermediary forms?... How is it that the most ancient fossil beds are rich in a variety of diverse forms of life, instead of the few early types Darwin's theory leads us to expect? How is it that no species has been seen to evolve during human history, and that the 4000 years which separates us from the mummies of Egypt have been insufficient to modify the crocodile and the ibis?" Pictet protested that, although slight variations might in time alter a species slightly, "all known facts demonstrate… that the prolonged influence of modifying causes has an action which is constantly restrained within sufficiently confined limits."

The anatomist Richard Owen likewise denied "that… variability is progressive and unlimited, so as, in the course of generations, to change the species, the genus, the order, or the class." The paleontologist Louis Agassiz insisted that organisms fall into discrete groups, based on uniquely different created plans, between which no intermediates could exist. He chose the birds as a group that showed the sharpest of boundaries. Only a few years later, in 1868, the fossil *Archaeopteryx*, an exquisite intermediate between birds and reptiles, demolished Agassiz's argument, and he had no more to say on the unique character of the birds.

Within twelve years of *The Origin of Species*, the evidence for evolution had been so thoroughly accepted that philosopher and mathematician Chauncey Wright could point out that among the students of science, "orthodoxy has been won over to the doctrine of evolution." However, Wright continued, "While the general doctrine of evolution has thus been successfully redeemed from theological condemnation, this is not yet true of the subordinate hypothesis of Natural Selection."

Natural selection turned out to be an extraordinarily difficult concept for people to grasp. St. George Mivart, a Catholic scholar and scientist, was not unusual in equating natural selection with chance. "The theory of Natural Selection may (though it need not) be taken in such a way as to lead man to regard the present organic world as formed, so to speak, *accidentally*, beautiful and wonderful as is the confessedly haphazard result." Many like him simply refused to understand that natural selection is the antithesis of chance and consequently could not see how selection might cause

adaptation or any kind of progressive evolutionary change. Even in the 1940s there were those, especially among paleontologists, who felt that the progressive evolution of groups like the horses, as revealed by the fossil record, must have had some unknown cause other than natural selection. Paradoxically, then, Darwin had convinced the scientific world of evolution where his predecessors had failed; but he had not convinced all biologists of his truly original theory, the theory of natural selection.

Natural selection fell into particular disrepute in the early part of the twentieth century because of the rise of genetics—which, as it happened, eventually became the foundation of the modern theory of evolution. Darwin's supposition that variation was unlimited, and so in time could give rise to strikingly different organisms, was not entirely convincing because he had no good idea of where variation came from. In 1865, the Austrian monk Gregor Mendel discovered, from his crosses of pea plants, that discretely different characteristics such as wrinkled versus smooth seeds were inherited from generation to generation without being altered, as if they were caused by particles that passed from parent to offspring. Mendel's work was ignored for thirty-five years, until, in 1900, three biologists discovered his paper and realized that it held the key to the mystery of heredity. One of the three, Hugo de Vries, set about to explore the problem as Mendel had, and in the course of his studies of evening primroses observed strikingly different variations arise, *de novo*. The new forms were so different that de Vries believed they represented new species, which had arisen in a single step by alteration or, as he called it, mutation, of the hereditary material.

In the next few decades, geneticists working with a great variety of organisms observed many other drastic changes arise by mutation: fruit flies (Drosophila), for example, with white instead of red eyes or curled instead of straight wings. These laboratory geneticists, especially Thomas Hunt Morgan, an outstanding geneticist at Columbia University, asserted that evolution must proceed by major mutational steps, and

that mutation, not natural selection, was the cause of evolution. In their eyes, Darwin's theory was dead on two counts: evolution was not gradual, and it was not caused by natural selection. Meanwhile, naturalists, taxonomists, and breeders of domesticated plants and animals continued to believe in Darwinism, because they saw that populations and species differed quantitatively and gradually rather than in big jumps, that most variation was continuous (like height in humans) rather than discrete, and that domesticated species could be altered by artificial selection from continuous variation.

The bitter conflict between the Mendelian geneticists and the Darwinians was resolved in the 1930s in a "New Synthesis" that brought the opposing views into a "neo-Darwinian" theory of evolution.[7] Slight variations in height, wing length, and other characteristics proved, under careful genetic analysis, to be inherited as particles, in the same way as the discrete variations studied by the Mendelians. Thus a large animal simply has inherited more particles, or genes, for large size than a smaller member of the species has. The Mendelians were simply studying particularly well marked variations, while the naturalists were studying more subtle ones. Variations could be very slight, or fairly pronounced, or very substantial, but all were inherited in the same manner. All these variations, it was shown, arose by a process of mutation of the genes.

Three mathematical theoreticians, Ronald Fisher and J. B. S. Haldane in England and Sewall Wright in the United States, proved that a newly mutated gene would not automatically form a new species. Nor would it automatically replace the preexisting form of the gene, and so transform the species. Replacement of one gene by a mutant form of the gene, they said, could happen in two ways. The mutation could enable its possessors to survive or reproduce more effectively than the old form; if so, it would increase by natural selection, just as Darwin had said. The new characteristic that evolved in this way would ordinarily be considered an improved adaptation.

Sewall Wright pointed out, however, that not all genetic changes in species need be adaptive. A new mutation might be no better or worse than the preexisting gene—it might simply be "neutral." In small populations such a mutation could replace the previous gene purely by chance—a process he called random genetic drift. The idea, put crudely, is this. Suppose there is a small population of land snails in a cow pasture, and that 5 percent of them are brown and the rest are yellow. Purely by chance, a greater percentage of yellow snails than of brown ones get crushed by cows' hooves in one generation. The snails breed, and there will now be a slightly greater percentage of yellow snails in the next generation than there had been. But in the next generation, the yellow ones may suffer more trampling, purely by chance. The proportion of yellow offspring will then be lower again. These random events cause fluctuations in the percentage of the two types. Wright proved mathematically that eventually, if no other factors intervene, these fluctuations will bring the population either to 100 percent yellow or 100 percent brown, purely by chance. The population will have evolved, then, but not by natural selection; and there is no improvement of adaptation.

During the period of the New Synthesis, though, genetic drift was emphasized less than natural selection, for which abundant evidence was discovered. Sergei Chetverikov in Russia, and later Theodosius Dobzhansky working in the United States, showed that wild populations of fruit flies contained an immense amount of genetic variation, including the same kinds of mutations that the geneticists had found arising in their laboratories. Dobzhansky and other workers went on to show that these variations affected survival and reproduction: that natural selection was a reality. They showed, moreover, that the genetic differences among related species were indeed compounded of the same kinds of slight genetic variations that they found within species. Thus the taxonomists and the geneticists converged onto a neo-Darwinian theory of evolution: evolution is due not to mutation *or* natural selection, but to both. Random mutations provide abundant genetic variation; natural selection, the antithesis of randomness,

sorts out the useful from the deleterious, and transforms the species.

In the following two decades, the paleontologist George Gaylord Simpson showed that this theory was completely adequate to explain the fossil record, and the ornithologists Bernhard Rensch and Ernst Mayr, the botanist G. Ledyard Stebbins, and many other taxonomists showed that the similarities and differences among living species could be fully explained by neo-Darwinism. They also clarified the meaning of "species." Organisms belong to different species if they do not interbreed when the opportunity presents itself, thus remaining genetically distinct. An ancestral species splits into two descendant species when different populations of the ancestor, living in different geographic regions, become so genetically different from each other that they will not or cannot interbreed when they have the chance to do so. As a result, evolution can happen without the formation of new species: a single species can be genetically transformed without splitting into several descendants. Conversely, new species can be formed without much genetic change. If one population becomes different from the rest of its species in, for example, its mating behavior, it will not interbreed with the other populations. Thus it has become a new species, even though it may be identical to its "sister species" in every respect except its behavior. Such a new species is free to follow a new path of genetic change, since it does not become homogenized with its sister species by interbreeding. With time, therefore, it can diverge and develop different adaptations.

The conflict between the geneticists and the Darwinians that was resolved in the New Synthesis was the last major conflict in evolutionary science. Since that time, an enormous amount of research has confirmed most of the major conclusions of neo-Darwinism. We now know that populations contain very extensive genetic variation that continually arises by mutation of pre-existing genes. We also know what genes are and how they become mutated. Many instances of the reality of natural selection in wild populations have been documented, and there is extensive evidence that many

species form by the divergence of different populations of an ancestral species.

The major questions in evolutionary biology now tend to be of the form, "All right, factors x and y both operate in evolution, but how important is x compared to y?" For example, studies of biochemical genetic variation have raised the possibility that nonadaptive, random change (genetic drift) may be the major reason for many biochemical differences among species. How important, then, is genetic drift compared to natural selection? Another major question has to do with rates of evolution: Do species usually diverge very slowly, as Darwin thought, or does evolution consist mostly of rapid spurts, interspersed with long periods of constancy? Still another question is raised by mutations, which range all the way from gross changes of the kind Morgan studied to very slight alterations. Does evolution consist entirely of the substitution of mutations that have very slight effects, or are major mutations sometimes important too? Partisans on each side of all these questions argue vigorously for their interpretation of the evidence, but they don't doubt that the major factors of evolution are known. They simply emphasize one factor or another. Minor battles of precisely this kind go on continually in every field of science; without them there would be very little advancement in our knowledge.

Within a decade or two of *The Origin of Species*, the belief that living organisms had evolved over the ages was firmly entrenched in biology. As of 1982, the historical existence of evolution is viewed as fact by almost all biologists. To explain how the fact of evolution has been brought about, a theory of evolutionary mechanisms—mutation, natural selection, genetic drift, and isolation—has been developed.[8] But exactly what is the evidence for the fact of evolution?

NOTES

1. Andrew Dickson White, *A History of the Warfare of Science with Theology in Christendom* vol. I (London: Macmillan, 1896; reprint ed., New York: Dover, 1960).

2. A. O. Lovejoy, *The Great Chain of Being* (Cambridge, Mass.: Harvard University Press, 1936).

3. Much of this history is provided by J. C. Greene, *The Death of Adam: Evolution and its Impact on Western Thought* (Ames: Iowa State University Press, 1959).

4. A detailed history of this and other developments in evolutionary biology is given by Ernst Mayr, *The Growth of Biological Thought: Diversity, Evolution, Inheritance* (Cambridge, Mass.: Harvard University Press, 1982).

5. See D. L. Hull, *Darwin and His Critics* (Cambridge, Mass.: Harvard University Press, 1973).

6. Ibid.

7. E. Mayr and W. B. Provine, *The Evolutionary Synthesis* (Cambridge, Mass.: Harvard University Press, 1980).

8. Our modern understanding of the mechanisms of evolution is described in many books. Elementary textbooks include G. L. Stebbins, *Processes of Organic Evolution*, (Englewood Cliffs, N.J.: Prentice-Hall, 1971), and J. Maynard Smith, *The Theory of Evolution* (New York: Penguin Books, 1975). More advanced textbooks include Th. Dobzhansky, F. J. Ayala, G. L. Stebbins, and J. W. Valentine, *Evolution* (San Francisco: Freeman, 1977), and D. J. Futuyma, *Evolutionary Biology* (Sunderland, Mass.: Sinauer, 1979). Unreferenced facts and theories described in the text are familiar enough to most evolutionary biologists that they will be found in most or all of the references cited above.

James D. Watson, a molecularbiologist, shared the Nobel Prize for his work in discovering the structure of DNA.

From *Science on Trial* by Douglas J. Futuyma, pp. 23–43. Published by Pantheon Books, a division of Random House, Inc. © 1982 by Douglas J. Futuyma. Reprinted by permission of the author.

Darwin's Influence on Modern Thought

Great minds shape the thinking of successive historical periods. Luther and Calvin inspired the Reformation; Locke, Leibniz, Voltaire and Rousseau, the Enlightenment. Modern thought is most dependent on the influence of Charles Darwin

by Ernst Mayr

Clearly, our conception of the world and our place in it is, at the beginning of the 21st century, drastically different from the zeitgeist at the beginning of the 19th century. But no consensus exists as to the source of this revolutionary change. Karl Marx is often mentioned; Sigmund Freud has been in and out of favor; Albert Einstein's biographer Abraham Pais made the exuberant claim that Einstein's theories "have profoundly changed the way modern men and women think about the phenomena of inanimate nature." No sooner had Pais said this, though, than he recognized the exaggeration. "It would actually be better to say 'modern scientists' than 'modern men and women,'" he wrote, because one needs schooling in the physicist's style of thought and mathematical techniques to appreciate Einstein's contributions in their fullness. Indeed, this limitation is true for all the extraordinary theories of modern physics, which have had little impact on the way the average person apprehends the world.

The situation differs dramatically with regard to concepts in biology. Many biological ideas proposed during the past 150 years stood in stark conflict with what everybody assumed to be true. The acceptance of these ideas required an ideological revolution. And no biologist has been responsible for more—and for more drastic—modifications of the aver-age person's worldview than Charles Darwin.

Darwin's accomplishments were so many and so diverse that it is useful to distinguish three fields to which he made major contributions: evolutionary biology; the philosophy of science; and the modern zeitgeist. Although I will be focusing on this last domain, for the sake of completeness I will put forth a short overview of his contributions—particularly as they inform his later ideas—to the first two areas.

A SECULAR VIEW OF LIFE

Darwin founded a new branch of life science, evolutionary biology. Four of his contributions to evolutionary biology are especially important, as they held considerable sway beyond that discipline. The first is the non-constancy of species, or the modern conception of evolution itself. The second is the notion of branching evolution, implying the common descent of all species of living things on earth from a single unique origin. Up until 1859, all evolutionary proposals, such as that of naturalist Jean-Baptiste Lamarck, instead endorsed linear evolution, a teleological march toward greater perfection that had been in vogue since Aristotle's concept of *Scala Naturae*, the chain of being. Darwin further noted that evolution must be gradual, with no major breaks or discontinuities. Finally, he reasoned that the mechanism of evolution was natural selection.

These four insights served as the foundation for Darwin's founding of a new branch of the philosophy of science, a philosophy of biology. Despite the passing of a century before this new branch of philosophy fully developed, its eventual form is based on Darwinian concepts. For example, Darwin introduced historicity into science. Evolutionary biology, in contrast with physics and chemistry, is a historical science—the evolutionist attempts to explain events and processes that have already taken place. Laws and experiments are inappropriate techniques for the explication of such events and processes. Instead one constructs a historical narrative, consisting of a tentative reconstruction of the particular scenario that led to the events one is trying to explain.

For example, three different scenarios have been proposed for the sudden extinction of the dinosaurs at the end of the Cretaceous: a devastating epidemic; a catastrophic change of climate; and the impact of an asteroid, known as the Alvarez theory. The first two narratives were ultimately refuted by evidence incompatible with them. All the known facts, however, fit the Alvarez theory, which is now widely accepted. The testing of historical narratives implies that the wide gap between science and the humanities that so troubled physicist C. P. Snow is actually nonexistent—by virtue of its methodology and its acceptance of the time factor that makes change possible, evolutionary biology serves as a bridge.

The discovery of natural selection, by Darwin and Alfred Russell Wallace, must itself be counted as an extraordinary philosophical advance. The principle remained unknown throughout the more than 2,000-year history of philosophy ranging from the Greeks to Hume, Kant and the Victorian era. The concept of natural selection had remarkable power for explaining directional and adaptive changes. Its nature is simplicity itself. It is not a force like the forces described in the laws of physics; its mechanism is simply the elimination of inferior individuals. This process of non-random elimination impelled Darwin's contemporary, philosopher Herbert Spencer, to describe evolution with the now familiar term "survival of the fittest." (This description was long ridiculed as circular reasoning: "Who are the fittest? Those who survive." In reality, a careful analysis can usually determine why certain individuals fail to thrive in a given set of conditions.)

The truly outstanding achievement of the principle of natural selection is that it makes unnecessary the invocation of "final causes"—that is, any teleological forces leading to a particular end. In fact, nothing is predetermined. Furthermore, the objective of selection even may change from one generation to the next, as environmental circumstances vary.

A diverse population is a necessity for the proper working of natural selection. (Darwin's success meant that typologists, for whom all members of a class are essentially identical, were left with an untenable viewpoint.) Because of the importance of variation, natural selection should be considered a two-step process: the production of abundant variation is followed by the elimination of inferior individuals. This latter step is directional. By adopting natural selection, Darwin settled the several-thousand-year-old argument among philosophers over chance or necessity. Change on the earth is the result of both, the first step being dominated by randomness, the second by necessity.

Darwin was a holist: for him the object, or target, of selection was primarily the individual as a whole. The geneticists, almost from 1900 on, in a rather reductionist spirit preferred to consider the gene the target of evolution. In the past 25 years, however, they have largely returned to the Darwinian view that the individual is the principal target.

For 80 years after 1859, bitter controversy raged as to which of four competing evolutionary theories was valid. "Transmutation" was the establishment of a new species or new type through a single mutation, or saltation. "Orthogenesis" held that intrinsic teleological tendencies led to transformation. Lamarckian evolution relied on the inheritance of acquired characteristics. And now there was Darwin's variational evolution, through natural selection. Darwin's theory clearly emerged as the victor during the evolutionary synthesis of the 1940s, when the new discoveries in genetics were married with taxonomic observations concerning systematics, the classification of organisms by their relationships. Darwinism is now almost unanimously accepted by knowledgeable evolutionists. In addition, it has become the basic component of the new philosophy of biology.

A most important principle of the new biological philosophy, undiscovered for almost a century after the publication of *On the Origin of Species*, is the dual nature of biological processes. These activities are governed both by the universal laws of physics and chemistry and by a genetic program, itself the result of natural selection, which has molded the genotype for millions of generations. The causal factor of the possession of a genetic program is unique to living organisms, and it is totally absent in the inanimate world. Because of the backward state of molecular and genetic knowledge in his time, Darwin was unaware of this vital factor.

Another aspect of the new philosophy of biology concerns the role of laws. Laws give way to concepts in Darwinism. In the physical sciences, as a rule, theories are based on laws; for example, the laws of motion led to the theory of gravitation. In evolutionary biology, however, theories are largely based on concepts such as competition, female choice, selection, succession and dominance. These biological concepts, and the theories based on them, cannot be reduced to the laws and theories of the physical sciences. Darwin himself never stated this idea plainly. My assertion of Darwin's importance to modern thought is the result of an analysis of Darwinian theory over the past century. During this period, a pronounced change in the methodology of biology took place. This transformation was not caused exclusively by Darwin, but it was greatly strengthened by developments in evolutionary biology. Observation, comparison and classification, as well as the testing of competing historical narratives, became the methods of evolutionary biology, outweighing experimentation.

I do not claim that Darwin was single-handedly responsible for all the intellectual developments in this period. Much of it, like the refutation of French mathematician and physicist Pierre-Simon Laplace's determinism, was "in the air." But Darwin in most cases either had priority or promoted the new views most vigorously.

THE DARWINIAN ZEITGEIST

A 21st-century person looks at the world quite differently than a citizen of the Victorian era did. This shift had multiple sources, particularly the incredible advances in technology. But what is not at all appreciated is the great extent to which this shift in thinking indeed resulted from Darwin's ideas.

Remember that in 1850 virtually all leading scientists and philosophers were Christian men. The world they inhabited had been created by God, and as the natural theologians claimed, He had instituted wise laws that brought about the perfect adaptation of all organisms to one another and to their environment. At the same time, the architects of the scientific revolution had constructed a worldview based on physicalism (a reduction to spatiotemporal things or events or their properties), teleology, determinism and other basic principles. Such was the thinking of Western man prior to the 1859 publication of *On the Origin of*

Species. The basic principles proposed by Darwin would stand in total conflict with these prevailing ideas.

First, Darwinism rejects all supernatural phenomena and causations. The theory of evolution by natural selection explains the adaptedness and diversity of the world solely materialistically. It no longer requires God as creator or designer (although one is certainly still free to believe in God even if one accepts evolution). Darwin pointed out that creation, as described in the Bible and the origin accounts of other cultures, was contradicted by almost any aspect of the natural world. Every aspect of the "wonderful design" so admired by the natural theologians could be explained by natural selection. (A closer look also reveals that design is often not so wonderful—see "Evolution and the Origins of Disease," by Randolph M. Nesse and George C. Williams; [&smallcaps]Scientific American[&stop], November 1998). Eliminating God from science made room for strictly scientific explanations of all natural phenomena; it gave rise to positivism; it produced a powerful intellectual and spiritual revolution, the effects of which have lasted to this day.

Second, Darwinism refutes typology. From the time of the Pythagoreans and Plato, the general concept of the diversity of the world emphasized its invariance and stability. This viewpoint is called typology, or essentialism. The seeming variety, it was said, consisted of a limited number of natural kinds (essences or types), each one forming a class. The members of each class were thought to be identical, constant, and sharply separated from the members of other essences.

Variation, in contrast, is nonessential and accidental. A triangle illustrates essentialism: all triangles have the same fundamental characteristics and are sharply delimited against quadrangles or any other geometric figures. An intermediate between a triangle and a quadrangle is inconceivable. Typological thinking, therefore, is unable to accommodate variation and gives rise to a misleading conception of human races. For the typologist, Caucasians, Africans, Asians or Inuits are types that conspicuously differ from other human ethnic groups. This mode of thinking leads to racism. (Although the ignorant misapplication of evolutionary theory known as "social Darwinism" often gets blamed for justifications of racism, adherence to the disproved essentialism preceding Darwin in fact can lead to a racist viewpoint.)

Darwin completely rejected typological thinking and introduced instead the entirely different concept now called population thinking. All groupings of living organisms, including humanity, are populations that consist of uniquely different individuals. No two of the six billion humans are the same. Populations vary not by their essences but only by mean statistical differences. By rejecting the constancy of populations, Darwin helped to introduce history into scientific thinking and to promote a distinctly new approach to explanatory interpretation in science.

Third, Darwin's theory of natural selection made any invocation of teleology unnecessary. From the Greeks onward, there existed a universal belief in the existence of a teleological force in the world that led to ever greater perfection. This "final cause" was one of the causes specified by Aristotle. After Kant, in the *Critique of Judgment*, had unsuccessfully attempted to describe biological phenomena with the help of a physicalist Newtonian explanation, he then invoked teleological forces. Even after 1859, teleological explanations (orthogenesis) continued to be quite popular in evolutionary biology. The acceptance of the *Scala Naturae* and the explanations of natural theology were other manifestations of the popularity of teleology. Darwinism swept such considerations away.

(The designation "teleological" actually applied to various different phenomena. Many seemingly end-directed processes in inorganic nature are the simple consequence of natural laws—a stone falls or a heated piece of metal cools because of laws of physics, not some end-directed process. Processes in living organisms owe their apparent goal-directedness to the operation of an inborn genetic or acquired program. Adapted systems, such as the heart or kidneys, may engage in activities that can be considered goal seeking, but the systems themselves were acquired during evolution and are continuously fine-tuned by natural selection. Finally, there was a belief in cosmic teleology, with a purpose and predetermined goal ascribed to everything in nature. Modern science, however, is unable to substantiate the existence of any such cosmic teleology.)

Fourth, Darwin does away with determinism. Laplace notoriously boasted that a complete knowledge of the current world and all its processes would enable him to predict the future to infinity. Darwin, by comparison, accepted the universality of randomness and chance throughout the process of natural selection. (Astronomer and philosopher John Herschel referred to natural selection contemptuously as "the law of the higgledy-piggledy.") That chance should play an important role in natural processes has been an unpalatable thought for many physicists. Einstein expressed this distaste in his statement, "God does not play dice." Of course, as previously mentioned, only the first step in natural selection, the production of variation, is a matter of chance. The character of the second step, the actual selection, is to be directional.

Despite the initial resistance by physicists and philosophers, the role of contingency and chance in natural processes is now almost universally acknowledged. Many biologists and philosophers deny the existence of universal laws in biology and suggest that all regularities be stated in probabilistic terms, as nearly all so-called biological laws have exceptions. Philosopher of science Karl Popper's famous test of falsification therefore cannot be applied in these cases.

Fifth, Darwin developed a new view of humanity and, in turn, a new anthropocentrism. Of all of Darwin's proposals, the one his contemporaries found most difficult to accept was that the theory of common descent applied to Man. For the theologians and philosophers alike, Man was a creature above and apart from other living beings. Aristotle, Descartes and Kant agreed on this sentiment, no matter how else their thinking diverged. But biologists Thomas Huxley and Ernst Haeckel revealed through rigorous comparative anatomical study that humans and living apes clearly had common ancestry, an assessment that has never again been seriously questioned in science. The application of the theory of common descent to Man deprived man of his former unique position.

Ironically, though, these events did not lead to an end to anthropocentrism. The study of man showed that, in spite of his descent, he is indeed unique among all organisms. Human intelligence is unmatched by that of any other creature. Humans are the only animals with true language, including grammar and syntax. Only humanity, as Darwin emphasized, has developed genuine ethical systems. In addition, through high intelligence, language and long parental care, humans are the only creatures to have created a rich culture. And by these means, humanity has attained, for better or worse, an unprecedented dominance over the entire globe.

Sixth, Darwin provided a scientific foundation for ethics. The question is frequently raised—and usually rebuffed—as to whether evolution adequately explains healthy human ethics. Many wonder how, if selection rewards the individual only for behavior that enhances his own survival and reproductive success, such pure selfishness can lead to any sound ethics. The widespread thesis of social Darwinism, promoted at the end of the 19th century by Spencer, was that evolutionary explanations were at odds with the development of ethics.

We now know, however, that in a social species not only the individual must be considered—an entire social group can be the target of selection. Darwin applied this reasoning to the human species in 1871 in *The Descent of Man*. The survival and prosperity of a social group depends to a large extent on the harmonious cooperation of the members of the group, and this behavior must be based on altruism. Such altruism, by furthering the survival and prosperity of the group, also indirectly benefits the fitness of the group's individuals. The result amounts to selection favoring altruistic behavior.

Kin selection and reciprocal helpfulness in particular will be greatly favored in a social group. Such selection for altruism has been demonstrated in recent years to be widespread among many other social animals. One can then perhaps encapsulate the relation between ethics and evolution by saying that a propensity for altruism and harmonious cooperation in social groups *is* favored by natural selection. The old thesis of social Darwinism—strict selfishness—was based on an incomplete understanding of animals, particularly social species.

THE INFLUENCE OF NEW CONCEPTS

Let me now try to summarize my major findings. No educated person any longer questions the validity of the so-called theory of evolution, which we now know to be a simple fact. Likewise, most of Darwin's particular theses have been fully confirmed, such as that of common descent, the gradualism of evolution, and his explanatory theory of natural selection.

I hope I have successfully illustrated the wide reach of Darwin's ideas. Yes, he established a philosophy of biology by introducing the time factor, by demonstrating the importance of chance and contingency, and by showing that theories in evolutionary biology are based on concepts rather than laws. But furthermore—and this is perhaps Darwin's greatest contribution—he developed a set of new principles that influence the thinking of every person: the living world, through evolution, can be explained without recourse to supernaturalism; essentialism or typology is invalid, and we must adopt population thinking, in which all individuals are unique (vital for education and the refutation of racism); natural selection, applied to social groups, is indeed sufficient to account for the origin and maintenance of altruistic ethical systems; cosmic teleology, an intrinsic process leading life automatically to ever greater perfection, is fallacious, with all seemingly teleological phenomena explicable by purely material processes; and determinism is thus repudiated, which places our fate squarely in our own evolved hands.

To borrow Darwin's phrase, there is grandeur in this view of life. New modes of thinking have been, and are being, evolved. Almost every component in modern man's belief system is somehow affected by Darwinian principles.

This article is based on the September 23, 1999, lecture that Mayr delivered in Stockholm on receiving the Crafoord Prize from the Royal Swedish Academy of Science.

FURTHER INFORMATION

DARWIN ON MAN: A PSYCHOLOGICAL STUDY OF SCIENTIFIC CREATIVITY. Second edition. Howard E. Gruber. University of Chicago Press, 1981.

ONE LONG ARGUMENT: CHARLES DARWIN AND THE GENESIS OF MODERN EVOLUTIONARY THOUGHT. Ernst Mayr. Harvard University Press, 1993.

CHARLES DARWIN: VOYAGING: A BIOGRAPHY. Janet Browne. Princeton University Press, 1996.

THE DESCENT OF MAN. Charles Darwin. Popular current edition. Prometheus Books, 1997.

THE ORIGIN OF SPECIES. Charles Darwin. Popular current edition. Bantam Classic, 1999.

ERNST MAYR is one of the towering figures in the history of evolutionary biology. Following his graduation from the University of Berlin in 1926, ornithological expeditions to New Guinea fueled his interest in theoretical evolutionary biology. Mayr emigrated to the U.S. in 1931 and in 1953 joined the faculty of Harvard University, where he is now Alexander Agassiz Professor of Zoology, Emeritus. His conception of rapid speciation of isolated populations formed the basis for the well-known neoevolutionary concept of punctuated equilibrium. The author of some of the 20th century's most influential volumes on evolution, Mayr is the recipient of numerous awards, including the National Medal of Science.

From *Scientific American*, July 2000, pp. 79–83. © 2000 by Ernst Mayr. Reprinted by permission of the author.

Curse and Blessing of the Ghetto

Tay-Sachs disease is a choosy killer, one that for centuries targeted Eastern European Jews above all others. By decoding its lethal logic, we can learn a lot about how genetic diseases evolve— and how they can be conquered.

Jared Diamond

Marie and I hated her at first sight, even though she was trying hard to be helpful. As our obstetrician's genetics counselor, she was just doing her job, explaining to us the unpleasant results that might come out of the genetic tests we were about to have performed. As a scientist, though, I already knew all I wanted to know about Tay-Sachs disease, and I didn't need to be reminded that the baby sentenced to death by it could be my own.

Fortunately, the tests would reveal that my wife and I were not carriers of the Tay-Sachs gene, and our preparenthood fears on that matter at least could be put to rest. But at the time I didn't yet know that. As I glared angrily at that poor genetics counselor, so strong was my anxiety that now, four years later, I can still clearly remember what was going through my mind: If I were an evil deity, I thought, trying to devise exquisite tortures for babies and their parents, I would be proud to have designed Tay-Sachs disease.

Tay-Sachs is completely incurable, unpreventable, and preprogrammed in the genes. A Tay-Sachs infant usually appears normal for the first few months after birth, just long enough for the parents to grow to love him. An exaggerated "startle reaction" to sounds is the first ominous sign. At about six months the baby starts to lose control of his head and can't roll over or sit without support. Later he begins to drool, breaks out into unmotivated bouts of laughter, and suffers convulsions. Then his head grows abnormally large, and he becomes blind. Perhaps what's most frightening for the parents is that their baby loses all contact with his environment and becomes virtually a vegetable. By the child's third birthday, if he's still alive, his skin will turn yellow and his hands pudgy. Most likely he will die before he's four years old.

My wife and I were tested for the Tay-Sachs gene because at the time we rated as high-risk candidates, for two reasons. First, Marie was carrying twins, so we had double the usual chance to bear a Tay-Sachs baby. Second, both she and I are of Eastern European Jewish ancestry, the population with by far the world's highest Tay-Sachs frequency.

In peoples around the world Tay-Sachs appears once in every 400,000 births. But it appears a hundred times more frequently—about once in 3,600 births—among descendants of Eastern European Jews, people known as Ashkenazim. For descendants of most other groups of Jews—Oriental Jews, chiefly from the Middle East, or Sephardic Jews, from Spain and other Mediterranean countries—the frequency of Tay-Sachs disease is no higher than in non-Jews. Faced with such a clear correlation, one cannot help but wonder: What is it about this one group of people that produces such an extraordinarily high risk of this disease?

Finding the answer to this question concerns all of us, regardless of our ancestry. Every human population is especially susceptible to certain diseases, not only because of its life-style but also because of its genetic inheritance. For example, genes put European whites at high risk for cystic fibrosis, African blacks for sickle-cell disease, Pacific Islanders for diabetes—and Eastern European Jews for ten different diseases, including Tay-Sachs. It's not that Jews are notably susceptible to genetic diseases in general; but a combination of historical factors has led to Jews' being intensively studied, and so their susceptibilities are far better known than those of, say, Pacific Islanders.

Tay-Sachs exemplifies how we can deal with such diseases; it has been the object of the most successful screening program to date. Moreover, Tay-Sachs is helping us understand how ethnic diseases evolve. Within the past couple of years discoveries by molecular biologists have provided tantalizing clues to precisely how a deadly gene can persist and spread over the centuries. Tay-Sachs may be primarily a disease of Eastern European Jews, but through this affliction of one group of people, we gain a window on how our genes simultaneously curse and bless us all.

The disease's hyphenated name comes from the two physicians—British ophthalmologist W. Tay and New York neurologist B. Sachs—who independently first recognized the disease, in 1881 and 1887, respectively. By 1896 Sachs had seen enough cases to realize that the disease was most common among Jewish children.

Not until 1962, however, were researchers able to trace the cause of the affliction to a single biochemical abnormality: the excessive accumulation in nerve cells of a fatty substance called G_{M2} ganglioside. Normally G_{M2} ganglioside is present at only modest levels in cell membranes, because it is constantly being broken down as well as synthesized. The breakdown depends on the enzyme hexosaminidase A, which is found in the tiny structures within our cells known as lysosomes. In the unfortunate Tay-Sachs victims this enzyme is lacking, and without it the ganglioside piles up and produces all the symptoms of the disease.

We have two copies of the gene that programs our supply of hexosaminidase A, one inherited from our father, the other from our mother; each of our parents, in turn, has two copies derived from their own parents. As long as we have one good copy of the gene, we can produce enough hexosaminidase A to prevent a buildup of G_{M2} ganglioside and we won't get Tay-Sachs. This genetic disease is of the sort termed recessive rather than dominant—meaning that to get it, a child must inherit a defective gene not just from one parent but from both of them. Clearly, each parent must have had one good copy of the gene along with the defective copy—if either had had two defective genes, he or she would have died of the disease long before reaching the age of reproduction. In genetic terms the diseased child is homozygous for the defective gene and both parents are heterozygous for it.

None of this yet gives any hint as to why the Tay-Sachs gene should be most common among Eastern European Jews. To come to grips with that question, we must take a short detour into history.

From their biblical home of ancient Israel, Jews spread peacefully to other Mediterranean lands, Yemen, and India. They were also dispersed violently through conquest by Assyrians, Babylonians, and Romans. Under the Carolingian kings of the eighth and ninth centuries Jews were invited to settle in France and Germany as traders and financiers. In subsequent centuries, however, persecutions triggered by the Crusades gradually drove Jews out of Western Europe; the process culminated in their total expulsion from Spain in 1492. Those Spanish Jews—called Sephardim—fled to other lands around the Mediterranean. Jews of France and Germany—the Ashkenazim—fled east to Poland and from there to Lithuania and western Russia, where they settled mostly in towns, as businessmen engaged in whatever pursuit they were allowed.

There the Jews stayed for centuries, through periods of both tolerance and oppression. But toward the end of the nineteenth century and the beginning of the twentieth, waves of murderous anti-Semitic attacks drove millions of Jews out of Eastern Europe, with most of them heading for the United States. My mother's parents, for example, fled to New York from Lithuanian pogroms of the 1880s, while my father's parents fled from the Ukrainian pogroms of 1903–6. The more modern history of Jewish migration is probably well known to you all: most Jews who remained in Eastern Europe were exterminated during World War II, while most the survivors immigrated to the United States and Israel. Of the 13 million Jews alive today, more than three-quarters are Ashkenazim, the descendants of the Eastern European Jews and the people most at risk for Tay-Sachs.

Have these Jews maintained their genetic distinctness through the thousands of years of wandering? Some scholars claim that there has been so much intermarriage and conversion that Ashkenazic Jews are now just Eastern Europeans who adopted Jewish culture. However, modern genetic studies refute that speculation.

First of all, there are those ten genetic diseases that the Ashkenazim have somehow acquired, by which they differ both from other Jews and from Eastern European non-Jews. In addition, many Ashkenazic genes turn out to be ones typical of Palestinian Arabs and other peoples of the Eastern Mediterranean areas where Jews originated. (In fact, by genetic standards the current Arab-Israeli conflict is an internecine civil war.) Other Ashkenazic genes have indeed diverged from Mediterranean ones (including genes of Sephardic and Oriental Jews) and have evolved to converge on genes of Eastern European non-Jews subject to the same local forces of natural selection. But the degree to which Ashkenazim prove to differ genetically from Eastern European non-Jews implies an intermarriage rate of only about 15 percent.

Can history help explain why the Tay-Sachs gene in particular is so much more common in Ashkenazim than in their non-Jewish neighbors or in other Jews? At the risk of spoiling a mystery, I'll tell you now that the answer is yes, but to appreciate it, you'll have to understand the four possible explanations for the persistence of the Tay-Sachs gene.

First, new copies of the gene might be arising by mutation as fast as existing copies disappear with the death of Tay-Sachs children. That's the most likely explanation for the gene's persistence in most of the world, where the disease frequency is only one in 400,000 births—that frequency reflects a typical human mutation rate. But for this explanation to apply to the Ashkenazim would require a mutation rate of at least one per 3,600 births—far above the frequency observed for any human gene. Furthermore, there would be no precedent for one particular gene mutating so much more often in one human population than in others.

As a second possibility, the Ashkenazim might have acquired the Tay-Sachs gene from some other people who already had the gene at high frequency. Arthur Koestler's controversial book *The Thirteenth Tribe*, for example, popularized the view that the Ashkenazim are really not a Semitic people but are instead descended from the Khazar, a Turkic tribe whose rulers converted to Judaism in the eighth century. Could the Khazar have brought the Tay-Sachs gene to Eastern Europe? This speculation makes good romantic reading, but there is no good evidence to support it. Moreover, it fails to explain why deaths of Tay-Sachs children didn't eliminate the gene by natural selection in the past 1,200 years, nor how the Khazar acquired high frequencies of the gene in the first place.

Founder effect in Full Effect (handwritten)

The third hypothesis was the one preferred by a good many geneticists until recently. It invokes two genetic processes, termed the founder effect and genetic drift, that may operate in small populations. To understand these concepts, imagine that 100 couples settle in a new land and found a population that then increases. Imagine further that one parent among those original 100 couples happens to have some rare gene, one, say, that normally occurs at a frequency of one in a million. The gene's frequency in the new population will now be one in 200 as a result of the accidental presence of that rare founder.

Or suppose again that 100 couples found a population, but that one of the 100 men happens to have lots of kids by his wife or that he is exceptionally popular with other women, while the other 99 men are childless or have few kids or are simply less popular. That one man may thereby father 10 percent rather than a more representative one percent of the next generation's babies, and their genes will disproportionately reflect that man's genes. In other words, gene frequencies will have drifted between the first and second generation.

Through these two types of genetic accidents a rare gene may occur with an unusually high frequency in a small expanding population. Eventually, if the gene is harmful, natural selection will bring its frequency back to normal by killing off gene bearers. But if the resultant disease is recessive—if heterozygous individuals don't get the disease and only the rare, homozygous individuals die of it—the gene's high frequency may persist for many generations.

These accidents do in fact account for the astonishingly high Tay-Sachs gene frequency found in one group of Pennsylvania Dutch: out of the 333 people in this group, 98 proved to carry the Tay-Sachs gene. Those 333 are all descended from one couple who settled in the United States in the eighteenth century and had 13 children. Clearly, one of that founding couple must have carried the gene. A similar accident may explain why Tay-Sachs is also relatively common among French Canadians, who number 5 million today but are descended from fewer than 6,000 French immigrants who arrived in the New World between 1638 and 1759. In the two or three centuries since both these founding events, the high Tay-Sachs gene frequency among Pennsylvania Dutch and French Canadians has not yet had enough time to decline to normal levels.

The same mechanisms were one proposed to explain the high rate of Tay-Sachs disease among the Ashkenazim. Perhaps, the reasoning went, the gene just happened to be overrepresented in the founding Jewish population that settled in Germany or Eastern Europe. Perhaps the gene just happened to drift up in frequency in the Jewish populations scattered among the isolated towns of Eastern Europe.

It seems unlikely that genetic accidents would have pumped up the frequency of the same gene not once but twice in the same population.

But geneticists have long questioned whether the Ashkenazim population's history was really suitable for these genetic accidents to have been significant. Remember, the founder effect and genetic drift become significant only in small populations, and the founding populations of Ashkenazim may have been quite large. Moreover, Ashkenazic communities were considerably widespread; drift would have sent gene frequencies up in some towns but down in others. And, finally, natural selection has by now had a thousand years to restore gene frequencies to normal.

Granted, those doubts are based on historical data, which are not always as precise or reliable as one might want. But within the past several years the case against those accidental explanations for Tay-Sachs disease in the Ashkenazim has been bolstered by discoveries by molecular biologists.

Like all proteins, the enzyme absent in Tay-Sachs children is coded for by a piece of our DNA. Along that particular stretch of DNA there are thousands of different sites where a mutation could occur that would result in no enzyme and hence in the same set of symptoms. If molecular biologists had discovered that all cases of Tay-Sachs in Ashkenazim involved damage to DNA at the same site, that would have been strong evidence that in Ashkenazim the disease stems from a single mutation that has been multiplied by the founder effect or genetic drift—in other words, the high incidence of Tay-Sachs among Eastern European Jews is accidental.

In reality, though, several different mutations along this stretch of DNA have been identified in Ashkenazim, and two of them occur much more frequently than in non-Ashkenazim populations. It seems unlikely that genetic accidents would have pumped up the frequency of the same gene not once but twice in the same population.

And that's not the sole unlikely coincidence arguing against accidental explanations. Recall that Tay-Sachs is caused by the excessive accumulation of one fatty substance, G_{M2} ganglioside, from a defect in one enzyme, hexosaminidase A. But Tay-Sachs is one of ten genetic diseases characteristic of Ashkenazim. Among those other nine, two—Gaucher's disease and Niemann-Pick disease—result from the accumulation of two other fatty substances similar to G_{M2} ganglioside, as a result of defects in two other enzymes similar to hexosaminidase A. Yet our bodies contain thousands of different enzymes. It would have been an incredible roll of the genetic dice if, by nothing more than chance, Ashkenazim had independently acquired mutations in three closely related enzymes—and had acquired mutations in one of those enzymes twice.

All these facts bring us to the fourth possible explanation of why the Tay-Sachs gene is so prevalent among Ashkenazim: namely, that something about them favored accumulation of G_{M2} ganglioside and related fats.

For comparison, suppose that a friend doubles her money on one stock while you are getting wiped out with your investments. Taken alone, that could just mean she was lucky on that one occasion. But suppose that she doubles her money on each of two different stocks and at the same time rings up big profits in real estate while also making a killing in bonds. That implies more than lady luck; it suggests that something about your friend—like shrewd judgment—favors financial success.

What could be the blessings of fat accumulation in Eastern European Jews? At first this question sounds weird. After all, that fat accumulation was noticed only because of the curses it bestows: Tay-Sachs, Gaucher's, or Niemann-Pick disease. But many of our common genetic diseases may persist because they bring both blessings and curses (see "The Cruel Logic of Our Genes," *Discover*, November 1989). They kill or impair individuals who inherit two copies of the faulty gene, but they help those who receive only one defective gene by protecting them against other diseases. The best understood example is the sickle-cell gene of African blacks, which often kills homozygotes but protects heterozygotes against malaria. Natural selection sustains such genes because more heterozygotes than normal individuals survive to pass on their genes, and those extra gene copies offset the copies lost through the deaths of homozygotes.

So let us refine our question and ask, What blessing could the Tay-Sachs gene bring to those individuals who are heterozygous for it? A clue first emerged back in 1972, with the publication of the results of a questionnaire that had asked U.S. Ashkenzaic parents of Tay-Sachs children what their own Eastern European-born parents had died of. Keep in mind that since these unfortunate children had to be homozygotes, with two copies of the Tay-Sachs gene, all their parents had to be heterozygotes, with one copy, and half of the parents' parents also had to be heterozygotes.

As it turned out, most of those Tay-Sachs grandparents had died of the usual causes: heart disease, stroke, cancer, and diabetes. But strikingly, only one of the 306 grandparents had died of tuberculosis, even though TB was generally one of the big killers in these grandparents' time. Indeed, among the general population of large Eastern European cities in the early twentieth century, TB caused up to 20 percent of all deaths.

This big discrepancy suggested that Tay-Sachs heterozygotes might somehow have been protected against TB. Interestingly, it was already well known that Ashkenazim in general had some such protection: even when Jews and non-Jews were compared within the same European city, class, and occupational group (for example, Warsaw garment workers), Jews had only half the TB death rate of non-Jews, despite their being equally susceptible to infection. Perhaps, one could reason, the Tay-Sachs gene furnished part of that well-established Jewish resistance.

We're not a melting pot, and we won't be for a long time. Each ethnic group has some characteristic genes of its own, a legacy of its distinct history.

A second clue to a heterozygote advantage conveyed by the Tay-Sachs gene emerged in 1983, with a fresh look at the data concerning the distributions of TB and the Tay-Sachs gene within Europe. The statistics showed that the Tay-Sachs gene was nearly three times more frequent among Jews originating from Austria, Hungary, and Czechoslovakia—areas where an amazing 9 to 10 percent of the population were heterozygotes—than among Jews from Poland, Russia, and Germany. At the same time records from an old Jewish TB sanatorium in Denver in 1904 showed that among patients born in Europe between 1860 and 1910, Jews from Austria and Hungary were overrepresented.

Initially, in putting together these two pieces of information, you might be tempted to conclude that because the highest frequency of the Tay-Sachs gene appeared in the same geographic region that produced the most cases of TB, the gene in fact offers no protection whatsoever. Indeed, this was precisely the mistaken conclusion of many researchers who had looked at these data before. But you have to pay careful attention to the numbers here: even at its highest frequency the Tay-Sachs gene was carried by far fewer people than would be infected by TB. What the statistics really indicate is that where TB is the biggest threat, natural selection produces the biggest response.

Think of it this way: You arrive at an island where you find that all the inhabitants of the north end wear suits of armor, while all the inhabitants of the south end wear only cloth shirts. You'd be pretty safe in assuming that warfare is more prevalent in the north—and that war-related injuries account for far more deaths there than in the south. Thus, if the Tay-Sachs gene does indeed lend heterozygotes some protection against TB, you would expect to find the gene most often precisely where you find TB most often. Similarly, the sickle-cell gene reaches its highest frequencies in those parts of Africa where malaria is the biggest risk.

But you may believe there's still a hole in the argument: If Tay-Sachs heterozygotes are protected against TB, you may be asking, why is the gene common just in the Ashkenazim? Why did it not become common in the non-Jewish populations also exposed to TB in Austria, Hungary, and Czechoslovakia?

At this point we must recall the peculiar circumstances in which the Jews of Eastern Europe were forced to live. They were unique among the world's ethnic groups in having been virtually confined to towns for most of the past 2,000 years. Being forbidden to own land, Eastern European Jews were not peasant farmers living in the countryside, but businesspeople forced to live in crowded ghettos, in an environment where tuberculosis thrived.

Of course, until recent improvements in sanitation, these towns were not very healthy places for non-Jews either. Indeed, their populations couldn't sustain themselves: deaths exceeded births, and the number of dead had to be balanced by continued emigration from the countryside. For non-Jews, therefore, there was no genetically distinct urban population. For ghetto-bound Jews, however, there could be no emigration from the countryside; thus the Jewish population was under the strongest selection to evolve genetic resistance to TB.

Those are the conditions that probably led to Jewish TB resistance, whatever particular genetic factors prove to underlie it. I'd speculate that G_{M2} and related fats accumulate at slightly higher-than-normal levels in heterozygotes, although not at the lethal levels seen in homozygotes. (The fat accumulation in heterozygotes probably takes place in the cell membrane, the cell's "armor.") I'd also speculate that the accumulation provides heterozygotes with some protection against TB, and that that's why the genes for Tay-Sachs, Gaucher's, and Niemann-Pick disease reached high frequencies in the Ashkenazim.

Having thus stated the case, let me make clear that I don't want to overstate it. The evidence is still speculative. Depending on how you do the calculation, the low frequency of TB deaths in Tay-Sachs grandparents either barely reaches or doesn't quite reach the level of proof that statisticians require to accept an effect as real rather than as one that's arisen by chance. Moreover, we have no idea of the biochemical mechanism by which fat accumulation might confer resistance against TB. For the moment, I'd say that the evidence points to some selective advantage of Tay-Sachs heterozygotes among the Ashkenazim, and that TB resistance is the only plausible hypothesis yet proposed.

For now Tay-Sachs remains a speculative model for the evolution of ethnic diseases. But it's already a proven model

of what to do about them. Twenty years ago a test was developed to identify Tay-Sachs heterozygotes, based on their lower-than-normal levels of hexosaminidase A. The test is simple, cheap, and accurate: all I did was to donate a small sample of my blood, pay $35, and wait a few days to receive the results.

If that test shows that at least one member of a couple is not a Tay-Sachs heterozygote, then any child of theirs can't be a Tay-Sachs homozygote. If both parents prove to be heterozygotes, there's a one-in-four chance of their child being a homozygote; that can then be determined by other tests performed on the mother early in pregnancy. If the results are positive, it's early enough for her to abort, should she choose to. That critical bit of knowledge has enabled parents who had gone through the agony of bearing a Tay-Sachs baby and watching him die to find the courage to try again.

The Tay-Sachs screening program launched in the United States in 1971 was targeted at the high-risk population: Ashkenazic Jewish couples of childbearing age. So successful has this approach been that the number of Tay-Sachs babies born each year in this country has declined tenfold. Today, in fact, more Tay-Sachs cases appear here in non-Jews than in Jews, because only the latter couples are routinely tested. Thus, what used to be the classic genetic disease of Jews is so no longer.

There's also a broader message to the Tay-Sachs story. We commonly refer to the United States as a melting pot, and in many ways that metaphor is apt. But in other ways we're not a melting pot, and we won't be for a long time. Each ethnic group has some characteristic genes of its own, a legacy of its distinct history. Tuberculosis and malaria are not major causes of death in the United States, but the genes that some of us evolved to protect ourselves against them are still frequent. Those genes are frequent only in certain ethnic groups, though, and they'll be slow to melt through the population.

With modern advances in molecular genetics, we can expect to see more, not less, ethnically targeted practice of medicine. Genetic screening for cystic fibrosis in European whites, for example, is one program that has been much discussed recently; when it comes, it will surely be based on the Tay-Sachs experience. Of course, what that may mean someday is more anxiety-ridden parents-to-be glowering at more dedicated genetics counselors. It will also mean fewer babies doomed to the agonies of diseases we may understand but that we'll never be able to accept.

Contributing editor Jared Diamond is a professor of physiology at the UCLA School of Medicine.

Reprinted with permission from *Discover* magazine, March 1991, pp. 60–65. © 1991 by The Walt Disney Company.

The Saltshaker's Curse

Physiological adaptations that helped American blacks
survive slavery may now be predisposing
their descendants to hypertension

[handwritten margin note: implies that white medicine did not notice problems afflicting other races such as...]

Jared Diamond

On the walls of the main corridor at UCLA Medical School hang thirty-seven photographs that tell a moving story. They are the portraits of each graduating class, from the year that the school opened (Class of 1955) to the latest crop (Class of 1991). Throughout the 1950s and early 1960s the portraits are overwhelmingly of young white men, diluted by only a few white women and Asian men. The first black student graduated in 1961, an event not repeated for several more years. When I came to UCLA in 1966, I found myself lecturing to seventy-six students, of whom seventy-four were white. Thereafter the numbers of blacks, Hispanics, and Asians exploded, until the most recent photos show the number of white medical students declining toward a minority.

In these changes of racial composition, there is of course nothing unique about UCLA Medical School. While the shifts in its student body mirror those taking place, at varying rates, in other professional groups throughout American society, we still have a long way to go before professional groups truly mirror society itself. But ethnic diversity among physicians is especially important because of the dangers inherent in a profession composed of white practitioners for whom white biology is the norm.

Different ethnic groups face different health problems, for reasons of genes as well as of life style. Familiar examples include the prevalence of skin cancer and cystic fibrosis in whites, stomach cancer and stroke in Japanese, and diabetes in Hispanics and Pacific islanders. Each year, when I teach a seminar course in ethnically varying disease patterns, these by-now-familiar textbook facts assume a gripping reality, as my various students choose to discuss some disease that affects themselves or their relatives. To read about the molecular biology of sickle-cell anemia is one thing. It's quite another thing when one of my students, a black man homozygous for the sickle-cell gene, describes the pain of his own sickling attacks and how they have affected his life. *[handwritten: this is reality]*

Sickle-cell anemia is a case in which the evolutionary origins of medically important genetic differences among peoples are well understood. (It evolved only in malarial regions because it confers resistance against malaria.) But in many other cases the evolutionary origins are not nearly so transparent. Why is it, for example, that only some human populations have a high frequency of the Tay-Sachs gene or of diabetes?…

Compared with American whites of the same age and sex, American blacks have, on the average, higher blood pressure, double the risk of developing hypertension, and nearly ten times the risk of dying of it. By age fifty, nearly half of U.S. black men are hypertensive. For a given age and blood pressure, hypertension more often causes heart disease and especially kidney failure and strokes in U.S. blacks than whites. Because the frequency of kidney disease in U.S. blacks is eighteen times that in whites, blacks account for about two-thirds of U.S. patients with hypertensive kidney failure, even though they make up only about one-tenth of the population. Around the world, only Japanese exceed U.S. blacks in their risk of dying from stroke. Yet it was not until 1932 that the average difference in blood pressure between U.S. blacks and whites was clearly demonstrated, thereby exposing a major health problem outside the norms of white medicine.

What is it about American blacks that makes them disproportionately likely to develop hypertension and then to die of its consequences? While this question is of course especially "interesting" to black readers, it also concerns all Americans, because other ethnic groups in the United States are not so far behind blacks in their risk of hypertension. If *Natural History* readers are a cross section of the United States, then about one-quarter of you now have high blood pressure, and

...lf of you will die of a heart ... stroke to which high blood ...predisposes. Thus, we all have ...easons for being interested in hy...ension.

First, some background on what those numbers mean when your doctor inflates a rubber cuff about your arm, listens, deflates the cuff, and finally pronounces, "Your blood pressure is 120 over 80." The cuff device is called a sphygmomanometer, and it measures the pressure in your artery in units of millimeters of mercury (that's the height to which your blood pressure would force up a column of mercury in case, God forbid, your artery were suddenly connected to a vertical mercury column). Naturally, your blood pressure varies with each stroke of your heart, so the first and second numbers refer, respectively, to the peak pressure at each heartbeat (systolic pressure) and to the minimum pressure between beats (diastolic pressure). Blood pressure varies somewhat with position, activity, and anxiety level, so the measurement is usually made while you are resting flat on your back. Under those conditions, 120 over 80 is an average reading for Americans.

There is no magic cutoff between normal blood pressure and high blood pressure. Instead, the higher your blood pressure, the more likely you are to die of a heart attack, stroke, kidney failure, or ruptured aorta. Usually, a pressure reading higher than 140 over 90 is arbitrarily defined as constituting hypertension, but some people with lower readings will die of a stroke at age fifty, while others with higher readings will die in a car accident in good health at age ninety.

Why do some of us have much higher blood pressure than others? In about 5 percent of hypertensive patients there is an identifiable single cause, such as hormonal imbalance or use of oral contraceptives. In 95 percent of such cases, though, there is no such obvious cause. The clinical euphemism for our ignorance in such cases is "essential hypertension."

Nowadays, we know that there is a big genetic component in essential hypertension, although the particular genes involved have not yet been identified. Among people living in the same house-

hold, the correlation coefficient for blood pressure is 0.63 between identical twins, who share all of their genes. (A correlation coefficient of 1.00 would mean that the twins share identical blood pressures as well and would suggest that pressure is determined entirely by genes and not at all by environment.) Fraternal twins or ordinary siblings or a parent and child, who share half their genes and whose blood pressure would therefore show a correlation coefficient of 0.5 if purely determined genetically, actually have a coefficient of about 0.25. Finally, adopted siblings or a parent and adopted child, who have no direct genetic connection, have a correlation coefficient of only 0.05. Despite the shared household environment, their blood pressures are barely more similar than those of two people pulled randomly off the street. In agreement with this evidence for genetic factors underlying blood pressure itself, your risk of actually developing hypertensive disease increases from 4 percent to 20 percent to 35 percent if, respectively, none or one or both of your parents were hypertensive.

But these same facts suggest that environmental factors also contribute to high blood pressure, since identical twins have similar but not identical blood pressures. Many environmental or life style factors contributing to the risk of hypertension have been identified by epidemiological studies that compare hypertension's frequency in groups of people living under different conditions. Such contributing factors include obesity, high intake of salt or alcohol or saturated fats, and low calcium intake. The proof of this approach is that hypertensive patients who modify their life styles so as to minimize these putative factors often succeed in reducing their blood pressure. Patients are especially advised to reduce salt intake and stress, reduce intake of cholesterol and saturated fats and alcohol, lose weight, cut out smoking, and exercise regularly.

Here are some examples of the epidemiological studies pointing to these risk factors. Around the world, comparisons within and between populations show that both blood pressure and the frequency of hypertension increase hand in hand with salt intake. At the one ex-

treme, Brazil's Yanomamö Indians have the world's lowest-known salt consumption (somewhat above 10 milligrams per day!), lowest average blood pressure (95 over 61!), and lowest incidence of hypertension (no cases!). At the opposite extreme, doctors regard Japan as the "land of apoplexy" because of the high frequency of fatal strokes (Japan's leading cause of death, five times more frequent than in the United States), linked with high blood pressure and notoriously salty food. Within Japan itself these factors reach their extremes in Akita Prefecture, famous for its tasty rice, which Akita farmers flavor with salt, wash down with salty miso soup, and alternate with salt pickles between meals. Of 300 Akita adults studied, not one consumed less than five grams of salt daily, the average consumption was twenty-seven grams, and the most salt-loving individual consumed an incredible sixty-one grams—enough to devour the contents of the usual twenty-six-ounce supermarket salt container in a mere twelve days. The average blood pressure in Akita by age fifty is 151 over 93, making hypertension (pressure higher than 140 over 90) the norm. Not surprisingly, Akitas' frequency of death by stroke is more than double even the Japanese average, and in some Akita villages 99 percent of the population dies before age seventy.

Why salt intake often (in about 60 percent of hypertensive patients) leads to high blood pressure is not fully understood. One possible interpretation is that salt intake triggers thirst, leading to an increase in blood volume. In response, the heart increases its output and blood pressure rises, causing the kidneys to filter more salt and water under that increased pressure. The result is a new steady state, in which salt and water excretion again equals intake, but more salt and water are stored in the body and blood pressure is raised.

At this point, let's contrast hypertension with a simple genetic disease like Tay-Sachs disease. Tay-Sachs is due to a defect in a single gene; every Tay Sachs patient has a defect in that same gene. Everybody in whom that gene is defective is certain to die of Tay-Sachs, regardless of their life style or environment. In contrast, hypertension in-

No hope for Tay-Sachs - it is in the genes destined to die

volves several different genes whose molecular products remain to be identified. Because there are many causes of raised blood pressure, different hypertensive patients may owe their condition to different gene combinations. Furthermore, whether someone genetically predisposed to hypertension actually develops symptoms depends a lot on life style. Thus, hypertension is not one of those uncommon, homogeneous, and intellectually elegant diseases that geneticists prefer to study. Instead, like diabetes and ulcers, hypertension is a shared set of symptoms produced by heterogeneous causes, all involving an interaction between environmental agents and a susceptible genetic background.

Since U.S. blacks and whites differ on the average in the conditions under which they live, could those differences account for excess hypertension in U.S. blacks? Salt intake, the dietary factor that one thinks of first, turns out on the average not to differ between U.S. blacks and whites. Blacks do consume less potassium and calcium, do experience more stress associated with more difficult socioeconomic conditions, have much less access to medical care, and are therefore much less likely to be diagnosed or treated until it is too late. Those factors surely contribute to the frequency and severity of hypertension in blacks.

However, those factors don't seem to be the whole explanation: hypertensive blacks aren't merely like severely hypertensive whites. Instead, physiological differences seem to contribute as well. On consuming salt, blacks retain it on average far longer before excreting it into the urine, and they experience a greater rise in blood pressure on a high-salt diet. Hypertension is more likely to be "salt-sensitive" in blacks than in whites, meaning that blood pressure is more likely to rise and fall with rises and falls in dietary salt intake. By the same token, black hypertension is more likely to be treated successfully by drugs that cause the kidneys to excrete salt (the so-called thiazide diuretics) and less likely to respond to those drugs that reduce heart rate and cardiac output (so-called beta blockers, such as propanolol). These facts suggest that there are some qualitative differences between the causes of black and white hypertension, with black hypertension more likely to involve how the kidneys handle salt.

Physicians often refer to this postulated feature as a "defect": for example, "kidneys of blacks have a genetic defect in excreting sodium." As an evolutionary biologist, though, I hear warning bells going off inside me whenever a seemingly harmful trait that occurs frequently in an old and large human population is dismissed as a "defect." Given enough generations, genes that greatly impede survival are extremely unlikely to spread, unless their net effect is to increase survival and reproductive success. Human medicine has furnished the best examples of seemingly defective genes being propelled to high frequency by counterbalancing benefits. For example, sickle-cell hemoglobin protects far more people against malaria than it kills of anemia, while the Tay-Sachs gene may have protected far more Jews against tuberculosis than it killed of neurological disease. Thus, to understand why U.S. blacks now are prone to die as a result of their kidneys' retaining salt, we need to ask under what conditions people might have benefited from kidneys good at retaining salt.

That question is hard to understand from the perspective of modern Western society, where saltshakers are on every dining table, salt (sodium chloride) is cheap, and our bodies' main problem is getting rid of it. But imagine what the world used to be like before saltshakers became ubiquitous. Most plants contain very little sodium, yet animals require sodium at high concentrations in all their extracellular fluids. As a result, carnivores readily obtain their needed sodium by eating herbivores, but herbivores themselves face big problems in acquiring that sodium. That's why the animals that one sees coming to salt licks are deer and antelope, not lions and tigers. Similarly, some human hunter-gatherers obtained enough salt from the meat that they ate. But when we began to take up farming ten thousand years ago, we either had to evolve kidneys superefficient at conserving salt or learn to extract salt at great effort or trade for it at great expense.

Examples of these various solutions abound. I already mentioned Brazil's Yanomamö Indians, whose staple food is low-sodium bananas and who excrete on the average only 10 milligrams of salt daily—barely one-thousandth the salt excretion of the typical American. A single Big Mac hamburger analyzed by *Consumer Reports* contained 1.5 grams (1,500 milligrams) of salt, representing many weeks of intake for a Yanomamö. The New Guinea highlanders with whom I work, and whose diet consists up to 90 percent of low-sodium sweet potatoes, told me of the efforts to which they went to make salt a few decades ago, before Europeans brought it as trade goods. They gathered leaves of certain plant species, burned them, scraped up the ash, percolated water through it to dissolve the solids, and finally evaporated the water to obtain small amounts of bitter salt.

Thus, salt has been in very short supply for much of recent human evolutionary history. Those of us with efficient kidneys able to retain salt even on a low-sodium diet were better able to survive our inevitable episodes of sodium loss (of which more in a moment). Those kidneys proved to be a detriment only when salt became routinely available, leading to excessive salt retention and hypertension with its fatal consequences. That's why blood pressure and the frequency of hypertension have shot up recently in so many populations around the world as they have made the transition from being self-sufficient subsistence farmers to members of the cash economy and patrons of supermarkets.

This evolutionary argument has been advanced by historian-epidemiologist Thomas Wilson and others to explain the current prevalence of hypertension in American blacks in particular. Many West African blacks, from whom most American blacks originated via the slave trade, must have faced the chronic problem of losing salt through sweating in their hot environment. Yet in West Africa, except on the coast and certain inland areas, salt was traditionally as scarce for African farmers as it has been for Yanomamö and New Guinea farmers. (Ironically, those Africans who sold other Africans as slaves often took payment in salt traded from the Sahara.) By this argument, the genetic basis for hypertension in U.S. blacks was already widespread in many of their West African ancestors. It required only the ubiquity of saltshakers in twentieth-century America for that genetic basis to express itself as hypertension. This argument also predicts that as Africa's life style becomes increasingly Westernized, hypertension could become as prevalent in West Africa as it now is among U.S. blacks. In this view, American blacks would be no different from the many Polynesian, Melanesian, Kenyan, Zulu, and other populations that have recently developed high blood pressure under a Westernized life style.

But there's an intriguing extension to this hypothesis, proposed by Wilson and physician Clarence Grim, collaborators at the Hypertension Research Center of Drew University in Los Angeles. They suggest a scenario in which New World blacks may now be at more risk for hypertension than their African ancestors. That scenario involves very recent selection for super-efficient kidneys, driven by massive mortality of black slaves from salt loss.

Grim and Wilson's argument goes as follows. Black slavery in the Americas began about 1517, with the first imports of slaves from West Africa, and did not end until Brazil freed its slaves barely a century ago in 1888. In the course of the slave trade an estimated 12 million Africans were brought to the Americas. But those imports were winnowed by deaths at many stages, from an even larger number of captives and exports.

First, slaves captured by raids in the interior of West Africa were chained together, loaded with heavy burdens, and marched for one or two months, with little food and water, to the coast. About 25 percent of the captives died en route. While awaiting purchase by slave traders, the survivors were held on the coast in hot, crowded buildings called barracoons, where about 12 percent of them died. The traders went up and down the coast buying and loading slaves for a few weeks or months until a ship's cargo was full (5 percent more died). The dreaded Middle Passage across the Atlantic killed 10 percent of the slaves, chained together in a hot, crowded, unventilated

hold without sanitation. (Picture to yourself the result of those toilet "arrangements.") Of those who lived to land in the New World, 5 percent died while awaiting sale, and 12 percent died while being marched or shipped from the sale yard to the plantation. Finally, of those who survived, between 10 and 40 percent died during the first three years of plantation life, in a process euphemistically called seasoning. At that stage, about 70 percent of the slaves initially captured were dead, leaving 30 percent as seasoned survivors.

Even the end of seasoning, however, was not the end of excessive mortality. About half of slave infants died within a year of birth because of the poor nutrition and heavy workload of their mothers. In plantation terminology, slave women were viewed as either "breeding units" or "work units," with a built-in conflict between those uses: "These Negroes breed the best, whose labour is least," as an eighteenth-century observer put it. As a result, many New World slave populations depended on continuing slave imports and couldn't maintain their own numbers because death rates exceeded birth rates. Since buying new slaves cost less than rearing slave children for twenty years until they were adults, slave owners lacked economic incentive to change this state of affairs.

Recall that Darwin discussed natural selection and survival of the fittest with respect to animals. Since many more animals die than survive to produce offspring, each generation becomes enriched in the genes of those of the preceding generation that were among the survivors. It should now be clear that slavery represented a tragedy of unnatural selection in humans on a gigantic scale. From examining accounts of slave mortality, Grim and Wilson argue that death was indeed selective: much of it was related to unbalanced salt loss, which quickly brings on collapse. We think immediately of salt loss by sweating under hot conditions: while slaves were working, marching, or confined in unventilated barracoons or ships' holds. More body salt may have been spilled with vomiting from seasickness. But the biggest salt loss at every stage was from diarrhea due to crowding and lack of san-

itation—ideal conditions for the spread of gastrointestinal infections. Cholera and other bacterial diarrheas kill us by causing sudden massive loss of salt and water. (Picture your most recent bout of *turista*, multiplied to a diarrheal fluid output of twenty quarts in one day, and you'll understand why.) All contemporary accounts of slave ships and plantation life emphasized diarrhea, or "fluxes" in eighteenth-century terminology, as one of the leading killers of slaves.

Grim and Wilson reason, then, that slavery suddenly selected for superefficient kidneys surpassing the efficient kidneys already selected by thousands of years of West African history. Only those slaves who were best able to retain salt could survive the periodic risk of high salt loss to which they were exposed. Salt supersavers would have had the further advantage of building up, under normal conditions, more of a salt reserve in their body fluids and bones, thereby enabling them to survive longer or more frequent bouts of diarrhea. Those superkidneys became a disadvantage only when modern medicine began to reduce diarrhea's lethal impact, thereby transforming a blessing into a curse.

Thus, we have two possible evolutionary explanations for salt retention by New World blacks. One involves slow selection by conditions operating in Africa for millennia; the other, rapid recent selection by slave conditions within the past few centuries. The result in either case would make New World blacks more susceptible than whites to hypertension, but the second explanation would, in addition, make them more susceptible than African blacks. At present, we don't know the relative importance of these two explanations. Grim and Wilson's provocative hypothesis is likely to stimulate medical and physiological comparisons of American blacks with African blacks and thereby to help resolve the question.

While this piece has focused on one medical problem in one human population, it has several larger morals. One, of course, is that our differing genetic heritages predispose us to different diseases, depending on the part of the world where our ancestors lived. Another is that our genetic differences reflect not only ancient conditions in different parts of the world but also recent episodes of migration and mortality. A well-established example is the decrease in the frequency of the sickle-cell hemoglobin gene in U.S. blacks compared with African blacks, because selection for resistance to malaria is now unimportant in the United States. The example of black hypertension that Grim and Wilson discuss opens the door to considering other possible selective effects of the slave experience. They note that occasional periods of starvation might have selected slaves

for superefficient sugar metabolism, leading under modern conditions to a propensity for diabetes.

Finally, consider a still more universal moral. Almost all people alive today exist under very different conditions from those under which every human lived 10,000 years ago. It's remarkable that our old genetic heritage now permits us to survive at all under such different circumstances. But our heritage still catches up with most of us, who will die of life style related diseases such as cancer, heart attack, stroke, and diabetes. The risk factors for these diseases are the strange new conditions prevailing in

modern Western society. One of the hardest challenges for modern medicine will be to identify for us which among all those strange new features of diet, life style, and environment are the ones getting us into trouble. For each of us, the answers will depend on our particular genes, hence on our ancestry. Only with such individually tailored advice can we hope to reap the benefits of modern living while still housed in bodies designed for life before saltshakers.

Jared Diamond is a professor of physiology at UCLA Medical School.

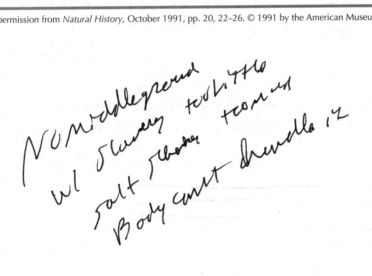

UNIT 2
Primates

Unit Selections

Key Points to Consider

- What is the role of deception among primates, and how might it have led to greater intelligence?

- Why is friendship important to olive baboons? What implications does this have for the origins of pair-bonding in hominid evolution?

- What are the implications for human evolution of tool use, social hunting, and food sharing among Ivory Coast chimpanzees?

- Should chimpanzee behavioral patterns be classified as "cultural"?

- Why is the mountain gorilla in danger of extinction?

- How do primates cope with crowding? Under what circumstances do they turn to violence?

- To what extent do apes have language skills?

- Are we in anthropodenial? Explain your answer.

 **Links: www.dushkin.com/online/**
These sites are annotated in the World Wide Web pages.

African Primates at Home
http://www.indiana.edu/~primate/primates.html

Chimpanzee and Great Ape Language Resources—Anthropology
http://www.brown.edu/Departments/Anthropology/apelang.html

Electronic Zoo/NetVet-Primate Page
http://netvet.wustl.edu/primates.htm

Jane Goodall Research Center
http://www.usc.edu/dept/elab/anth/goodall.html

Primates are fun. They are active, intelligent, colorful, emotionally expressive, and unpredictable. In other words, observing them is like holding up an opaque mirror to ourselves. The image may not be crystal-clear or, indeed, what some would consider flattering, but it is certainly familiar enough to be illuminating.

Primates are, of course, but one of many orders of mammals that adaptively radiated into the variety of ecological niches vacated at the end of the Age of Reptiles about 65 million years ago. Whereas some mammals took to the sea (cetaceans), and some took to the air (chiroptera, or bats), primates are characterized by an arboreal or forested adaptation. Whereas some mammals can be identified by their food-getting habits, such as the meat-eating carnivores, primates have a penchant for eating almost anything and are best described as omnivorous. In taking to the trees, primates did not simply develop a full-blown set of distinguishing characteristics that set them off easily from other orders of mammals. Rather, each primate seems to represent degrees of anatomical, biological, and behavioral characteristics on a continuum of progress with respect to the particular traits we humans happen to be interested in.

None of this is meant to imply, of course, that the living primates are our ancestors. Since the prosimians, monkeys, and apes are our contemporaries, they are no more our ancestors than we are theirs, and, as living end-products of evolution, we have all descended from a common stock in the distant past. So, if we are interested primarily in our own evolutionary past, why study primates at all? Because, by the criteria we have set up as significant milestones in the evolution of humanity, an inherent reflection of our own bias, primates have not evolved as far as we have. They and their environments, therefore, may represent glimmerings of the evolutionary stages and ecological circumstances through which our own ancestors may have gone. What we stand to gain, for instance, is an educated guess as to how our own ancestors might have appeared and behaved as semierect creatures before becoming bipedal. Aside from being a pleasure to observe, then, living primates can teach us something about our past.

Another reason for studying primates is that they allow us to test certain notions too often taken for granted. For instance, in "Coping With Crowding," Frans de Waal, Filippo Aureli, and Peter Judge call into question the notion that high population densities in primates necessarily lead to violence. In another example, Barbara Smuts, in "What Are Friends For?" reveals that friendship bonds, as illustrated by the olive baboons of East Africa, have little if anything to do with a sexual division of labor or even sexual exclusivity between a pair-bonded male and female. Smuts challenges the traditional male-oriented idea that primate societies are dominated solely by males for males.

This unit demonstrates that relationships between the sexes are subject to wide variation, that the kinds of answers that are obtained depend upon the kinds of questions that are asked, and that we have to be very careful in making inferences about human beings from any one particular primate study. We may, if we are not careful, draw conclusions that say more about our own skewed perspectives than about that which we claim to understand. Still another benefit of primate field research is that it provides us with perspectives that the bones and stones of the fossil hunters will never reveal: a sense of the richness and variety of social patterns that must have existed in the primate order for many tens of millions of years. (See James Shreeve's report "Machiavellian Monkeys," Robert Sapolsky's essay, "Fossey in the Mist," and Jane Goodall's "The Mind of the Chimpanzee.")

Even if we had the physical remains of the earliest hominids in front of us, which we do not have, there is no way such evidence could thoroughly answer the questions that physical anthropologists care most deeply about: How did these creatures move about and get their food? Did they cooperate and share? On what levels did they think and communicate? Did they have a sense of family, let alone a sense of self? In one way or another, all of the previously mentioned articles on primates relate to these issues, as do some of the subsequent ones on the fossil evidence. But what sets off this unit from the others is how some of the authors attempt to deal with these matters head-on, even in the absence of direct fossil evidence. Christophe Boesch and Hedwige Boesch-Achermann, in "Dim Forest, Bright Chimps," indicate that some aspects of "hominization" (the acquisition of such humanlike qualities as cooperative hunting and food sharing) actually may have begun in the African rain forest rather than in the dry savanna, as has usually been proposed. They base their suggestions on some remarkable first-hand observations of forest-dwelling chimpanzees.

As if to show that chimpanzee behavior may vary according to local circumstances, just as we know human behavior does, Craig Stanford, in "To Catch a Colobus," contrasts his observations of chimpanzee hunting in Gombe National Park with the findings of the Boesches. In fact, behavioral variations in chimpanzees are so extensive that Andrew Whiten and Christophe Boesch (in "The Culture of Chimpanzees") make a strong case for such differences to be classified as cultural.

Recent research has shown some striking resemblances between apes and humans, hinting that such qualities might have been characteristic of our common ancestors. Following this line of reasoning, Frans de Waal ("Are We in Anthropodenial?") argues that we can make educated guesses as to the mental and physical processes of our hominid predecessors. Moreover, Sharon Begley ("Aping Language") suggests that the common ancestor of chimpanzees and humans may have even possessed rudimentary language abilities.

Taken collectively, the articles in this section show how far anthropologists are willing to go to construct theoretical formulations based upon limited data. Although making so much out of so little may be seen as a fault and may generate irreconcilable differences among theorists, a readiness to entertain new ideas should be welcomed for what it is—a stimulus for more intensive and meticulous research.

Machiavellian Monkeys

The sneaky skills of our primate cousins suggest that we may owe our great intelligence to an inherited need to deceive.

James Shreeve

This is a story about frauds, cheats, liars, faithless lovers, incorrigible con artists, and downright thieves. You're gonna love 'em.

Let's start with a young rascal named Paul. You'll remember his type from your days back in the playground. You're minding your own business, playing on the new swing set, when along comes Paul, such a little runt that you hardly notice him sidle up to you. All of a sudden he lets out a scream like you've run him through with a white-hot barbed harpoon or something. Of course the teacher comes running, and the next thing you know you're being whisked inside with an angry finger shaking in your face. That's the end of recess for you. But look out the window: there's Paul, having a great time on *your* swing. Cute kid.

Okay, you're a little older now and a little smarter. You've got a bag of chips stashed away in your closet, where for once your older brother won't be able to find them. You're about to open the closet door when he pokes his head in the room. Quickly you pretend to be fetching your high tops; he gives you a look but he leaves. You wait a couple of minutes, lacing up the sneakers in case he walks back in, then you dive for the chips. Before you can get the bag open, he's over your shoulder, snatching it out of your hands. "Nice try, punk," he says through a mouthful, "but I was hiding outside your room the whole time."

This sort of trickery is such a common part of human interaction that we hardly notice how much time we spend defending ourselves against it or perpetrating it ourselves. What's so special about the fakes and cheaters here, however, is that they're not human. Paul is a young baboon, and your big brother is, well, a chimpanzee. With some admittedly deceptive alterations of scenery and props, the situations have been lifted from a recent issue of *Primate Report*. The journal is the work of Richard Byrne and Andrew Whiten, two psychologists at the University of St. Andrews in Scotland, and it is devoted to cataloging the petty betrayals of monkeys and apes as witnessed by primatologists around the world. It is a testament to the evolutionary importance of what Byrne and Whiten call Machiavellian intelligence—a facility named for the famed sixteenth-century author of *The Prince*, the ultimate how-to guide to prevailing in a complex society through the judicious application of cleverness, deceit, and political acumen.

Deception is rife in the natural world. Stick bugs mimic sticks. Harmless snakes resemble deadly poisonous ones. When threatened, blowfish puff themselves up and cats arch their backs and bristle their hair to seem bigger than they really are. All these animals could be said to practice deception because they fool other animals—usually members of other species—into thinking they are something that they patently are not. Even so, it would be overreading the situation to attribute Machiavellian cunning to a blowfish, or to accuse a stick

bug of being a lying scoundrel. Their deceptions, whether in their looks or in their actions, are programmed genetic responses. Biology leaves them no choice but to dissemble: they are just being true to themselves.

The kind of deception that interests Byrne and Whiten—what they call tactical deception—is a different kettle of blowfish altogether. Here an animal has the mental flexibility to take an "honest" behavior and use it in such a way that another animal—usually a member of the deceiver's own social group—is misled, thinking that a normal, familiar state of affairs is under way, while, in fact, something quite different is happening.

Take Paul, for example. The real Paul is a young chacma baboon that caught Whiten's attention in 1983, while he and Byrne were studying foraging among the chacma in the Drakensberg Mountains of southern Africa. Whiten saw a member of Paul's group, an adult female named Mel, digging in the ground, trying to extract a nutritious plant bulb. Paul approached and looked around. There were no other baboons within sight. Suddenly he let out a yell, and within seconds his mother came running, chasing the startled Mel over a small cliff. Paul then took the bulb for himself.

In this case the deceived party was Paul's mother, who was misled by his scream into believing that Paul was being attacked, when actually no such attack was taking place. As a result of her apparent misinterpretation Paul was left alone to eat the bulb that Mel had carefully extracted—a morsel, by the way, that he would not have had the strength to dig out on his own.

If Paul's ruse had been an isolated case, Whiten might have gone on with his foraging studies and never given it a second thought. But when he compared his field notes with Byrne's, he noticed that both their notebooks were sprinkled with similar incidents and had been so all summer long. After they returned home to Scotland, they boasted about their "dead smart" baboons to their colleagues in pubs after conferences, expecting them to be suitably impressed. Instead the other researchers countered with tales about their own shrewd vervets or Machiavellian macaques.

"That's when we realized that a whole phenomenon might be slipping through a sieve," says Whiten. Researchers had assumed that this sort of complex trickery was a product of the sophisticated human brain. After all, deceitful behavior seemed unique to humans, and the human brain is unusually large, even for primates—"three times as big as you would expect for a primate of our size," notes Whiten, if you're plotting brain size against body weight.

But if primates other than humans deceived one another on a regular basis, the two psychologists reasoned, then it raised the extremely provocative possibility that the primate brain, and ultimately the human brain, is an instrument crafted for social manipulation. Humans evolved from the same evolutionary stock as apes, and if tactical deception was an important part of the lives of our evolutionary ancestors, then the sneakiness and subterfuge that human beings are so manifestly capable of might not be simply a result of our great intelligence and oversize brain, but a driving force behind their development.

To Byrne and Whiten these were ideas worth pursuing. They fit in with a theory put forth some years earlier by English psychologist Nicholas Humphrey. In 1976 Humphrey had eloquently suggested that the evolution of primate intelligence might have been spurred not by the challenges of environment, as was generally thought, but rather by the complex cognitive demands of living with one's own companions. Since then a number of primatologists had begun to flesh out his theory with field observations of politically astute monkeys and apes.

Suddenly Paul let out a yell, and his mother came running, chasing Mel over a small cliff.

Deception, however, had rarely been reported. And no wonder: If chimps, baboons, and higher primates generally are skilled deceivers, how could one ever know it? The best deceptions would by their very nature go undetected by the other members of the primate group, not to mention by a human stranger. Even those ruses that an observer could see through would have to be rare, for if used too often, they would lose their effectiveness. If Paul always cried wolf, for example, his mother would soon learn to ignore his ersatz distress. So while the monkey stories swapped over beers certainly suggested that deception was widespread among higher primates, it seemed unlikely that one or even a few researchers could observe enough instances of it to scientifically quantify how much, by whom, when, and to what effect. *maybe maybe not*

Byrne and Whiten's solution was to extend their pub-derived data base with a more formal survey. In 1985 they sent a questionnaire to more than 100 primatologists working both in the field and in labs, asking them to report back any incidents in which they felt their subjects had perpetrated deception on one another. The questionnaire netted a promising assortment of deceptive tactics used by a variety of monkeys and all the great apes. Only the relatively small-brained and socially simple lemur family, which includes bush babies and lorises, failed to elicit a single instance. This supported the notion that society, sneakiness, brain size, and intelligence are intimately bound up with one another. The sneakier the primate, it seemed, the bigger the brain.

Byrne and Whiten drew up a second, much more comprehensive questionnaire in 1989 and sent it to hundreds more primatologists and animal behaviorists, greatly increasing the data base. Once again, when the results were tallied, only the lemur family failed to register a single case of deception.

All the other species, however, represented a simian rogues' gallery of liars and frauds. Often deception was used to distract another animal's attention. In one cartoonish example, a young baboon, chased by some angry elders, suddenly stopped, stood on his hind legs, and stared at a spot on the horizon, as if he noticed the presence of a predator or a foreign troop of baboons. His pursuers braked to a halt and looked in the same direction, giving up the chase. Powerful field binoculars revealed that no predator or baboon troop was anywhere in sight.

Sometimes the deception was simply a matter of one animal hiding a choice bit of food from the awareness of those strong enough to take it away. One of Jane Goodall's chimps, for example, named Figan, was once given some bananas after the more dominant members of the troop had wandered off. In the excitement, he uttered some loud "food barks"; the others quickly returned and took the bananas away. The next day Figan again waited behind the others and got some bananas. This time, however, he kept silent, even though the human observers, Goodall reported, "could hear faint choking sounds in his throat."

Concealment was a common ruse in sexual situations as well. Male monkeys and chimpanzees in groups have fairly strict hierarchies that control their access to females. Animals at the top of the order intimidate those lower down, forcing them away from females. Yet one researcher reported seeing a male stump-tailed macaque of a middle rank leading a female out of sight of the more dominant males and then mating with her silently, his climax unaccompanied by the harsh, low-pitched grunts that the male stump-tailed normally makes. At one point during the tryst the female turned and stared into his face, then covered his mouth with her hand. In another case a subordinate chimpanzee, aroused by the presence of a female in estrus, covered his erect penis with his hand when a dominant male approached, thus avoiding a likely attack.

In one particularly provocative instance a female hamadryas baboon slowly shuffled toward a large rock, appearing to forage, all the time keeping an eye on the most dominant male in the group. After 20 minutes she ended up with her head and shoulders visible to the big, watchful male, but with her hands happily engaged in the elicit activity of grooming a favorite subordinate male, who was hidden from view behind the rock.

Baboons proved singularly adept at a form of deception that Byrne and Whiten call "using a social tool." Paul's scam is a perfect example: he fools his mother into acting as a lever to pry the plant bulb away from the adult female, Mel. But can it be said unequivocally that he intended to deceive her? Perhaps Paul had simply learned through trial and error that letting out a yell brought his mother running and left him with food, in which case there is no reason to endow his young baboon intellect with Machiavellian intent. How do we know that Mel didn't actually threaten Paul in some way that Byrne and Whiten, watching, could not comprehend? While we're at it, how do we know that any of the primate deceptions reported here were really deliberate, conscious acts?

"It has to be said that there is a whole school of psychology that would deny such behavior even to humans," says Byrne. The school in question—strict behaviorism—would seek an explanation for the baboons' behavior not by trying to crawl inside their head but by carefully analyzing observable behaviors and the stimuli that might be triggering them. Byrne and Whiten's strategy against such skepticism was to be hyperskeptical themselves. They accepted that trial-and-error learning or simple conditioning, in which an animal's actions are reinforced by a reward, might account for a majority of the incidents reported to them—even when they believed that tactical deception was really taking place. But when explaining things "simply" led to a maze of extraordinary coincidences and tortuous logic, the evidence for deliberate deception seemed hard to dismiss.

Paul, for instance, *might* have simply learned that screaming elicits the reward of food, via his mother's intervention. But Byrne witnessed him using the same tactic several times, and in each case his mother was out of sight, able to hear his yell but not able to see what was really going on. If Paul was simply conditioned to scream, why would he do so only when his mother could not see who was—or was not—attacking her son?

Society, sneakiness, brain size, and intelligence are intimately bound up with one another.

Still, it is possible that she was not intentionally deceived. But in at least one other, similar case there is virtually no doubt that the mother was responding to a bogus attack, because the alleged attacker was quite able to verbalize his innocence. A five-year-old male chimp named Katabi, in the process of weaning, had discovered that the best way to get his reluctant mother to suckle him was to convince her he needed reassurance. One day Katabi approached a human observer—Japanese primatologist Toshisada Nishida—and began to screech, circling around the researcher and waving an accusing hand at him. The chimp's mother and her escort immediately glared at Nishida, their hair erect. Only by slowly backing away from the screaming youngster did Nishida avoid a possible attack from the two adult chimps.

"In fact I did nothing to him," Nishida protested. It follows that the adults were indeed misled by Katabi's hysterics—unless there was some threat in Nishida unknown even to himself.

"If you try hard enough," says Byrne, "you can explain every single case without endowing the animal with the ability to deceive. But if you look at the whole body of work, there comes a point where you have to strive officiously to deny it."

The cases most resistant to such officious denials are the rarest—and the most compelling. In these interactions the primate involved not only employed

tactical deception but clearly understood the concept. Such comprehension would depend upon one animal's ability to "read the mind" of another: to attribute desires, intentions, or even beliefs to the other creature that do not necessarily correspond to its own view of the world. Such mind reading was clearly evident in only 16 out of 253 cases in the 1989 survey, all of them involving great apes.

For example, consider Figan again, the young chimp who suppressed his food barks in order to keep the bananas for himself. In his case, mind reading is not evident: he might simply have learned from experience that food barks in certain contexts result in a loss of food, and thus he might not understand the nature of his own ruse, even if the other chimps are in fact deceived.

But contrast Figan with come chimps observed by Dutch primatologist Frans Plooij. One of these chimps was alone in a feeding area when a metal box containing food was opened electronically. At the same moment another chimp happened to approach. (Sound familiar? It's your older brother again.) The first chimp quickly closed the metal box (that's you hiding your chips), walked away, and sat down, looking around as if nothing had happened. The second chimp departed, but after going some distance away he hid behind a tree and peeked back at the first chimp. When the first chimp thought the coast was clear, he opened the box. The second chimp ran out, pushed the other aside, and ate the bananas.

Chimp One might be a clever rogue, but Chimp Two, who counters his deception with a ruse of his own, is the true mind reader. The success of his ploy is based on his insight that Chimp One was trying to deceive *him* and on his ability to adjust his behavior accordingly. He has in fact performed a prodigious cognitive leap—proving himself capable of projecting himself into another's mental space, and becoming what Humphrey would call a natural psychologist.

Niccolò Machiavelli might have called him good raw material. It is certainly suggestive that only the great apes—our closest relatives—seem capable of deceits based on such mind reading, and chimpanzees most of all. This does not necessarily mean that chimps are inherently more intelligent: the difference may be a matter of social organization. Orangutans live most of their lives alone, and thus they would not have much reason to develop such a complex social skill. And gorillas live in close family groups, whose members would be more familiar, harder to fool, and more likely to punish an attempted swindle. Chimpanzees, on the other hand, spend their lives in a shifting swirl of friends and relations, where small groups constantly form and break apart and reform with new members.

"What an opportunity for lying and cheating!" muses Byrne. Many anthropologists now believe that the social life of early hominids—our first non-ape ancestors—was much like that of chimps today, with similar opportunities to hone their cognitive skills on one another. Byrne and Whiten stop just short of saying that mind reading is the key to understanding the growth of human intelligence. But it would be disingenuous to ignore the possibility. If you were an early hominid who could comprehend the subjective impressions of others and manipulate them to your own ends, you might well have a competitive advantage over those less psychosocially nimble, perhaps enjoying slightly easier access to food and to the mating opportunities that would ensure your genetic survival.

Consider too how much more important your social wits would be in a world where the targets of your deceptions were constantly trying to outsmart *you*. After millennia of intrigue and counter-intrigue, a hominid species might well evolve a brain three times bigger than it "should" be—and capable of far more than deceiving other hominids. "The ability to attribute other intentions to other people could have been an enormous building block for many human achievements, including language," says Whiten. "That this leap seems to have been taken by chimps and possibly the other great apes puts that development in human mentality quite early."

So did our intellect rise to its present height on a tide of manipulation and deceit? Some psychologists, even those who support the notion that the evolution of intelligence was socially driven, think that Bryne and Whiten's choice of the loaded adjective *Machiavellian* might be unnecessarily harsh.

"In my opinion," says Humphrey, "the word gives too much weight to the hostile use of intelligence. One of the functions of intellect in higher primates and humans is to keep the social unit together and make it able to successfully exploit the environment. A lot of intelligence could better be seen as driven by the need for cooperation and compassion." To that, Byrne and Whiten only point out that cooperation is itself an excellent Machiavellian strategy—sometimes. *Feeding strategies*

The Scottish researchers are not, of course, the first to have noticed this. "It is good to appear clement, trustworthy, humane, religious, and honest, and also to be so," Machiavelli advised his aspiring Borgia prince in 1513. "But always with the mind so disposed that, when the occasion arises not to be so, you can become the opposite."

Reprinted with permission from *Discover* magazine, June 1991, pp. 69–73. © 1991 The Walt Disney Company.

a social group based on deception would lead to extinction

(handwritten note: Focuses on other go? Time when they can't mate)

What Are Friends For?

*Among East African baboons, friendship means companions, health, safety...
and, sometimes, sex*

Barbara Smuts

Virgil, a burly adult male olive baboon, closely followed Zizi, a middle-aged female easily distinguished by her grizzled coat and square muzzle. On her rump Zizi sported a bright pink swelling, indicating that she was sexually receptive and probably fertile. Virgil's extreme attentiveness to Zizi suggested to me—and all rival males in the troop—that he was her current and exclusive mate.

Zizi, however, apparently had something else in mind. She broke away from Virgil, moved rapidly through the troop, and presented her alluring sexual swelling to one male after another. Before Virgil caught up with her, she had managed to announce her receptive condition to several of his rivals. When Virgil tried to grab her, Zizi screamed and dashed into the bushes with Virgil in hot pursuit. I heard sounds of chasing and fighting coming from the thicket. Moments later Zizi emerged from the bushes with an older male named Cyclops. They remained together for several days, copulating often. In Cyclops's presence, Zizi no longer approached or even glanced at other males.

Primatologists describe Zizi and other olive baboons (*Papio cynocephalus anubis*) as promiscuous, meaning that both males and females usually mate with several members of the opposite sex within a short period of time. Promiscuous mating behavior characterizes many of the larger, more familiar primates, including chimpanzees, rhesus macaques, and gray langurs, as well as olive, yellow, and chacma baboons, the three sub-

species of savanna baboon. In colloquial usage, promiscuity often connotes wanton and random sex, and several early studies of primates supported this stereotype. However, after years of laboriously recording thousands of copulations under natural conditions, the Peeping Toms of primate fieldwork have shown that, even in promiscuous species, sexual pairings are far from random.

Some adult males, for example, typically copulate much more often than others. Primatologists have explained these differences in terms of competition: the most dominant males monopolize females, and prevent lower-ranking rivals from mating. But exceptions are frequent. Among baboons, the exceptions often involve scruffy, older males who mate in full view of younger, more dominant rivals.

A clue to the reason for these puzzling exceptions emerged when primatologists began to question an implicit assumption of the dominance hypothesis—that females were merely passive objects of male competition. But what if females were active arbiters in this system? If females preferred some males over others and were able to express these preferences, then models of mating activity based on male dominance alone would be far too simple.

Once researchers recognized the possibility of female choice, evidence for it turned up in species after species. The story of Zizi, Virgil, and Cyclops is one of hundreds of examples of female primates rejecting the sexual advances of

particular males and enthusiastically cooperating with others. But what is the basis for female choice? Why might they prefer some males over others?

This question guided my research on the Eburru Cliffs troop of olive baboons, named after one of their favorite sleeping sites, a sheer rocky outcrop rising several hundred feet above the floor of the Great Rift Valley, about 100 miles northwest of Nairobi, Kenya. The 120 members of Eburru Cliffs spent their days wandering through open grassland studded with occasional acacia thorn trees. Each night they retired to one of a dozen sets of cliffs that provided protection from nocturnal predators such as leopards.

Most previous studies of baboon sexuality had focused on females who, like Zizi, were at the peak of sexual receptivity. A female baboon does not mate when she is pregnant or lactating, a period of abstinence lasting about eighteen months. The female then goes into estrus, and for about two weeks out of every thirty-five-day cycle, she mates. Toward the end of this two-week period she may ovulate, but usually the female undergoes four or five estrous cycles before she conceives. During pregnancy, she once again resumes a chaste existence. As a result, the typical female baboon is sexually active for less than 10 percent of her adult life. I thought that by focusing on the other 90 percent, I might learn something new. In particular, I suspected that routine, day-to-day relationships between males and pregnant or lactating (nonestrous) females might provide clues to female mating preferences.

Nearly every day for sixteen months, I joined the Eburru Cliffs baboons at their sleeping cliffs at dawn and traveled several miles with them while they foraged for roots, seeds, grass, and occasionally, small prey items, such as baby gazelles or hares (see "Predatory Baboons of Kekopey," *Natural History*, March 1976). Like all savanna baboon troops, Eburru Cliffs functioned as a cohesive unit organized around a core of related females, all of whom were born in the troop. Unlike the females, male savanna baboons leave their natal troop to join another where they may remain for many years, so most of the Eburru Cliffs adult males were immigrants. Since membership in the troop remained relatively constant during the period of my study, I learned to identify each individual. I relied on differences in size, posture, gait, and especially, facial features. To the practiced observer, baboons look as different from one another as human beings do.

As soon as I could recognize individuals, I noticed that particular females tended to turn up near particular males again and again. I came to think of these pairs as friends. Friendship among animals is not a well-documented phenomenon, so to convince skeptical colleagues that baboon friendship was real, I needed to develop objective criteria for distinguishing friendly pairs.

I began by investigating grooming, the amiable simian habit of picking through a companion's fur to remove dead skin and ectoparasites (see "Little Things That Tick Off Baboons," *Natural History*, February 1984). Baboons spend much more time grooming than is necessary for hygiene, and previous research had indicated that it is a good measure of social bonds.

Although eighteen adult males lived in the troop, each nonestrous female performed most of her grooming with just one, two, or occasionally, three males. For example, of Zizi's twenty-four grooming bouts with males, Cyclops accounted for thirteen, and a second male, Sherlock, accounted for all the rest. Different females tended to favor different males as grooming partners.

Another measure of social bonds was simply who was observed near whom. When foraging, traveling, or resting, each pregnant or lactating female spent a lot of time near a few males and associated with the others no more often than expected by chance. When I compared the identities of favorite grooming partners and frequent companions, they overlapped almost completely. This enabled me to develop a formal definition of friendship: any male that scored high on both grooming and proximity measures was considered a friend.

Virtually all baboons made friends; only one female and three males who had most recently joined the troop lacked such companions. Out of more than 600 possible adult female-adult male pairs in the troop, however, only about one in ten qualified as friends; these really were special relationships.

Several factors seemed to influence which baboons paired up. In most cases, friends were unrelated to each other, since the male had immigrated from another troop. (Four friendships, however, involved a female and an adolescent son who had not yet emigrated. Unlike other friends, these related pairs never mated.) Older females tended to be friends with older males; younger females with younger males. I witnessed occasional May–December romances, usually involving older females and young adult males. Adolescent males and females were strongly rule-bound, and with the exception of mother-son pairs, they formed friendships only with one another.

Regardless of age or dominance rank, most females had just one or two male friends. But among males, the number of female friends varied greatly from none to eight. Although high-ranking males enjoyed priority of access to food and sometimes mates, dominant males did not have more female friends than low-ranking males. Instead it was the older males who had lived in the troop for many years who had the most friends. When a male had several female friends, the females were often closely related to one another. Since female baboons spend a lot of time near their kin, it is probably easier for a male to maintain

bonds with several related females at once.

When collecting data, I focused on one nonestrous female at a time and kept track of her every movement toward or away from any male; similarly, I noted every male who moved toward or away from her. Whenever the female and male moved close enough to exchange intimacies, I wrote down exactly what happened. When foraging together, friends tended to remain a few yards apart. Males more often wandered away from females than the reverse, and females, more often than males, closed the gap. The female behaved as if she wanted to keep the male within calling distance, in case she needed his protection. The male, however, was more likely to make approaches that brought them within actual touching distance. Often, he would plunk himself down right next to his friend and ask her to groom him by holding a pose with exaggerated stillness. The female sometimes responded by grooming, but more often, she exhibited the most reliable sign of true intimacy: she ignored her friend and simply continued whatever she was doing.

In sharp contrast, when a male who was not a friend moved close to a female, she dared not ignore him. She stopped whatever she was doing and held still, often glancing surreptitiously at the intruder. If he did not move away, she sometimes lifted her tail and presented her rump. When a female is not in estrus, this is a gesture of appeasement, not sexual enticement. Immediately after this respectful acknowledgement of his presence, the female would slip away. But such tense interactions with nonfriend males were rare, because females usually moved away before the males came too close.

These observations suggest that females were afraid of most of the males in their troop, which is not surprising: male baboons are twice the size of females, and their canines are longer and sharper than those of a lion. All Eburru Cliffs males directed both mild and severe aggression toward females. Mild aggression, which usually involved threats and chases but no body contact, occurred most often during feeding competition or when the male redirected aggression toward a female after losing a fight with another male. Females and juveniles showed aggression toward other females and juveniles in similar circumstances and occasionally inflicted superficial wounds. Severe aggression by males, which involved body contact and sometimes biting, was less common and also more puzzling, since there was no apparent cause.

An explanation for at least some of these attacks emerged one day when I was watching Pegasus, a young adult male, and his friend Cicily, sitting together in the middle of a small clearing. Cicily moved to the edge of the clearing to feed, and a higher-ranking female, Zora, suddenly attacked her. Pegasus stood up and looked as if he were about to intervene when both females disappeared into the bushes. He sat back down, and I remained with him. A full ten minutes later, Zora appeared at the edge of the clearing; this was the first time she had come into view since her attack on Cicily. Pegasus instantly pounced on Zora, repeatedly grabbed her neck in his mouth and lifted her off the ground, shook her whole body, and then dropped her. Zora screamed continuously and tried to escape. Each time, Pegasus caught her and continued his brutal attack. When he finally released her five minutes later she had a deep canine gash on the palm of her hand that made her limp for several days.

This attack was similar in form and intensity to those I had seen before and labeled "unprovoked." Certainly, had I come upon the scene after Zora's aggression toward Cicily, I would not have understood why Pegasus attacked Zora. This suggested that some, perhaps many, severe attacks by males actually represented punishment for actions that had occurred some time before.

Whatever the reasons for male attacks on females, they represent a serious threat. Records of fresh injuries indicated that Eburru Cliffs adult females received canine slash wounds from males at the rate of one for every female each year, and during my study, one female died of her injuries. Males probably pose an even greater threat to infants. Although only one infant was killed during my study, observers in Botswana and

Tanzania have seen recent male immigrants kill several young infants.

Protection from male aggression, and from the less injurious but more frequent aggression of other females and juveniles, seems to be one of the main advantages of friendship for a female baboon. Seventy times I observed an adult male defend a female or her offspring against aggression by another troop member, not infrequently a high-ranking male. In all but six of these cases, the defender was a friend. Very few of these confrontations involved actual fighting; no male baboon, subordinate or dominant, is anxious to risk injury by the sharp canines of another.

Males are particularly solicitous guardians of their friends' youngest infants. If another male gets too close to an infant or if a juvenile female plays with it too roughly, the friend may intervene. Other troop members soon learn to be cautious when the mother's friend is nearby, and his presence provides the mother with a welcome respite from the annoying pokes and prods of curious females and juveniles obsessed with the new baby. Male baboons at Gombe Park in Tanzania and Amboseli Park in Kenya have also been seen rescuing infants from chimpanzees and lions. These several forms of male protection help to explain why females in Eburru Cliffs stuck closer to their friends in the first few months after giving birth than at any other time.

The male-infant relationship develops out of the male's friendship with the mother, but as the infant matures, this new bond takes on a life of its own. My co-worker Nancy Nicolson found that by about nine months of age, infants actively sought out their male friends when the mother was a few yards away, suggesting that the male may function as an alternative caregiver. This seemed to be especially true for infants undergoing unusually early or severe weaning. (Weaning is generally a gradual, prolonged process, but there is tremendous variation among mothers in the timing and intensity of weaning. See "Mother Baboons," *Natural History*, September 1980). After being rejected by the mother, the crying infant often approached the male friend and sat huddled

against him until its whimpers subsided. Two of the infants in Eburru Cliffs lost their mothers when they were still quite young. In each case, their bond with the mother's friend subsequently intensified, and—perhaps as a result—both infants survived.

A close bond with a male may also improve the infant's nutrition. Larger than all other troop members, adult males monopolize the best feeding sites. In general, the personal space surrounding a feeding male is inviolate, but he usually tolerates intrusions by the infants of his female friends, giving them access to choice feeding spots.

Although infants follow their male friends around rather than the reverse, the males seem genuinely attached to their tiny companions. During feeding, the male and infant express their pleasure in each other's company by sharing spirited, antiphonal grunting duets. If the infant whimpers in distress, the male friend is likely to cease feeding, look at the infant, and grunt softly, as if in sympathy, until the whimpers cease. When the male rests, the infants of his female friends may huddle behind him, one after the other, forming a "train," or, if feeling energetic, they may use his body as a trampoline.

When I returned to Eburru Cliffs four years after my initial study ended, several of the bonds formed between males and the infants of their female friends were still intact (in other cases, either the male or the infant or both had disappeared). When these bonds involved recently matured females, their long-time male associates showed no sexual interest in them, even though the females mated with other adult males. Mothers and sons, and usually maternal siblings, show similar sexual inhibitions in baboons and many other primate species.

The development of an intimate relationship between a male and the infant of his female friend raises an obvious question: Is the male the infant's father? To answer this question definitely we would need to conduct genetic analysis, which was not possible for these baboons. Instead, I estimated paternity probabilities from observations of the temporary (a few hours or days) exclusive mating relationships, or consortships, that estrous females form with a series of different males. These estimates were apt to be fairly accurate, since changes in the female's sexual swelling allow one to pinpoint the timing of conception to within a few days. Most females consorted with only two or three males during this period, and these males were termed likely fathers.

In about half the friendships, the male was indeed likely to be the father of his friend's most recent infant, but in the other half he was not—in fact, he had never been seen mating with the female. Interestingly, males who were friends with the mother but not likely fathers nearly always developed a relationship with her infant, while males who had mated with the female but were not her friend usually did not. Thus friendship with the mother, rather than paternity, seems to mediate the development of male-infant bonds. Recently, a similar pattern was documented for South American capuchin monkeys in a laboratory study in which paternity was determined genetically.

These results fly in the face of a prominent theory that claims males will invest in infants only when they are closely related. If males are not fostering the survival of their own genes by caring for the infant, then why do they do so? I suspected that the key was female choice. If females preferred to mate with males who had already demonstrated friendly behavior, then friendships with mothers and their infants might pay off in the future when the mothers were ready to mate again. *Be friends to mate*

To find out if this was the case, I examined each male's sexual behavior with females he had befriended before they resumed estrus. In most cases, males consorted considerably more often with their friends than with other females. Baboon females typically mate with several different males, including both friends and nonfriends, but prior friendship increased a male's probability of mating with a female above what it would have been otherwise.

This increased probability seemed to reflect female preferences. Females occasionally overtly advertised their disdain for certain males and their desire for others. Zizi's behavior, described above,

is a good example. Virgil was not one of her friends, but Cyclops was. Usually, however, females expressed preferences and aversions more subtly. For example, Delphi, a petite adolescent female, found herself pursued by Hector, a middle-aged adult male. She did not run away or refuse to mate with him, but whenever he wasn't watching, she looked around for her friend Homer, an adolescent male. When she succeeded in catching Homer's eye, she narrowed her eyes and flattened her ears against her skull, the friendliest face one baboon can send another. This told Homer she would rather be with him. Females expressed satisfaction with a current consort partner by staying close to him, initiating copulations, and not making advances toward other males. Baboons are very sensitive to such cues, as indicated by an experimental study in which rival hamadryas baboons rarely challenged a male-female pair if the female strongly preferred her current partner. Similarly, in Eburru Cliffs, males were less apt to challenge consorts involving a pair that shared a long-term friendship.

Even though females usually consorted with their friends, they also mated with other males, so it is not surprising that friendships were most vulnerable during periods of sexual activity. In a few cases, the female consorted with another male more often than with her friend, but the friendship survived nevertheless. One female, however, formed a strong sexual bond with a new male. This bond persisted after conception, replacing her previous friendship. My observations suggest that adolescent and young adult females tend to have shorter, less stable friendships than do older females. Some friendships, however, last a very long time. When I returned to Eburru Cliffs six years after my study began, five couples were still together. It is possible that friendships occasionally last for life (baboons probably live twenty to thirty years in the wild), but it will require longer studies, and some very patient scientists to find out.

By increasing both the male's chances of mating in the future and the likelihood that a female's infant will survive, friendship contributes to the reproductive success of both partners. This

clarifies the evolutionary basis of friendship-forming tendencies in baboons, but what does friendship mean to a baboon? To answer this question we need to view baboons as sentient beings with feelings and goals not unlike our own in similar circumstances. Consider, for example, the friendship between Thalia and Alexander.

The affair began one evening as Alex and Thalia sat about fifteen feet apart on the sleeping cliffs. It was like watching two novices in a singles bar. Alex stared at Thalia until she turned and almost caught him looking at her. He glanced away immediately, and then she stared at him until his head began to turn toward her. She suddenly became engrossed in grooming her toes. But as soon as Alex looked away, her gaze returned to him. They went on like this for more than fifteen minutes, always with split-second timing. Finally, Alex managed to catch Thalia looking at him. He made the friendly eyes-narrowed, ears-back face and smacked his lips together rhythmically. Thalia froze, and for a second she looked into his eyes. Alex approached, and Thalia, still nervous, groomed him. Soon she calmed down, and I found them still together on the cliffs the next morning. Looking back on this event months later, I realized that it marked the beginning of their friendship. Six years later, when I returned to Eburru Cliffs, they were still friends.

If flirtation forms an integral part of baboon friendship, so does jealousy. Overt displays of jealousy, such as chasing a friend away from a potential rival, occur occasionally, but like humans, baboons often express their emotions in more subtle ways. One evening a colleague and I climbed the cliffs and settled down near Sherlock, who was friends with Cybelle, a middle-aged female still foraging on the ground below the cliffs. I observed Cybelle while my colleague watched Sherlock, and we kept up a running commentary. As long as Cybelle was feeding or interacting with females, Sherlock was relaxed, but each time she approached another male, his body would stiffen, and he would stare intently at the scene below. When Cybelle presented politely to a male who had recently tried to befriend her, Sherlock even made threatening sounds under his breath. Cybelle was not in estrus at the time, indicating that male baboon jealousy extends beyond the sexual arena to include affiliative interactions between a female friend and other males.

Because baboon friendships are embedded in a network of friendly and antagonistic relationships, they inevitably lead to repercussions extending beyond the pair. For example, Virgil once provoked his weaker rival Cyclops into a fight by first attacking Cyclops's friend Phoebe. On another occasion, Sherlock chased Circe, Hector's best friend, just after Hector had chased Antigone, Sherlock's friend.

In another incident, the prime adult male Triton challenged Cyclops's possession of meat. Cyclops grew increasingly tense and seemed about to abandon the prey to the younger male. Then Cyclops's friend Phoebe appeared with her infant Phyllis. Phyllis wandered over to Cyclops. He immediately grabbed her, held her close, and threatened Triton away from the prey. Because any challenge to Cyclops now involved a threat to Phyllis as well, Triton risked being mobbed by Phoebe and her relatives and friends. For this reason, he backed down. Males frequently use the infants of their female friends as buffers in this way. Thus, friendship involves costs as well as benefits because it makes the participants vulnerable to social manipulation or redirected aggression by others.

Finally, as with humans, friendship seems to mean something different to each baboon. Several females in Eburru Cliffs had only one friend. They were devoted companions. Louise and Pandora, for example, groomed their friend Virgil and no other male. Then there was Leda, who, with five friends, spread herself more thinly than any other female. These contrasting patterns of friendship were associated with striking personality differences. Louise and Pandora were unobtrusive females who hung around quietly with Virgil and their close relatives. Leda seemed to be everywhere at once, playing with infants, fighting with juveniles, and making friends with males. Similar differences were apparent among the males. Some devoted a great deal of time and energy to cultivating friendships with females, while others focused more on challenging other males. Although we probably will never fully understand the basis of these individual differences, they contribute immeasurably to the richness and complexity of baboon society.

Male-female friendships may be widespread among primates. They have been reported for many other groups of savanna baboons, and they also occur in rhesus and Japanese Macaques, capuchin monkeys, and perhaps in bonobos (pygmy chimpanzees). These relationships should give us pause when considering popular scenarios for the evolution of male-female relationships in humans. Most of these scenarios assume that, except for mating, males and females had little to do with one another until the development of a sexual division of labor, when, the story goes, females began to rely on males to provide meat in exchange for gathered food. This, it has been argued, set up new selection pressures favoring the development of long-term bonds between individual males and females, female sexual fidelity, and as paternity certainty increased, greater male investment in the offspring of these unions. In other words, once women began to gather and men to hunt, presto—we had the nuclear family.

This scenario may have more to do with cultural biases about women's economic dependence on men and idealized views of the nuclear family than with the actual behavior of our hominid ancestors. The nonhuman primate evidence challenges this story in at least three ways.

First, long-term bonds between the sexes can evolve in the absence of a sexual division of labor of food sharing. In our primate relatives, such relationships rest on exchanges of social, not economic, benefits.

Second, primate research shows that highly differentiated, emotionally intense male-female relationships can occur without sexual exclusivity. Ancestral men and women may have experienced intimate friendships long before they invented marriage and norms of sexual fidelity.

Third, among our closest primate relatives, males clearly provide mothers and infants with social benefits even when they are unlikely to be the fathers of those infants. In return, females provide a variety of benefits to the friendly males, including acceptance into the group and, at least in baboons, increased mating opportunities in the future. This suggests that efforts to reconstruct the evolution of hominid societies may have overemphasized what the female must supposedly do (restrict her mating to just one male) in order to obtain male parental investment.

Maybe it is time to pay more attention to what the male must do (provide benefits to females and young) in order to obtain female cooperation. Perhaps among our ancestors, as in baboons today, sex and friendship went hand in hand. As for marriage—well, that's another story.

Fossey in the Mist

'MY WORK IN THE BUSH AS A PRIMATOLOGIST ALWAYS makes me think of someone whose unlikely job would be to collect snowflakes, then rush into a warm room and observe their unique patterns under a microscope before they melt and are never seen again. This is an account of my time of Africa's Mt. Karisimbi, where the snowflakes are the rarest and nearest to melting....'

By Robert M. Sapolsky

OH, WHAT NEW CAN I SAY ABOUT Dian Fossey? She's been featured in in books, enshrined in the movies. She was clearly the stuff of legend. She was a large, imposing, awkward woman who looked not one bit like Sigourney Weaver, who played her in the 1988 film *Gorillas in the Mist*. By chance, the mother of a member of my lab at Stanford University went to high school with Fossey in the late 1940s; she related that Fossey was already difficult, withdrawn, marked. I saw Fossey's yearbook photo. At age 17, she had the hunted, unhappy look of the high-school weirdo destined to become either a reclusive field biologist or a serial murderer.

At a relatively late age, Fossey fell in love with the ideas of Africa and of the mountain gorilla—the largest and last-discovered great ape by Western man, studied in the field only once, cloaked in legend and misconception. Without any formal training, she make up her mind to go to Africa and live with them. In 1963, she encountered Louis Leakey, the famed paleontologist and sponsor of female primatologists, and convinced him to send her to the rain forest of the Virunga mountains to study the gorillas for a short stretch. She stayed on for decades.

She immersed herself utterly in the gorillas, broke all the objective rules about not touching them, not interacting with them, and managed to observe astounding things about their behavior. In the process, she became more reclusive, more difficult, drove away possible collaborators and colleagues. She did little science of note beyond observing amazing things by sheer dint of her persistence, was openly contemptuous of most scientists doing fieldwork, and clearly wanted little more than to be a gorilla herself. I could understand the last. As a child, something primal had clicked in me the first time I stood before the mountain gorilla diorama at the American Museum of Natural History in New York City, and I had set on a path to become a primatologist.

> Fossey fought with the poachers and the tribesmen, and the rangers who led the tourists that she loathed

I met Fossey once, as an undergrad at Harvard, in the mid-1970s. Gorillas resonated emotionally with me in an extraordinary way (although eventually I would study baboons), and Fossey was one of the humans I most admired. I thought I would swoon with pleasure at meeting her.

Fossey was in Cambridge against her will, forced by her funding sources to act like a proper citizen of the scientific community. It was an evening seminar in the living room of the senior primatology professor, and it was jammed. Quickly, one had the sickened, guilty, voyeuristic sense of watching a bear forced to perform in some medieval circus. She sat with her knees drawn up to her chest, and then suddenly burst out, pacing back and forth in front of the room, bent so that her hands hung near her knees. She mostly talked to herself, in a monotone, and nearly yelled at people when they asked questions. Once, she did yell. One professor had his young kid sitting on his lap, the kid making occasional sounds typical of a four-year-old, and suddenly Fossey stopped, pointed, and said "Child, shut thy mouth or I will shut it for you."

I was mesmerized and more than a little bit horrified. Afterward, I went up to her and asked the question I had been preparing since I was 10: Could I go to Rwanda as her research assistant and devote my life to the gorillas? She scowled at me, said yes, and told me to write to her. I returned to my dorm in a transcendent euphoria and sent her that letter by midnight. She never answered. I later learned that this was her standard way of dealing with the acolytes and petitioners; say yes to anything, tell them to write, never answer.

Soon after that, her difficulties began. The rain forest of Rwanda were inhabited by Batwa tribesmen, hunter-gatherers who lived by catching forest bucks with snares, Inevitably, a gorilla would

step on a snare now and then and be trapped. Gangrene, death. The best evidence indicates that these first deaths were accidental. Fossey freaked. She began to fight the tribesmen, destroying their snares, their source of food. And they began to fight back. Soon they were killing her gorillas intentionally, dumping their decapitated bodies on the path to her cabin, high up in the volcanoes, while she, in turn, kidnapped those tribesmen's children.

Fossey, in a turnaround, became extroverted. She ran around the world lecturing about the killings of her animals and demanding help. She opened the field site to students, collaborators—so long as they would fight the gorilla killers. Before long, there was a split in the conservation community. Some said, yes, let's pour money in there, but not to her. She is too inflammatory, too provocative. Get her out of there, and pour money into the dirt-poor Rwandan game park service to get some rangers up there, armed, to make the place a real wildlife preserve. The other half said, give her money, give her guns. If there are going to be any gorillas surviving, it will be because of her. Who else cares?

The former group prevailed. Money poured into the Digit Fund, named for her most beloved animal, whose butchered body was left for her to find. A real, functioning, protective park service was established. Enough interest was gener-

ated to start gorilla-watching tourism that has continued to fund the park and the local economy. The gorillas started to do better, perhaps increasing in numbers.

And Fossey was sent away. Some sort of visiting adjunct professorship was rigged up for her at Cornell, where, by most reports, she sank into depression and alcoholism.

Against everyone's pleading, she returned to Rwanda and her gorillas. She fought with the poachers, with the rangers who led the tourists that she loathed, with the agricultural tribesmen whose slash-and-burning was decimating the remnants of the rain forest, fought with the government. Her health was destroyed by drinking, chain-smoking and emphysema, and by trying to live in humid, high-altitude conditions. She could barely walk, had to be carried up to her cabin. That's where she was murdered one night in late December 1985. The government lamely and unconvincingly blamed an American grad student and condemned him to death in absentia after making sure he had left the country, and everyone felt sure it was poachers or government rangers.

The funeral service was held near her cabin, a week after Christmas, and was conducted by a missionary who said, "Last week the world did honor to a long-ago event that changed its history.... the coming of the Lord to Earth.... We see at our feet here a parable of that magnifi-

cent condescension—Dian Fossey, born to a home of comfort and privilege that she left by her own choice to live among a race facing extinction.... And if you think that the distance Christ had to come to take the likeness of man is not so great as that from man to gorilla, then you don't know men. Or gorillas. Or God." And, as per her wish, she was buried in the graveyard of her slain gorillas, next to Digit.

NINE MONTHS AFTER FOSSEY'S murder I flew with two friends from Kenya, where I had been studying baboons for eight years, to Kigali, Rwanda's capital. It was a country of staggering population density. As we headed toward the gorillas, we passed endless hills with endless terraces and endless farms, every inch under cultivation, up to the very west, the very last edge of the country. There, forming the border between Zaire (now the Democratic Republic of the Congo) to the west and Uganda to the east, are the Ruwenzoris, the famed Mountains of the Moon, which are followed to the south by the Virungas, a ribbon of mammoth volcanoes between Congo and Rwanda. The peaks there rise up more than 14,000 feet, rugged, jutting, one after another after another, snow on top spilling into the Congo, wild rain forest below. And because they are too steep for even the desperate farmers to try to squeeze food out of, on the saddles and slopes survive the last mountain gorillas on Earth.

We splurged and stayed in the only real hotel in Ruhengeri, the town at the entrance to the park. It was ramshackle old jobbie, dripping with colonial nostalgia. We slept fitfully, feeling the volcanoes hovering over us, and were agitatedly ready by dawn. We hiked up with park rangers, the men who find the gorilla groups each day for the 18 tourists allowed in to see the three groups on display. The rangers were silent men who moved with smooth, frictionless gestures.

We set off through the farm fields, already angled steeply where they weren't terraced, weaving our way through huts and rows of corn until we reached a wall of bamboo with a slight forest path through it. We plunged in, winding up steep unstable slopes thick with bamboo and moss-covered hagenia trees that have always looked silly to me unless they are shrouded in mist. Higher, onto a saddle of one of the volcanoes, a view of forest ahead of us, a small lake, fields of bushes. Onward, the rangers macheteing a way through fields of stinging nettles. Clouds and mist and chills and heat, somehow all simultaneously. Sweating and shivering. Sliding down a deep ravine, clambering the way back up to other side, more nettles, more bamboo.

A few hours had passed yet the rangers continued their silent, coordinated movement. One would examine some broken bamboo shoots, another would sniff the flattened grass around there. Gorillas, but from yesterday, they concluded. Another hour. Misty rain, but somehow warmer. More nettles. Something resembling a real path and a flattened clump of grass to the left of it. Large, fibrous, shredded turds in the middle, the type you would expect from a pro football player gone vegetarian. The gorilla. Fresh, late night's nest.

Pushing ahead, tired and excited and impatient. Down another ravine, and one of the rangers hears a murmur up the other side. We stopped, silent, willing to invent the sound to convince ourselves that they were close, and suddenly, we heard the unmistakable murmur, deep, throaty, slow-motion, paternal. We rushed, tiptoed up the other side and, on top of the ridge, I saw my first wild mountain gorillas.

When tribesmen's snares accidentally killed some gorillas, Fossey freaked and began destroying the traps. Soon the hunters were killing gorillas intentionally, dumping the bodies near her cabin. She in turn kidnapped their children

---

It was a group of perhaps a dozen. A prime-aged male—a silverback. Some females with infants, a few lurking younger males, some adolescents. The silverback played with the kids. The mothers fed, lumbering about with the infants carried dorsal. The two young males spent most of an hour wrestling, rolling around with each other, mouthing each other in restrained bites. They'd pant as they rolled and tickled each other, get exhausted from the excitement, and have to retreat to separate corners to catch their breaths. Refreshed, one would pound its chest and they'd launch themselves at each other again. At one point, both ambled over to sit next to me and stare, one leaning in so close that the rangers forced me to lean back. They had a comforting, musty, damp smell to them, like opening a trunk from the mildewed corners of a cellar that contains forgotten beloved objects.

I had a flood of thoughts and feelings. At the first sight, I thought, "Now my eyes will well up with tears," but I was too intent on watching for that to happen. I wondered what my social rank would be if I had wound up a mountain gorilla. I was mesmerized by their eyes; their faces seemed less emotionally expressive than those of chimps or even baboons, but their eyes, you wanted to go swimming in. I tried not to make eye contact, not only because it's bad field technique and discomforts primates, but because the act would make me want to confess to unlikely crimes. I found myself with the barely controllable urge to scream, or to gibber dangerously among them, or to rudely kiss one, so that they would stomp me to death then and there and stop my suspense.

That night, sleeping in my tent on the mountain's slopes, I had a dream that summarized my feelings far better than I could when awake. It was a dream so tender, so ludicrously sentimental, so full of beliefs that I do not have when awake, that I still marvel at it. I dreamt that God and angels and seraphs and devils all existed, in a very literal way, each with potential strengths and frailties much like our own. And I dreamt that the rain forests of the Mountains of the Moon were where God placed the occasional angel born with Down syndrome.

MY FRIENDS LEFT THE NEXT DAY. I stayed another week, going back to the gorillas repeatedly. It was heaven, but with each day, I felt more depressed. The gorillas were wondrous, but the weight of what was gone, removed, unmentioned, unanswered, irrevocable, became heavier. I felt it in the park headquarters, where the posters on the park's history made more mention of 19th-century Belgian colonials than of Fossey. With the rangers, who would say, yes, we knew Fossey, and then change the subject. With the gorillas, where you would watch a mother hold her child and nibble at bamboo, and all the while hear the farmers, their chickens, the school kids, 200 yards down the slope, where the slash-and-burning had finally stopped. On the miles and miles of empty rain forests paths aching with no more gorillas. And finally, from atop the nearly 15,000-foot Mt. Karisimbi, the highest point in the range, where I climbed to peer down and discover that the massive, endless, magisterial, mythic Virungas were nearly gone, a tiny narrow ribbon of forest engulfed by the infinity of terraces spreading from Rwanda to Uganda.

It was on top of that mountain that the week finally got to me and I had a night of African paranoia. You weren't allowed to hike alone in the range. Instead, a ranger had to be hired as a guide. Hauling to the top of the highest volcano around was clearly not their idea of fun, and the most junior of the rangers was given the task. From previous days of hanging around the rangers, I had noticed him and already had a dislike for him; even the other rangers seemed to ostracize him. He was a sullen, sloe-eyed kid, with a face like a mask and a tense air of violence about him. He mostly sat off on the side of the camp and seemed to get into a lot of monosyllabic arguments when he did interact.

As we started hiking, my dislike for my guide began to build. I could elicit nothing more than grunts out of him, as I tried in French, Swahili, English, my 20 words of Kirwanda. I slipped and fell on a wet rock at one point, and he laughed; it had a sneering, dismissive whine to it. Once, he flung stones at grazing forest bucks, probably both to hurt them and to deprive me of the view.

Our dislike for each other simmered. Somehow, these mutual feelings evolved, wordlessly, into competition. We began to hike faster, moving more relentlessly, until we were racing up the mountain, seeing who would first ask to rest. We pushed harder and harder, through the rain forest, montane forest, patchy woodland, open moorland where we sank to our knees in mud, to stark open rock with patches of frost, from 7,000 to 14,000 feet. The air got thinner, I felt an edge of altitude sickness, my vision got blurry, my chest throbbed. He climbed these mountains for a living, and I had the heavier pack, but sheer anger let me keep pace with him. "*Fatigué*?" he would ask in French and I would gasp, "*Non*." Once, he spoke his longest pronouncement: "*Je pense tu es fatigué. Tu es mzee* [Swahili for old man]." I nearly sprinted after him, hoping to kill him. At one triumphant point, I got ahead for a minute, and was able to whisper the same breathless "*Fatigué*?" to him, while he gasped, "*Non*."

We reached our goal, a corrugated metal shelter near the rim of the crater, just as an ice storm let loose. We lay in there, gasping, as the storm closed in and pounded on the metal. And there we stayed, from mid-afternoon until the next

morning. We ate a bit, rice and French bread, but everything tends to taste sickening at that altitude. Your eyes throb, your head hurts constantly, your chest aches with each breath. At that altitude, my resting heart rate is usually about 110, which means you wake from presumably relaxing sleep already feeling like you've been climbing stairs.

We lay on the wooden floor, as far away from each other as the small shelter would allow. I tried to play the recorder, but didn't have the breath; instead, I mostly thought about gorillas. He muttered to himself and scraped his name, *Bonaventre*, into the metal with his machete, all the while smoking in our closed hut at 14,000 feet.

So the hours passed, until sometime around nightfall, as I still lay there with my eyeballs throbbing, it occurred to me for the first time to become afraid. Fossey was murdered just nine months before on this mountain. Not only was it probably a ranger who did it (I had now decided), but it was probably this kid with the very same machete he was now holding. And tonight was almost certainly my night to get it. I was suddenly terribly frightened, near to panic. I desperately wanted to escape. I struggled to control my breathing, thought to cry out for help. I lay awake most of the night, with my pocketknife opened at my side, and truly thought I was going to die. The ranger, meanwhile, spent the night talking in his sleep—mutterings, and harsh muffled barks.

At dawn, I felt foolish and angry and relieved and lucky. We struggled up the ice-coated rocks and were at the summit by 7:00. He sat, looked impatient, and kicked at rocks. I looked out over Rwanda, Uganda, Zaire, and tried to imagine that it was once all rain forest full with gorillas. He clearly wanted us to head down immediately; I could have stayed there forever. He was saved from that fate, as the clouds rolled in, obscuring all view and forcing us down.

We ran over the ice-covered rocks. We ran through the near frozen mud

fields of the moorland down past the groves of trees and the rain forest and past the bamboo. And as we came to the saddle of the mountain, coming down a different path than we had taken up yesterday, the ranger slowed down. He didn't seem tired, and I couldn't imagine he was slowing out of concern for me. He suddenly seemed cautious, even uncomfortable. It was the nearest I could detect to an emotion on his face.

The forest had opened a bit, there were longer views, and a beautiful stream running alongside our path. We were walking slowly now, the ground was level. We crossed the stream on a log. Another minute walking, and the grove of trees near us parted. And then, with no warning, we were standing in front of Fossey's cabin.

It was plain, small, boarded. A Rwandan flag was flying over it. I walked over toward it, and the ranger motioned me away. I walked closer, and this silent kid told me in French, in Swahili, even in broken but understandable English, that it was not allowed. I walked past the cabin, and for the moment before he forced me away, I stood at the grave of Fossey and the other primates.

FOSSEY, FOSSEY, YOU CRANKY difficult strong-arming self-destructive misanthrope, mediocre scientist, deceiver of earnest college students, probable cause of more deaths of the gorillas than if you had never set foot in Rwanda, Fossey, you pain-in-the-ass saint, I do not believe in prayers or souls, but I will pray for your soul, I will remember you for all of my days, in gratitude for that moment by the graves when all I felt was the pure, cleansing sadness of returning home and finding nothing but ghosts.

From the forthcoming book A Primate's Memoir *by Robert M. Sapolsky. Copyright © 2001 by Robert M. Sapolsky. Reprinted by permission of Scribner, an imprint of Simon & Schuster, Inc.*

The Mind of the Chimpanzee

Jane Goodall

Often I have gazed into a chimpanzee's eyes and wondered what was going on behind them. I used to look into Flo's, she so old, so wise. What did she remember of her young days? David Greybeard had the most beautiful eyes of them all, large and lustrous, set wide apart. They somehow expressed his whole personality, his serene self-assurance, his inherent dignity—and, from time to time, his utter determination to get his way. For a long time I never liked to look a chimpanzee straight in the eye—I assumed that, as is the case with most primates, this would be interpreted as a threat or at least as a breach of good manners. No so. As long as one looks with gentleness, without arrogance, a chimpanzee will understand, and may even return the look. And then—or such is my fantasy—it is as though the eyes are windows into the mind. Only the glass is opaque so that the mystery can never be fully revealed.

I shall never forget my meeting with Lucy, an eight-year-old home-raised chimpanzee. She came and sat beside me on the sofa and, with her face very close to mine, searched in my eyes—for what? Perhaps she was looking for signs of mistrust, dislike, or fear, since many people must have been somewhat disconcerted when, for the first time, they came face to face with a grown chimpanzee. Whatever Lucy read in my eyes clearly satisfied her for she suddenly put one arm round my neck and gave me a generous and very chimp-like kiss, her mouth wide open and laid over mine. I was accepted.

For a long time after that encounter I was profoundly disturbed. I had been at Gombe for about fifteen years then and I was quite familiar with chimpanzees in the wild. But Lucy, having grown up as a human child, was like a changeling, her essential chimpanzeeness overlaid by the various human behaviours she had acquired over the years. No longer purely chimp yet eons away from humanity, she was man-made, some other kind of being. I watched, amazed, as she opened the refrigerator and various cupboards, found bottles and a glass, then poured herself a gin and tonic. She took the drink to the TV, turned the set on, flipped from one channel to another then, as though in disgust, turned it off again. She selected a glossy magazine from the table and, still carrying her drink, settled in a comfortable chair. Occasionally, as she leafed through the magazine she identified something she saw, using the signs of ASL, the American Sign Language used by the deaf. I, of course, did not understand, but my hostess, Jane Temerlin (who was also Lucy's 'mother'), translated: 'That dog,' Lucy commented, pausing at a photo of a small white poodle. She turned the page. 'Blue,' she declared, pointing then signing as she gazed at a picture of a lady advertising some kind of soap powder and wearing a brilliant blue dress. And finally, after some vague hand movements—perhaps signed mutterings—'This Lucy's, this mine,' as she closed the magazine and laid it on her lap. She had just been taught, Jane told me, the use of the possessive pronouns during the thrice weekly ASL lessons she was receiving at the time.

The book written by Lucy's human 'father,' Maury Temerlin, was entitled *Lucy, Growing Up Human*. And in fact, the chimpanzee is more like us than is any other living creature. There is close resemblance in the physiology of our two species and genetically, in the structure of the DNA, chimpanzees and humans differ by only just over one per cent. This is why medical research uses chimpanzees as experimental animals when they need substitutes for humans in the testing of some drug or vaccine. Chimpanzees can be infected with just about all known human infectious diseases including those, such as hepatitis B and AIDS, to which other non-human animals (except gorillas, orangutans and gibbons) are immune. There are equally striking similarities between humans and chimpanzees in the anatomy and wiring of the brain and nervous system, and—although many scientists have been reluctant to admit to this—in social behaviour, intellectual ability, and the emotions. The notion of an evolutionary continuity in physical structure from pre-human ape to modern man has long been morally acceptable to most scientists. That the same might hold good for mind was generally considered an absurd hypothesis—particularly by those who used, and often misused, animals in their laboratories. It is, after all, convenient to believe that the creature you are using, while it may react in disturbingly human-like ways, is, in fact, merely a mindless and, above all, unfeeling, 'dumb' animal.

When I began my study at Gombe in 1960 it was not permissible—at least not in ethological circles—to talk about an animal's mind. Only humans had minds. Nor was it quite proper to talk about animal personality. Of course everyone

idea would be laughed at

[handwritten margin note, top right: humans don't NPK know how other humans feel, write (How can't they know?)]

[handwritten margin note, left side, vertical: Sars]

[handwritten margin note, lower left, vertical: Fight KEPTQuiet]

knew that they *did* have their own unique characters—everyone who had ever owned a dog or other pet was aware of that. But ethologists, striving to make theirs a 'hard' science, shied away from the task of trying to explain such things objectively. One respected ethologist, while acknowledging that there was 'variability between individual animals,' wrote that it was best that this fact be 'swept under the carpet.' At that time ethological carpets fairly bulged with all that was hidden beneath them.

How naive I was. As I had not had an undergraduate science education I didn't realize that animals were not supposed to have personalities, or to think, or to feel emotions or pain. I had no idea that it would have been more appropriate to assign each of the chimpanzees a number rather than a name when I got to know him or her. I didn't realize that it was not scientific to discuss behaviour in terms of motivation or purpose. And no one had told me that terms such as *childhood* and *adolescence* were uniquely human phases of the life cycle, culturally determined, not to be used when referring to young chimpanzees. Not knowing, I freely made use of all those forbidden terms and concepts in my initial attempt to describe, to the best of my ability, the amazing things I had observed at Gombe.

I shall never forget the response of a group of ethologists to some remarks I made at an erudite seminar. I described how Figan, as an adolescent, had learned to stay behind in camp after senior males had left, so that we could give him a few bananas for himself. On the first occasion he had, upon seeing the fruits, uttered loud, delighted food calls: whereupon a couple of the older males had charged back, chased after Figan, and taken his bananas. And then, coming to the point of the story, I explained how, on the next occasion, Figan had actually suppressed his calls. We could hear little sounds, in his throat, but so quiet that none of the others could have heard them. Other young chimps, to whom we tried to smuggle fruit without the knowledge of their elders, never learned such self-control. With shrieks of glee they would fall to, only to be robbed of their booty when the big males charged back.

I had expected my audience to be as fascinated and impressed as I was. I had hoped for an exchange of views about the chimpanzee's undoubted intelligence. Instead there was a chill silence, after which the chairman hastily changed the subject. Needless to say, after being thus snubbed, I was very reluctant to contribute any comments, at any scientific gatherings, for a very long time. Looking back, I suspect that everyone was interested, but it was, of course, not permissible to present a mere 'anecdote' as evidence for anything.

The editorial comments on the first paper I wrote for publication demanded that every *he* or *she* be replaced with *it*, and every *who* be replaced with *which*. Incensed, I, in my turn, crossed out the *its* and *whichs* and scrawled back the original pronouns. As I had no desire to carve a niche for myself in the world of science, but simply wanted to go on living among and learning about chimpanzees, the possible reaction of the editor of the learned journal did not trouble me. In fact I won that round: the paper when finally published did confer upon the chimpanzees the dignity of their appropriate genders and properly upgraded them from the status of mere 'things' to essential Beingness.

[handwritten margin note, vertical: most likely wrong, not thoughtful]

However, despite my somewhat truculent attitude, I did want to learn, and I was sensible of my incredible good fortune in being admitted to Cambridge. I wanted to get my PhD, if only for the sake of Louis Leakey and the other people who had written letters in support of my admission. And how lucky I was to have, as my supervisor, Robert Hinde. Not only because I thereby benefitted from his brilliant mind and clear thinking, but also because I doubt that I could have found a teacher more suited to my particular needs and personality. Gradually he was able to cloak me with at least some of the trappings of a scientist. Thus although I continued to hold to most of my convictions—that animals had personalities; that they could feel happy or sad or fearful; that they could feel pain; that they could strive towards planned goals and achieve greater success if they were highly motivated—I soon realized that these personal convictions were, indeed, difficult to prove. It was best to be circumspect—at least until I had gained some credentials and credibility. And Robert gave me wonderful advice on how best to tie up some of my more rebellious ideas with scientific ribbon. 'You can't *know* that Fifi was jealous,' had admonished on one occasion. We argued a little. And then: 'Why don't you just say *If Fifi were a human child we would say she was jealous.*' I did.

It is not easy to study emotions even when the subjects are human. I know how I feel if I am sad or happy or angry, and if a friend tells me that he is feeling sad, happy or angry, I assume that his feelings are similar to mine. But of course I cannot know. As we try to come to grips with the emotions of beings progressively more different from ourselves the task, obviously, becomes increasingly difficult. If we ascribe human emotions to non-human animals we are accused of being anthropomorphic—a cardinal sin in ethology. But is it so terrible? If we test the effect of drugs on chimpanzees because they are biologically so similar to ourselves, if we accept that there are dramatic similarities in chimpanzee and human brain and nervous system, is it not logical to assume that there will be similarities also in at least the more basic feelings, emotions, moods of the two species?

In fact, all those who have worked long and closely with chimpanzees have no hesitation in asserting that chimps experience emotions similar to those which in ourselves we label pleasure, joy, sorrow, anger, boredom and so on. Some of the emotional states of the chimpanzee are so obviously similar to ours that even an inexperienced observer can understand what is going on. An infant who hurls himself screaming to the ground, face contorted, hitting out with his arms at any nearby object, banging his head, is clearly having a tantrum. Another youngster, who gambols around his mother, turning somersaults, pirouetting and, every so often, rushing up to her and tumbling into her lap, patting her or pulling her hand towards him in a request for tickling, is obviously filled with *joie de vivre*. There are few observers who would not unhesitatingly ascribe his behaviour to a happy, carefree state of well-being. And one cannot watch chimpanzee infants for long without realizing that they have the same emotional need for affection and reassurance as human children. An adult male, reclining in the shade after a good meal, reaching benignly to play with an infant or idly groom an adult female, is clearly in a good mood. When he sits with bristling hair, glaring at his subordinates and threatening them, with irritated gestures, if they come too close, he is clearly feeling cross and grumpy. We make these judgements because the similarity of so much of a chimpanzee's behaviour to our own permits us to empathize.

It is hard to empathize with emotions we have not experienced. I can image, to some extent, the pleasure of a female chimpanzee during the act of procreation. The feelings of her male partner are beyond my knowledge—as are those of the human male in the same context. I have spent countless hours watching mother chimpanzees interacting with their infants. But not until I had an infant of my own did I begin to understand the basic, powerful instinct of mother-love. If someone accidentally did something to frighten Grub, or threaten his well-being in any way, I felt a surge of quite irrational anger. How much more easily could I then understand the feelings of the chimpanzee mother who furiously waves her arm and barks in threat at an individual who approaches her infant too closely, or at a playmate who inadvertently hurts her child. And it was not until I knew the numbing grief that gripped me after the death of my second husband that I could even begin to appreciate the despair and sense of loss that can cause young chimps to pine away and die when they lose their mothers.

Empathy and intuition can be of tremendous value as we attempt to understand certain complex behavioral interactions, provided that the behaviour, as it occurs, is recorded precisely and objectively. Fortunately I have seldom found it difficult to record facts in an orderly manner even during times of powerful emotional involvement. And "knowing" intuitively how a chimpanzee is feeling—after an attack, for example—may help one to understand what happens next. We should not be afraid at least to try to make use of our

close evolutionary relationship with the chimpanzees in our attempts to interpret complex behaviour.

Today, as in Darwin's time, it is once again fashionable to speak of and study the animal mind. This change came about gradually, and was, at least in part, due to the information collected during careful studies of animal societies in the field. As these observations became widely known, it was impossible to brush aside the complexities of social behaviour that were revealed in species after species. The untidy clutter under the ethological carpets was brought out and examined, piece by piece. Gradually it was realized that parsimonious explanations of apparently intelligent behaviours were often misleading. This led to a succession of experiments that, taken together, clearly prove that many intellectual abilities that had been thought unique to humans were actually present, though in a less highly developed form, in other, non-human beings. Particularly, of course, in the non-human primates and especially in chimpanzees.

When first I began to read about human evolution, I learned that one of the hallmarks of our own species was that we, and only we, were capable of making tools. *Man the Toolmaker* was an oft-cited definition—and this despite the careful and exhaustive research of Wolfgang Kohler and Robert Yerkes on the tool-using and tool-making abilities of chimpanzees. Those studies, carried out independently in the early twenties, were received with scepticism. Yet both Kohler and Yerkes were respected scientists, and both had a profound understanding of chimpanzee behaviour. Indeed, Kohler's descriptions of the personalities and behaviour of the various individuals in his colony, published in his book *The Mentality of Apes*, remain some of the most vivid and colourful ever written. And his experiments, showing how chimpanzees could stack boxes, then climb the unstable constructions to reach fruit suspended from the ceiling, or join two short sticks to make a pole long enough to rake in fruit otherwise out of reach, have become classic, appearing in almost all textbooks dealing

with intelligent behaviour in non-human animals.

By the time systematic observations of tool-using came from Gombe those pioneering studies had been largely forgotten. Moreover, it was one thing to know that humanized chimpanzees in the lab could use implements: it was quite another to find that this was a naturally occurring skill in the wild. I well remember writing to Louis about my first observations, describing how David Greybeard not only used bits of straw to fish for termites but actually stripped leaves from a stem and thus *made* a tool. And I remember too receiving the now oft-quoted telegram he sent in response to my letter: "Now we must redefine *tool*, redefine *Man*, or accept chimpanzees as humans."

There were initially, a few scientists who attempted to write off the termiting observations, even suggesting that I had taught the chimps! By and large, though, people were fascinated by the information and by the subsequent observations of the other contexts in which the Gombe chimpanzees used objects as tools. And there were only a few anthropologists who objected when I suggested that the chimpanzees probably passed their tool-using traditions from one generation to the next, through observations, imitation and practice, so that each population might be expected to have its own unique tool-using culture. Which, incidentally, turns out to be quite true. And when I described how one chimpanzee, Mike, spontaneously solved a new problem by using a tool (he broke off a stick to knock a banana to the ground when he was too nervous to actually take it from my hand) I don't believe there were any raised eyebrows in the scientific community. Certainly I was not attacked viciously, as were Kohler and Yerkes, for suggesting that humans were not the only beings capable of reasoning and insight.

The mid-sixties saw the start of a project that, along with other similar research, was to teach us a great deal about the chimpanzee mind. This was Project Washoe, conceived by Trixie and Allen Gardner. They purchased an infant chimpanzee and began to teach her the signs of ASL, the American Sign Language used by the deaf. Twenty years earlier another husband and wife team, Richard and Cathy Hayes, had tried, with an almost total lack of success, to teach a young chimp, Vikki, to talk. The Hayes's undertaking taught us a lot about the chimpanzee mind, but Vikki, although she did well in IQ tests, and was clearly an intelligent youngster, could not learn human speech. The Gardners, however, achieved spectacular success with their pupil, Washoe. Not only did she learn signs easily, but she quickly began to string them together in meaningful ways. It was clear that each sign evoked, in her mind, a mental image of the object it represented. If, for example, she was asked, in sign language, to fetch an apple, she would go and locate an apple that was out of sight in another room.

Other chimps entered the project, some starting their lives in deaf signing families before joining Washoe. And finally Washoe adopted an infant, Loulis. He came from a lab where no thought of teaching signs had ever penetrated. When he was with Washoe he was given no lessons in language acquisition—not by humans, anyway. Yet by the time he was eight years old he had made fifty-eight signs in their correct contexts. How did he learn them? Mostly, it seems, by imitating the behaviour of Washoe and the other three signing chimps, Dar, Moja and Tatu. Sometimes, though, he received tuition from Washoe herself. One day, for example, she began to swagger about bipedally, hair bristling, signing *food! food! food!* in great excitement. She had seen a human approaching with a bar of chocolate. Loulis, only eighteen months old, watched passively. Suddenly Washoe stopped her swaggering, went over to him, took his hand, and moulded the sign for *food* (fingers pointing towards mouth). Another time, in a similar context, she made the sign for *chewing gum*—but with *her* hand on *his* body. On a third occasion Washoe, apropos of nothing, picked up a small chair, took it over to Loulis, set it down in front of him, and very distinctly made the *chair* sign three times, watching him closely as she did so. The two food signs became incorporated into Loulis's vocabulary but the sign for chair did not. Obviously the priorities of a young

chimp are similar to those of a human child!

When news of Washoe's accomplishments first hit the scientific community it immediately provoked a storm of bitter protest. It implied that chimpanzees were capable of mastering a human language, and this, in turn, indicated mental powers of generalization, abstraction and concept-formation as well as an ability to understand and use abstract symbols. And these intellectual skills were surely the prerogatives of *Homo sapiens*. Although there were many who were fascinated and excited by the Gardners' findings, there were many more who denounced the whole project, holding that the data was suspect, the methodology sloppy, and the conclusions not only misleading, but quite preposterous. The controversy inspired all sorts of other language projects. And, whether the investigators were sceptical to start with and hoped to disprove the Gardners' work, or whether they were attempting to demonstrate the same thing in a new way, their research provided additional information about the chimpanzee's mind.

And so, with new incentive, psychologists began to test the mental abilities of chimpanzees in a variety of different ways; again and again the results confirmed that their minds are uncannily like our own. It had long been held that only humans were capable of what is called 'cross-modal transfer of information'—in other words, if you shut your eyes and someone allows you to feel a strangely shaped potato, you will subsequently be able to pick it out from other differently shaped potatoes simply by looking at them. And vice versa. It turned out that chimpanzees can 'know' with their eyes what they 'feel' with their fingers in just the same way. In fact, we now know that some other non-human primates can do the same thing. I expect all kinds of creatures have the same ability.

Then it was proved, experimentally and beyond doubt, that chimpanzees could recognize themselves in mirrors—that they had, therefore, some kind of self-concept. In fact, Washoe, some years previously, had already demonstrated the ability when she spontane-

ously identified herself in the mirror, staring at her image and making her name sign. But that observation was merely anecdotal. The proof came when chimpanzees who had been allowed to play with mirrors were, while anaesthetized, dabbed with spots of odourless paint in places, such as the ears or the top of the head, that they could see only in the mirror. When they woke they were not only fascinated by their spotted images, but immediately investigated, with their fingers, the dabs of paint.

The fact that chimpanzees have excellent memories surprised no one. Everyone, after all, has been brought up to believe that 'an elephant never forgets' so why should a chimpanzee be any different? The fact that Washoe spontaneously gave the name-sign of Beatrice Gardner, her surrogate mother, when she saw her after a separation of eleven years was no greater an accomplishment than the amazing memory shown by dogs who recognize their owners after separations of almost as long—and the chimpanzee has a much longer life span than a dog. Chimpanzees can plan ahead, too, at least as regards the immediate future. This, in fact, is well illustrated at Gombe, during the termiting season: often an individual prepares a tool for use on a termite mound that is several hundred yards away and absolutely out of sight.

This is not the place to describe in detail the other cognitive abilities that have been studied in laboratory chimpanzees. Among other accomplishments chimpanzees possess pre-mathematical skills: they can, for example, readily differentiate between *more* and *less*. They can classify things into specific categories according to a given criterion—thus they have no difficulty in separating a pile of food into *fruits* and *vegetables* on one occasion, and, on another, dividing the same pile of food into *large* versus *small* items, even though this requires putting some vegetables with some fruits. Chimpanzees who have been taught a language can combine signs creatively in order to describe objects for which they have no symbol. Washoe, for example, puzzled her caretakers by asking, repeatedly, for a *rock berry*. Eventually it transpired that she was referring to Brazil nuts which she had encountered for the first time a while before. Another language-trained chimp described a cucumber as a *green banana*, and another referred to an Alka-Seltzer as a *listen drink*. They can even invent signs. Lucy, as she got older, had to be put on a leash for her outings. One day, eager to set off but having no sign for *leash*, she signalled her wishes by holding a crooked index finger to the ring on her collar. This sign became part of her vocabulary. Some chimpanzees love to draw, and especially to paint. Those who have learned sign language sometimes spontaneously label their works, 'This [is] apple'—or bird, or sweetcorn, or whatever. The fact that the paintings often look, to our eyes, remarkably unlike the objects depicted by the artists either means that the chimpanzees are poor draughtsmen or that we have much to learn regarding ape-style representational art!

People sometimes ask why chimpanzees have evolved such complex intellectual powers when their lives in the wild are so simple. The answer is, of course, that their lives in the wild are not so simple! They use—and need—all their mental skills during normal day-to-day life in their complex society. They are always having to make choices—where to go, or with whom to travel. They need highly developed social skills—particularly those males who are ambitious to attain high positions in the dominance hierarchy. Low-ranking chimpanzees must learn deception—to conceal their intentions or to do things in secret—if they are to get their way in the presence of their superiors. Indeed, the study of chimpanzees in the wild suggests that their intellectual abilities evolved, over the millennia, to help them cope with daily life. And now, the solid core of data concerning chimpanzee intellect collected so carefully in the lab setting provides a background against which to evaluate the many examples of intelligent, rational behaviour that we see in the wild.

It is easier to study intellectual prowess in the lab where, through carefully devised tests and judicious use of rewards, the chimpanzees can be encouraged to exert themselves, to stretch their minds to the limit. It is more meaningful to study the subject in the wild, but much harder. It is more meaningful because we can better understand the environmental pressures that led to the evolution of intellectual skills in chimpanzee societies. It is harder because, in the wild, almost all behaviours are confounded by countless variables; years of observing, recording and analysing take the place of contrived testing; sample size can often be counted on the fingers of one hand; the only experiments are nature's own, and only time— eventually—may replicate them.

In the wild a single observation may prove of utmost significance, providing a clue to some hitherto puzzling aspect of behaviour, a key to the understanding of, for example, a changed relationship. Obviously it is crucial to see as many incidents of this sort as possible. During the early years of my study at Gombe it became apparent that one person alone could never learn more than a fraction of what was going on in a chimpanzee community at any given time. And so, from 1964 onwards, I gradually built up a research team to help in the gathering of information about the behaviour of our closest living relatives.

The Cultures of Chimpanzees

*Humankind's nearest relative is even closer than we thought:
chimpanzees display remarkable behaviors that can only be described as
social customs passed on from generation to generation*

by Andrew Whiten and Christophe Boesch

As researchers quietly approach a clearing in the Taï Forest of Ivory Coast, they hear a complex pattern of soft thuds and cracks. It sounds as though a small band of people are busy in the forest, applying some rudimentary technology to a routine task. On entering the clearing, the scientists observe several individuals working keenly at anvils, skillfully wielding wooden hammers. One or two juveniles have apprenticed themselves to the work and—more clumsily and with less success—are struggling to lift the best hammer they can find. All this activity is directed toward cracking rock-hard but nutritious coula nuts. Intermittently, individuals set aside their tools to gather more handfuls of nuts. An infant sits with her mother, gathering morsels of broken nuts.

In many ways, this group could indeed be a family of foraging people. The hammers and anvils they leave behind, some made of stone, would excite the imagination of any anthropologist searching for signs of a primitive civilization. Yet these forest residents are not humans but chimpanzees.

The similarities between chimpanzees and humans have been studied for years, but in the past decade researchers have determined that these resemblances run much deeper than anyone first thought. For instance, the nut cracking observed in the Taï Forest is far from a simple chimpanzee behavior; rather it is a singular adaptation found only in that particular part of Africa and a trait that biologists consider to be an expression of chimpanzee culture. Scientists frequently use the term culture to describe elementary animal behaviors—such as the regional dialects of different populations of songbirds—but as it turns out, the rich and varied cultural traditions found among chimpanzees are second in complexity only to human traditions.

During the past two years, an unprecedented scientific collaboration, involving every major research group studying chimpanzees, has documented a multitude of distinct cultural patterns extending across Africa, in actions ranging from the animals' use of tools to their forms of communication and social customs. This emerging picture of chimpanzees not only affects how we think of these amazing creatures but also alters human beings' conception of our own uniqueness and hints at very ancient foundations for humankind's extraordinary capacity for culture.

CONTEMPLATING CULTURE

Homo sapiens and *Pan troglodytes* have coexisted for hundreds of millennia and share more than 98 percent of their genetic material, yet only 40 years ago we still knew next to nothing about chimpanzee behavior in the wild. That began to change in the 1960s, when Toshisada Nishida of Kyoto University in Japan and Jane Goodall began their studies of wild chimpanzees at two field sites in Tanzania. (Goodall's research station at Gombe—the first of its kind—is more famous, but Nishida's site at Mahale is the second-oldest chimpanzee research site in the world.)

In these initial studies, as the chimpanzees became accustomed to close observation, the remarkable discoveries began. Researchers witnessed a range of unexpected behaviors, including fashioning and

The Culture Club

How an international team of chimpanzee experts conducted the most comprehensive survey of the animals ever attempted

Scientists have been investigating chimpanzee culture for several decades, but too often their studies contained a crucial flaw. Most attempts to document cultural diversity among chimpanzees have relied solely on officially published accounts of the behaviors recorded at each research site. But this approach probably overlooks a good deal of cultural variation for three reasons.

First, scientists typically don't publish an extensive list of all the activities they do *not* see at a particular location. Yet this is exactly what we need to know—which behaviors were and were not observed at each site. Second, many reports describe chimpanzee behaviors without saying how common they are; without this information, we can't determine whether a particular action was a once-in-a-lifetime aberration or a routine event that should be considered part of the animals' culture. Finally, researchers' descriptions of potentially significant chimpanzee behaviors frequently lack sufficient detail, making it difficult for scientists working at other spots to record the presence or absence of the activities.

To remedy these problems, the two of us decided to take a new approach. We asked field researchers at each site for a list of all the behaviors they suspected were local traditions. With this information in hand, we pulled together a comprehensive list of 65 candidates for cultural behaviors.

Then we distributed our list to the team leaders at each site. In consultation with their colleagues, they classified each behavior in terms of its occurrence or absence in the chimpanzee community studied. The key categories were customary behavior (occurs in most or all of the able-bodied members of at least one age or sex class, such as all adult males), habitual (less common than customary but occurs repeatedly in several individuals), present (seen at the site but not habitual), absent (never seen), and unknown.

Our inquiry concentrated on seven sites with chimpanzees habituated to human onlookers; all told, the study compiled a total of more than 150 years of chimpanzee observation. The behavior patterns we were particularly interested in, of course, were those absent in at least one community, yet habitual or customary in at least one other; this was our criterion for denoting any behavior a cultural variant. (Certain behaviors are absent for specific local reasons, however, and we excluded them from consideration. For example, although chimpanzees at Bossou scoop tasty algae from pools of water with a stick, chimpanzees elsewhere don't do this, simply because algae are not present.)

The extensive survey turned up no fewer than 39 chimpanzee patterns of behavior that should be labeled as cultural variations, including numerous forms of tool use, grooming techniques and courtship gambits, several of which are illustrated throughout this article. This cultural richness is far in excess of anything known for any other species of animal.

—*A.W. and C.B.*

using tools, hunting, meat eating, food sharing and lethal fights between members of neighboring communities. In the years that followed, other primatologists set up camp elsewhere, and, despite all the financial, political and logistical problems that can beset African fieldwork, several of these outposts became truly long-term projects. As a result, we live in an unprecedented time, when an intimate and comprehensive scientific record of chimpanzees' lives at last exists not just for one but for several communities spread across Africa.

As early as 1973, Goodall recorded 13 forms of tool use as well as eight social activities that appeared to differ between the Gombe chimpanzees and chimpanzee populations elsewhere. She ventured that some variations had what she termed a cultural origin. But what exactly did Goodall mean by "culture"? According to the *Oxford Encyclopedic English Dictionary*, culture is defined as "the customs... and achievements of a particular time or people." The diversity of human cultures extends from technological variations to marriage rituals, from culinary habits to myths and legends. Animals do not have myths and legends, of course. But they do have the capacity to pass on behavioral traits from generation to generation, not through their genes but by learning. For biologists, this is the fundamental criterion for a cultural trait: it must be something that can be learned by observing the established skills of others and thus passed on to future generations [*see box,* "Do Apes Ape?"].

By the 1990s the discovery of new behavioral differences among chimpanzees made it feasible to begin assembling comprehensive charts of cultural variations for these animals. William C. McGrew, in his 1992 book *Chimpanzee Material Cultures*, was able to list 19 different kinds of tool use in distinct communities. One of us (Boesch), along with colleague Michael Tomasello of the Max Planck Institute for Evolutionary Anthropology in Leipzig, Germany, identified 25 distinct activities as potential cultural traits in wild chimpanzee populations.

A Guide to the Cultures of Chimpanzees

In an effort to catalogue cultural variations among chimpanzees, we asked researchers working at six sites across central Africa to classify chimpanzee behaviors in terms of occurrence or absence in seven communities. (There are two communities at Mahale.) The key categories were customary behavior, which occurs in most or all members of one age or sex class; habitual, which is less common but which still occurs repeatedly; present; absent; and unknown. Certain behaviors are absent for ecological reasons (eco): for example, chimpanzees do not use hammers to open coula nuts at Budongo, because the nuts are not available. The survey turned up 39 chimpanzee rituals that are labeled as cultural variations; 18 are illustrated below. —*A.W. and C.B.*

Hammering nuts
To crack open nutritious coula nuts, chimpanzees use stones as rudimentary hammers and anvils.

Pounding with pestle
With the stalks of palm trees acting as makeshift pestles, chimpanzees can pound and deepen holes in trees.

Fishing for termites
Chimpanzees insert thin, flexible strips of bark into termite mounds to extract the insects, which they then eat.

Wiping ants off stick manually
Once the ants have swarmed almost halfway up sticks dipped into the insects' nests, chimpanzees pull the sticks through their fists and sweep the ants into their mouths.

Eating ants directly off stick
After a few ants climb onto sticks inserted into the nests, chimpanzees bring the sticks directly to their mouths and eat the ants.

Removing bone marrow
With the help of small sticks, chimpanzees eat the marrow found inside the long bones of monkeys they have killed and eaten.

Sitting on leaves
A few large leaves apparently serve as protection when chimpanzees sit on wet ground.

Fanning flies
To keep flies away, chimpanzees utilize leafy twigs as a kind of fan.

Tickling self
A large stone or stick can be used to probe especially ticklish areas on a chimpanzee's own body.

	BOSSOU	TAÏ FOREST	GOMBE	MAHALE M-GROUP	MAHALE K-GROUP	KIBALE	BUDONGO
Hammering nuts	customary	customary	absent	absent	absent	absent (eco?)	absent (eco)
Pounding with pestle	customary	absent	absent	absent (eco?)	absent (eco?)	absent (eco?)	absent (eco?)
Fishing for termites	absent	absent (eco)	customary	absent	customary	absent (eco)	absent (eco?)
Wiping ants off stick manually	present	absent	customary	absent	absent	absent	absent
Eating ants directly off stick	customary	customary	present	absent	absent	absent	absent
Removing bone marrow	absent	customary	absent	absent	absent	absent	absent
Sitting on leaves	present	habitual	absent	absent	absent	present	absent
Fanning flies	absent	habitual	present	absent	absent	absent	habitual
Tickling self	absent	absent	habitual	absent	absent	absent	absent

Chart continues on next page.

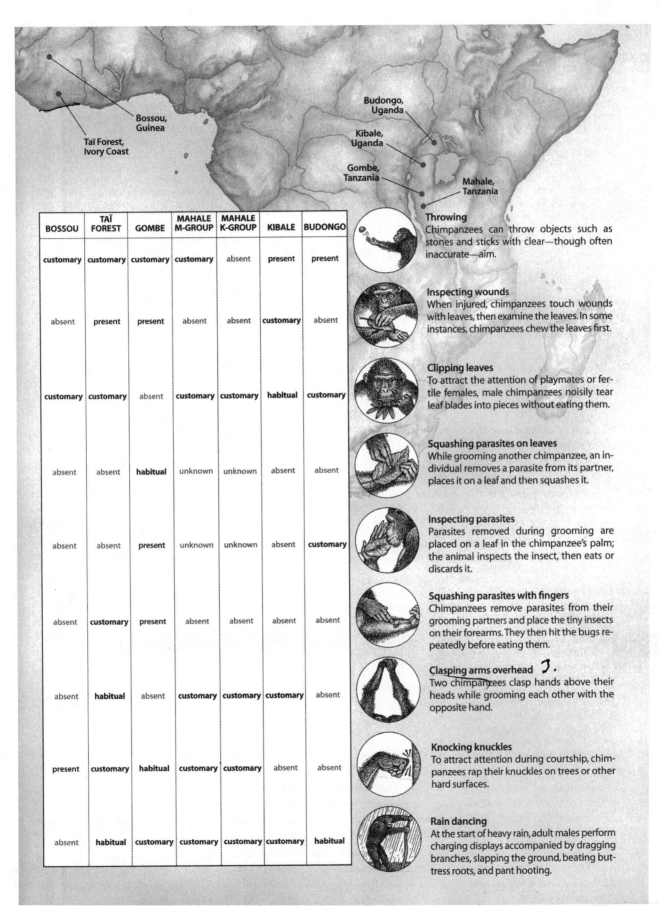

BOSSOU	TAÏ FOREST	GOMBE	MAHALE M-GROUP	MAHALE K-GROUP	KIBALE	BUDONGO
customary	customary	customary	customary	absent	present	present
absent	present	present	absent	absent	customary	absent
customary	customary	absent	customary	customary	habitual	customary
absent	absent	habitual	unknown	unknown	absent	absent
absent	absent	present	unknown	unknown	absent	customary
absent	customary	present	absent	absent	absent	absent
absent	habitual	absent	customary	customary	customary	absent
present	customary	habitual	customary	customary	absent	absent
absent	habitual	customary	customary	customary	customary	habitual

Throwing
Chimpanzees can throw objects such as stones and sticks with clear—though often inaccurate—aim.

Inspecting wounds
When injured, chimpanzees touch wounds with leaves, then examine the leaves. In some instances, chimpanzees chew the leaves first.

Clipping leaves
To attract the attention of playmates or fertile females, male chimpanzees noisily tear leaf blades into pieces without eating them.

Squashing parasites on leaves
While grooming another chimpanzee, an individual removes a parasite from its partner, places it on a leaf and then squashes it.

Inspecting parasites
Parasites removed during grooming are placed on a leaf in the chimpanzee's palm; the animal inspects the insect, then eats or discards it.

Squashing parasites with fingers
Chimpanzees remove parasites from their grooming partners and place the tiny insects on their forearms. They then hit the bugs repeatedly before eating them.

Clasping arms overhead
Two chimpanzees clasp hands above their heads while grooming each other with the opposite hand.

Knocking knuckles
To attract attention during courtship, chimpanzees rap their knuckles on trees or other hard surfaces.

Rain dancing
At the start of heavy rain, adult males perform charging displays accompanied by dragging branches, slapping the ground, beating buttress roots, and pant hooting.

Chart continued from previous page.

Do Apes Ape?

Recent studies show that chimpanzees and other apes can learn by imitation

The notion that the great apes—chimpanzees, gorillas, orangutans and gibbons—can imitate one another might seem unsurprising to anyone who has watched these animals playing at the zoo. But in scientific circles, the question of whether apes, well, *ape*, has become controversial.

Consider a young chimpanzee watching his mother crack open a coula nut, as has been observed in the Taï Forest of West Africa. In most cases, the youth will eventually take up the practice himself. Was this because he imitated his mother? Skeptics think perhaps not. They argue that the mother's attention to the nuts encouraged the youngster to focus on them as well. Once his attention had been drawn to the food, the young chimpanzee learned how to open the nut by trial and error, not by imitating his mother.

Such a distinction has important implications for any discussion of chimpanzee cultures. Some scientists define a cultural trait as one that is passed down not by genetic inheritance but instead when the younger generation copies adult behavior. If cracking open a coula is something that chimpanzees can simply figure out how to do on their own once they hold a hammer stone, then it can't be considered part of their culture. Furthermore, if these animals learn exclusively by trial and error, then chimpanzees must, in a sense, reinvent the wheel each time they tackle a new skill. No cumulative culture can ever develop.

The clearest way to establish how chimpanzees learn is through laboratory experiments. One of us (Whiten), in collaboration with Deborah M. Custance of Goldsmiths College, University of London, constructed artificial fruits to serve as analogues of those the animals must deal with in the wild. In a typical experiment, one group of chimpanzees watched a complex technique for opening one of the fruits, while a second group observed a very different method; we then recorded the extent to which the chimpanzees had been influenced by the method they observed. We also conducted similar experiments with three-year-old human children as subjects. Our results demonstrate that six-year-old chimpanzees show imitative behavior that is markedly like that seen in the children, although the fidelity of their copying tends to be poorer.

In a different kind of experiment, one of us (Boesch), along with some co-workers, gave chimpanzees in the Zurich Zoo in Switzerland hammers and nuts similar to those available in the wild. We then monitored the repertoire of behaviors displayed by the captive chimpanzees. As it turned out, the chimpanzees in the zoo exhibited a greater range of activities than the more limited and focused set of actions we had seen in the wild. We interpreted this to mean that a wild chimpanzee's cultural environment channeled the behavior of youngsters, steering them in the direction of the most useful skills. In the zoo, without benefit of existing traditions, the chimpanzees experimented with a host of less useful actions.

Interestingly, some of the results from the experiments involving the artificial fruits converge with this idea. In one study, chimpanzees copied an entire sequence of actions they had witnessed, but did so only after several viewings and after trying some alternatives. In other words, they tended to imitate what they had observed others doing at the expense of their own trial-and-error discoveries.

In our view, these findings taken together suggest that apes do ape and that this ability forms one strand in cultural transmission. Indeed, it is difficult to imagine how chimpanzees could develop certain geographic variations in activities such as ant-dipping and parasite-handling without copying established traditions. They must be imitating other members of their group.

We should note, however, that—just as is the case with humans—certain cultural traits are no doubt passed on by a combination of imitation and simpler kinds of social learning, such as having one's attention drawn to useful tools. Either way, learning from elders is crucial to growing up as a competent wild chimpanzee.

—A.W. and C.B.

The most recent catalogue of cultural variations results from a unique collaboration of nine chimpanzee experts (including the two of us) who pooled extensive field observations that, taken together, amounted to a total of 151 years of chimp watching [*see box,* "The Culture Club"]. The list cites 39 patterns of chimpanzee behavior that we believe to have a cultural origin, including such activities as using sticks to "fish" for ants, making dry seats from leaves, and a range of social grooming habits. At present, these 39 variants put chimpanzees in a class of their own, with far more elaborate customs than any other animal studied to date. Of course, chimpanzees also remain distinct from humans, for whom cultural variations are simply beyond count. (We must point out, however, that scientists are only beginning to uncover the behavioral complexity that exists among chimpanzees—and so the number 39 no doubt represents a minimum of cultural traits.)

MULTICULTURAL CHIMPANZEES

When describing human customs, anthropologists and sociologists often refer to "American culture" or "Chinese culture"; these terms encompass a wide spectrum of activities—language, forms of dress, eating habits, marriage rituals and so on. Among animals, however, culture has typically been established for a single behavior, such as song dialects among birds. Ornithologists haven't identified variation in courtship patterns or feeding practices, for example, to go alongside the differences in dialect.

Chimpanzees, though, do more than display singular cultural traits: each community exhibits an entire set of behaviors that differentiates it from other groups [see illustrations]. As a result, we can talk about "Gombe culture" or "Taï culture." Indeed, once we observe how a chimpanzee behaves, we can identify where the animal lives. For instance, an individual that cracks nuts, leaf-clips during drumming displays, fishes for ants with one hand using short sticks, and knuckle-knocks to attract females clearly comes from the Taï Forest. A chimp that leaf-grooms and hand-clasps during grooming can come from the Kibale Forest or the Mahale Mountains, but if you notice that he also ant-fishes, there is no doubt anymore—he comes from Mahale.

In addition, chimpanzee cultures go beyond the mere presence or absence of a particular behavior. For example, all chimpanzees dispatch parasites found during grooming a companion. But at Taï they will mash the parasites against their forearms with a finger, at Gombe they squash them onto leaves, and at Budongo they put them on a leaf to inspect before eating or discarding them. Each community has developed a unique approach for accomplishing the same goal. Alternatively, behaviors may look similar yet be used in different contexts: at Mahale, males "clip" leaves noisily with their teeth as a courtship gesture, whereas at Taï, chimpanzees incorporate leaf-clipping into drumming displays.

The implications of this new picture of chimpanzee culture are many. The information offers insight into our distinctiveness as a species. When we first published this work in the journal Nature, we found some people quite disturbed to realize that the characteristic that had appeared to separate us so starkly from the animal world—our capacity for cultural development—is not such an absolute difference after all.

But this seems a rather misdirected response. The differences between human customs and traditions, enriched and mediated by language as they are, are vast in contrast with what we see in the chimpanzee. The story of chimpanzee cultures sharpens our understanding of our uniqueness, rather than threatening it in any way that need worry us.

Human achievements have made enormous cumulative progress over the generations, a phenomenon Boesch and Tomasello have dubbed the "ratchet effect." The idea of a hammer—once simply a crude stone cobble—has been modified and improved on countless times until now we have electronically controlled robot hammers in our factories. Chimpanzees may show the beginnings of the ratchet effect—some that use stone anvils, for example, have gone a step further, as at Bossou, where they wedge a stone beneath their anvil when it needs leveling on bumpy ground—but such behavior has not become customary and is rudimentary indeed beside human advancements.

The cultural capacity we share with chimpanzees also suggests an ancient ancestry for the mentality that must underlie it. Our cultural nature did not emerge out of the blue but evolved from simpler beginnings. Social learning similar to that of chimpanzees would appear capable of sustaining the earliest stone-tool cultures of human ancestors living two million years ago.

Whether chimpanzees are the sole species on the planet that shares humankind's capacity for culture is too early to judge: nobody has undertaken the comprehensive research necessary to test the idea. Early evidence hints that other creatures should be included in these discussions, however. Carel P. van Schaik and his colleagues at Duke University have found orangutans in Sumatra that habitually use at least two different kinds of tools. Orangutans monitored for years elsewhere have never been seen to do this.

And Hal Whitehead of Dalhousie University and his colleagues have begun to document the ways in which pop-

ulations of whales that sing in different dialects also hunt in different ways. We hope that our comprehensive approach to documenting chimpanzee cultures may provide a template for the study of these other promising species.

What of the implications for chimpanzees themselves? We must highlight the tragic loss of chimpanzees, whose populations are being decimated just when we are at last coming to appreciate these astonishing animals more completely. Populations have plummeted in the past century and continue to fall as a result of illegal trapping, logging and, most recently, the bushmeat trade. The latter is particularly alarming: logging has driven roadways into the forest that are now used to ship wild-animal meat—including chimpanzee meat—to consumers as far afield as Europe. Such destruction threatens not only the animals themselves but also a host of fascinatingly different ape cultures.

Perhaps the cultural richness of the ape may yet help in its salvation, however. Some conservation efforts have already altered the attitudes of some local people. A few organizations have begun to show videotapes illustrating the cognitive prowess of chimpanzees. One Zairian viewer was heard to exclaim, "Ah, this ape is so like me, I can no longer eat him."

FURTHER INFORMATION

CHIMPANZEE MATERIAL CULTURE. William C. McGrew. Cambridge University Press, 1992.

CULTURES IN CHIMPANZEES. A. Whiten, J. Goodall, W. C. McGrew, T. Nishida, V. Reynolds, Y. Sugiyama, C.E.G. Tutin, R. W. Wrangham and C. Boesch in Nature, Vol. 399, pages 682–685; 1999.

CHIMPANZEES OF THE TAÏ FOREST: BEHAVIORAL ECOLOGY AND EVOLUTION. Christophe Boesch and Hedwige Boesch-Aschermann. Oxford University Press, 2000.

PRIMATE CULTURE AND SOCIAL LEARNING. Andrew Whiten in Cognitive Science. Special issue on primate cognition, Vol. 24, pages 477–508; 2000.

Chimpanzee Cultures Web site: http://chimp.stand.ac.uk/cultures/

Wild Chimpanzee Foundation Web site: http://www.wildchimps.org

ANDREW WHITEN and CHRISTOPHE BOESCH have collaborated since 1998 on the cross-cultural study of chimpanzees. Whiten, a fellow of the British Academy, is professor of evolutionary and developmental psychology at the University of St. Andrews in Scotland. Boesch is co-director of the Max Planck Institute for Evolutionary Anthropology in Leipzig, Germany, and a professor at the University of Leipzig. The chimpanzee field-study directors participating in the research described here are Jane Goodall, Jane Goodall Institute, Washington, D.C.; William C. McGrew, Miami University; Toshisada Nishida, Kyoto University, Japan; Vernon Reynolds, University of Oxford; Yukimaru Sugiyama, Tokaigakuen University, Japan; Caroline E. G. Tutin, University of Stirling, Scotland; and Richard W. Wrangham, Harvard University.

Dim Forest, Bright Chimps

*In the rain forest of Ivory Coast, chimpanzees meet
the challenge of life by hunting cooperatively
and using crude tools*

**Christophe Boesch and
Hedwige Boesch-Achermann**

Taï National Park, Ivory Coast, December 3, 1985. Drumming, barking, and screaming, chimps rush through the undergrowth, little more than black shadows. Their goal is to join a group of other chimps noisily clustering around Brutus, the dominant male of this seventy-member chimpanzee community. For a few moments, Brutus, proud and self-confident, stands fairly still, holding a shocked, barely moving red colobus monkey in his hand. Then he begins to move through the group, followed closely by his favorite females and most of the adult males. He seems to savor this moment of uncontested superiority, the culmination of a hunt high up in the canopy. But the victory is not his alone. Cooperation is essential to capturing one of these monkeys, and Brutus will break apart and share this highly prized delicacy with most of the main participants of the hunt and with the females. Recipients of large portions will, in turn, share more or less generously with their offspring, relatives, and friends.

In 1979, we began a long-term study of the previously unknown chimpanzees of Taï National Park, 1,600 square miles of tropical rain forest in the Republic of the Ivory Coast (Côte d'Ivoire). Early on, we were most interested in the chimps' use of natural hammers—

branches and stones—to crack open the five species of hard-shelled nuts that are abundant here. A sea otter lying on its back, cracking an abalone shell with a rock, is a familiar picture, but no primate had ever before been observed in the wild using stones as hammers. East Africa's savanna chimps, studied for decades by Jane Goodall in Gombe, Tanzania, use twigs to extract ants and termites from their nests or honey from a bees' nest, but they have never been seen using hammerstones.

As our work progressed, we were surprised by the many ways in which the life of the Taï forest chimpanzees differs from that of their savanna counterparts, and as evidence accumulated, differences in how the two populations hunt proved the most intriguing. Jane Goodall had found that chimpanzees hunt monkeys, antelope, and wild pigs, findings confirmed by Japanese biologist Toshida Nishida, who conducted a long-term study 120 miles south of Gombe, in the Mahale Mountains. So we were not surprised to discover that the Taï chimps eat meat. What intrigued us was the degree to which they hunt cooperatively. In 1953 Raymond Dart proposed that group hunting and cooperation were key ingredients in the evolution of *Homo sapiens*. The argument has been modified consid-

erably since Dart first put it forward, and group hunting has also been observed in some social carnivores (lions and African wild dogs, for instance), and even some birds of prey. Nevertheless, many anthropologists still hold that hunting cooperatively and sharing food played a central role in the drama that enabled early hominids, some 1.8 million years ago, to develop the social systems that are so typically human.

We hoped that what we learned about the behavior of forest chimpanzees would shed new light on prevailing theories of human evolution. Before we could even begin, however, we had to habituate a community of chimps to our presence. Five long years passed before we were able to move with them on their daily trips through the forest, of which "our" group appeared to claim some twelve square miles. Chimpanzees are alert and shy animals, and the limited field of view in the rain forest—about sixty-five feet at best—made finding them more difficult. We had to rely on sound, mostly their vocalizations and drumming on trees. Males often drum regularly while moving through the forest: pant-hooting, they draw near a big buttress tree; then, at full speed they fly over the buttress, hitting it repeatedly with their hands and feet. Such drum-

Tool finding

ming may resound more than half a mile in the forest. In the beginning, our ignorance about how they moved and who was drumming led to failure more often than not, but eventually we learned that the dominant males drummed during the day to let other group members know the direction of travel. On some days, however, intermittent drumming about dawn was the only signal for the whole day. If we were out of earshot at the time, we were often reduced to guessing.

During these difficult early days, one feature of the chimps' routine proved to be our salvation: nut cracking is a noisy business. So noisy, in fact, that in the early days of French colonial rule, one officer apparently even proposed the theory that some unknown tribe was forging iron in the impenetrable and dangerous jungle.

Nuts

Guided by the sounds made by the chimps as they cracked open nuts, which they often did for hours at a time, we were gradually able to get within sixty feet of the animals. We still seldom saw the chimps themselves (they fled if we came too close), but even so, the evidence left after a session of nut cracking taught us a great deal about what types of nuts they were eating, what sorts of hammer and anvil tools they were using, and—thanks to the very distinctive noise a nut makes when it finally splits open— how many hits were needed to crack a nut and how many nuts could be opened per minute.

After some months, we began catching glimpses of the chimpanzees before they fled, and after a little more time, we were able to draw close enough to watch them at work. The chimps gather nuts from the ground. Some nuts are tougher to crack than others. Nuts of the *Panda oleosa* tree are the most demanding, harder than any of the foods processed by present-day hunter-gatherers and breaking open only when a force of 3,500 pounds is applied. The stone hammers used by the Taï chimps range from stones of ten ounces to granite blocks of four to forty-five pounds. Stones of any size, however, are a rarity in the forest and are seldom conveniently placed near a nut-bearing tree. By observing closely, and in some cases imitating the way the chimps handle hammerstones,

we learned that they have an impressive ability to find just the right tool for the job at hand. Taï chimps could remember the positions of many of the stones scattered, often out of sight, around a panda tree. Without having to run around rechecking the stones, they would select one of appropriate size that was closest to the tree. These mental abilities in spatial representation compare with some of those of nine-year-old humans.

To extract the four kernels from inside a panda nut, a chimp must use a hammer with extreme precision. Time and time again, we have been impressed to see a chimpanzee raise a twenty-pound stone above its head, strike a nut with ten or more powerful blows, and then, using the same hammer, switch to delicate little taps from a height of only four inches. To finish the job, the chimps often break off a small piece of twig and use it to extract the last tiny fragments of kernel from the shell. Intriguingly, females crack panda nuts more often than males, a gender difference in tool use that seems to be more pronounced in the forest chimps than in their savanna counterparts.

After five years of fieldwork, we were finally able to follow the chimpanzees at close range, and gradually, we gained insights into their way of hunting. One morning, for example, we followed a group of six male chimps on a three-hour patrol that had taken them into foreign territory to the north. (Our study group is one of five chimpanzee groups more or less evenly distributed in the Taï forest.) As always during these approximately monthly incursions, which seem to be for the purpose of territorial defense, the chimps were totally silent, clearly on edge and on the lookout for trouble. Once the patrol was over, however, and they were back within their own borders, the chimps shifted their attention to hunting. They were after monkeys, the most abundant mammals in the forest. Traveling in large, multi-species groups, some of the forest's ten species of monkeys are more apt than others to wind up as a meal for the chimps. The relatively sluggish and large (almost thirty pounds) red colobus monkeys are the chimps' usual fare. (Antelope also live in the forest, but in our ten years at Taï, we have never

seen a chimp catch, or even pursue, one. In contrast, Gombe chimps at times do come across fawns, and when they do, they seize the opportunity—and the fawn.)

The six males moved on silently, peering up into the vegetation and stopping from time to time to listen for the sound of monkeys. None fed or groomed; all focused on the hunt. We followed one old male, Falstaff, closely, for he tolerates us completely and is one of the keenest and most experienced hunters. Even from the rear, Falstaff set the pace; whenever he stopped, the others paused to wait for him. After thirty minutes, we heard the unmistakable noises of monkeys jumping from branch to branch. Silently, the chimps turned in the direction of the sounds, scanning the canopy. Just then, a diana monkey spotted them and gave an alarm call. Dianas are very alert and fast; they are also about half the weight of colobus monkeys. The chimps quickly gave up and continued their search for easier, meatier prey.

Shortly after, we heard the characteristic cough of a red colobus monkey. Suddenly Rousseau and Macho, two twenty-year-olds, burst into action, running toward the cough. Falstaff seemed surprised by their precipitousness, but after a moment's hesitation, he also ran. Now the hunting barks of the chimps mixed with the sharp alarm calls of the monkeys. Hurrying behind Falstaff, we saw him climb up a conveniently situated tree. His position, combined with those of Schubert and Ulysse, two mature chimps in their prime, effectively blocked off three of the monkeys' possible escape routes. But in another tree, nowhere near any escape route and thus useless, waited the last of the hunters, Kendo, eighteen years old and the least experienced of the group. The monkeys, taking advantage of Falstaff's delay and Kendo's error, escaped.

The six males moved on and within five minutes picked up the sounds of another group of red colobus. This time, the chimps approached cautiously, nobody hurrying. They screened the canopy intently to locate the monkeys, which were still unaware of the approaching danger. Macho and Schubert chose two adjacent trees, both full of monkeys, and started climbing very quietly, taking care not to move any branches. Meanwhile, the other four chimps blocked off anticipated escape routes. When Schubert was halfway up, the monkeys finally detected the two chimps. As we watched the colobus monkeys take off in literal panic, the appropriateness of the chimpanzees' scientific name—*Pan* came to mind: with a certain stretch of the imagination, the fleeing monkeys could be shepherds and shepherdesses frightened at the sudden appearance of Pan, the wild Greek god of the woods, shepherds, and their flocks.

Taking off in the expected direction, the monkeys were trailed by Macho and Schubert. The chimps let go with loud hunting barks. Trying to escape, two colobus monkeys jumped into smaller trees lower in the canopy. With this, Rousseau and Kendo, who had been watching from the ground, sped up into the trees and tried to grab them. Only a third of the weight of the chimps, however, the monkeys managed to make it to the next tree along branches too small for their pursuers. But Falstaff had anticipated this move and was waiting for them. In the following confusion, Falstaff seized a juvenile and killed it with a bite to the neck. As the chimps met in a rush on the ground, Falstaff began to eat, sharing with Schubert and Rousseau. A juvenile colobus does not provide much meat, however, and this time, not all the chimps got a share. Frustrated individuals soon started off on another hunt, and relative calm returned fairly quickly: this sort of hunt, by a small band of chimps acting on their own at the edge of their territory, does not generate the kind of high excitement that prevails when more members of the community are involved.

So far we have observed some 200 monkey hunts and have concluded that success requires a minimum of three motivated hunters acting cooperatively. Alone or in pairs, chimps succeed less than 15 percent of the time, but when three or four act as a group, more than half the hunts result in a kill. The chimps seem well aware of the odds; 92 percent of all the hunts we observed were group affairs.

Gombe chimps also hunt red colobus monkeys, but the percentage of group hunts is much lower: only 36 percent. In addition, we learned from Jane Goodall that even when Gombe chimps do hunt in groups, their strategies are different. When Taï chimps arrive under a group of monkeys, the hunters scatter, often silently, usually out of sight of one another but each aware of the others' positions. As the hunt progresses, they gradually close in, encircling the quarry. Such movements require that each chimp coordinate his movements with those of the other hunters, as well as with those of the prey, at all times.

Coordinated hunts account for 63 percent of all those observed at Taï but only 7 percent of those at Gombe. Jane Goodall says that in a Gombe group hunt, the chimpanzees typically travel together until they arrive at a tree with monkeys. Then, as the chimps begin climbing nearby trees, they scatter as each pursues a different target. Goodall gained the impression that Gombe chimps boost their success by hunting independently but simultaneously, thereby disorganizing their prey; our impression is that the Taï chimps owe their success to being organized themselves.

Just why the Gombe and Taï chimps have developed such different hunting strategies is difficult to explain, and we plan to spend some time at Gombe in the hope of finding out. In the meantime, the mere existence of differences is interesting enough and may perhaps force changes in our understanding of human evolution. Most currently accepted theories propose that some three million years ago, a dramatic climate change in Africa east of the Rift Valley turned dense forest into open, drier habitat. Adapting to the difficulties of life under these new conditions, our ancestors supposedly evolved into cooperative hunters and began sharing food they caught. Supporters of this idea point out that plant and animal remains indicative of dry, open environments have been found at all early hominid excavation sites in Tanzania, Kenya, South Africa, and Ethiopia. That the large majority of apes in Africa today live west of the Rift Valley appears to many anthropologists to lend further support to the idea that a change in environment caused the common ancestor of apes and humans to evolve along a different line from those remaining in the forest.

Our observations, however, suggest quite another line of thought. Life in dense, dim forest may require more sophisticated behavior than is commonly assumed: compared with their savanna relatives, Taï chimps show greater complexity in both hunting and tool use. Taï chimps use tools in nineteen different ways and have six different ways of making them, compared with sixteen uses and three methods of manufacture at Gombe.

Anthropologist colleagues of mine have told me that the discovery that some chimpanzees are accomplished users of hammerstones forces them to look with a fresh eye at stone tools turned up at excavation sites. The important role played by female Taï chimps in tool use also raises the possibility that in the course of human evolution, women may have been decisive in the development of many of the sophisticated manipulative skills characteristic of our species. Taï mothers also appear to pass on their skills by actively teaching their offspring. We have observed mothers providing their young with hammers and then stepping in to help when the inexperienced youngsters encounter difficulty. This help may include carefully showing how to position the nut or hold the hammer properly. Such behavior has never been observed at Gombe.

Similarly, food sharing, for a long time said to be unique to humans, seems more general in forest than in savanna chimpanzees. Taï chimp mothers share with their young up to 60 percent of the nuts they open, at least until the latter become sufficiently adept, generally at about six years old. They also share other foods acquired with tools, including honey, ants, and bone marrow. Gombe mothers share such foods much less often, even with their infants. Taï chimps also share meat more frequently than do their Gombe relatives, sometimes dividing a chunk up and giving portions away, sometimes simply allowing beggars to grab pieces.

Any comparison between chimpanzees and our hominid ancestors can only be suggestive, not definitive. But our studies lead us to believe that the process of hominization may have begun independently of the drying of the environment. Savanna life could even have delayed the process; many anthropologists have been struck by how slowly hominid-associated remains, such as the hand ax, changed after their first appearance in the Olduvai age.

Will we have the time to discover more about the hunting strategies or other, perhaps as yet undiscovered abilities of these forest chimpanzees? Africa's tropical rain forests, and their inhabitants, are threatened with extinction by extensive logging, largely to provide the Western world with tropical timber and such products as coffee, co-

coa, and rubber. Ivory Coast has lost 90 percent of its original forest, and less than 5 percent of the remainder can be considered pristine. The climate has changed dramatically. The harmattan, a cold, dry wind from the Sahara previously unknown in the forest, has now swept through the Taï forest every year since 1986. Rainfall has diminished; all the rivulets in our study region are now dry for several months of the year.

In addition, the chimpanzee, biologically very close to humans, is in demand for research on AIDS and hepatitis vaccines. Captive-bred chimps are available, but they cost about twenty times more than wild-caught animals. Chimps

taken from the wild for these purposes are generally young, their mothers having been shot during capture. For every chimp arriving at its sad destination, nine others may well have died in the forest or on the way. Such priorities—cheap coffee and cocoa and chimpanzees—do not do the economies of Third World countries any good in the long run, and they bring suffering and death to innocent victims in the forest. Our hope is that Brutus, Falstaff, and their families will survive, and that we and others will have the opportunity to learn about them well into the future. But there is no denying that modern times work against them and us.

To Catch a Colobus

*Chimpanzees in Gombe National Park band together to kill nearly
a fifth of the red colobus monkeys in their range*

Craig B. Stanford

On a sunny July morning, I am sitting on the bank of Kakombe Stream in Gombe National Park, Tanzania. Forty feet above my head, scattered through large fig trees, is a group of red colobus monkeys. This is J group, whose twenty-five members I have come to know as individuals during several seasons of fieldwork. Gombe red colobus are large, long-tailed monkeys, with males sometimes weighing more than twenty pounds. Both sexes have a crown of red hair, a gray back, and buff underparts. The highlight of this particular morning has been the sighting of a new infant, born sometime in the previous two days. As the group feeds noisily on fruit and leaves overhead, I mull over the options for possible names for the infant.

While I watch the colobus monkeys, my attention is caught by the loud and excited pant-hoots of a party of chimpanzees farther down the valley. I judge the group to be of considerable size and traveling in my direction. As the calls come closer, the colobus males begin to give high-pitched alarm calls, and mothers gather up their infants and climb higher into the tree crowns.

A moment later, a wild chorus of pant-hoots erupts just behind me, followed by a cacophony of colobus alarm calls, and it is obvious to both J group and to me that the chimps have arrived. The male chimps immediately climb up to the higher limbs of the tall albizia tree into which most of the colobus group have retreated. Colobus females and their offspring huddle high in the crown, while a

phalanx of five adult males descends to meet the advancing ranks of four adult male chimpanzees, led by seventeen-year-old, 115-pound Frodo. Frodo is the most accomplished hunter of colobus monkeys at Gombe and the only one willing to take on several colobus males simultaneously in order to catch his prey. The other hunters keep their distance while Frodo first scans the group of monkeys, then advances upon the colobus defenders. Time and again he lunges at the colobus males, attempting to race past them and into the cluster of terrified females and infants. Each time he is driven back; at one point, the two largest males of J group leap onto Frodo's back until he retreats, screaming, a few yards away.

A brief lull in the hunt follows, during which the colobus males run to one another and embrace for reassurance, then part to renew their defense. Frodo soon charges again into the midst of the colobus males, and this time manages to scatter them long enough to pluck the newborn from its mother's abdomen. In spite of fierce opposition, Frodo has caught his quarry, and he now sits calmly and eats it while the other hunters and two female chimps—their swollen pink rumps a sign that they are in estrus, a period of sexual receptivity—sit nearby begging for meat. The surviving colobus monkeys watch nervously from a few feet away. Minutes later, the mother of the dead infant attempts to approach, perhaps to try to rescue her nearly consumed offspring. She is chased, falls from the tree to the forest floor, and is

pounced upon and killed by juvenile chimpanzees that have been watching the hunt from below. Seconds later, before these would-be hunters have had a chance to begin their meal, Wilkie, the chimpanzee group's dominant male, races down the tree and steals the carcass from them. He shows off his prize by charging across the forest floor, dead colobus in hand, and then, amid a frenzy of chimps eager for a morsel, he sits down to share the meat with his ally Prof and two females from the hunting party.

Until Jane Goodall observed chimpanzees eating meat in the early 1960s, they were thought to be complete vegetarians. We now know that a small but regular portion of the diet of wild chimps consists of the meat of such mammals as bush pigs, small antelopes, and a variety of monkey species. For example, chimpanzees in the Mahale Mountains of Tanzania, the Taï forest of Ivory Coast, and in Gombe all regularly hunt red colobus monkeys. Documenting the effect of such predation on wild primate populations, however, is extremely difficult because predators—whether chimps, leopards, or eagles—are generally too shy to hunt in the presence of people. The result is that even if predation is a regular occurrence, researchers are not likely to see it, let alone study it systematically.

Gombe is one of the few primate study sites where both predators and their prey have been habituated to human observers, making it possible to witness hunts. I have spent the past four field sea-

Look for food

sons at Gombe, studying the predator-prey relationship between the 45-member Kasakela chimpanzee community and the 500 red colobus monkeys that share the same twelve square miles of Gombe National Park. Gombe's rugged terrain is composed of steep slopes of open woodland, rising above stream valleys lush with riverine forest. The chimpanzees roam across these hills in territorial communities, which divide up each day into foraging parties of from one to forty animals. So far, I have clocked in more than a thousand hours with red colobus monkeys and have regularly followed the chimps on their daily rounds, observing some 150 encounters between the monkeys and chimps and more than 75 hunts. My records, together with those of my colleagues, show that the Gombe chimps may kill more than 100 red colobus each year, or nearly one-fifth of the colobus inhabiting their range. Most of the victims are immature monkeys under two years old. Also invaluable have been the data gathered daily on the chimps for the past two decades by a team of Tanzanian research assistants.

One odd outcome of my work has been that I am in the unique position of knowing both the hunters and their victims as individuals, which makes my research intriguing but a bit heart-wrenching. In October 1992, for example, a party of thirty-three chimpanzees encountered my main study group, J, in upper Kakombe valley. The result was devastating from the monkeys' viewpoint. During the hour-long hunt, seven were killed; three were caught and torn apart right in front of me. Nearly four hours later, the hunters were still sharing and eating the meat they had caught, while I sat staring in disbelief at the remains of many of my study subjects.

Determined to learn more about the chimp-colobus relationship, however, I continued watching, that day and many others like it. I will need several more field seasons before I can measure the full impact of chimpanzee hunting on the Gombe red colobus, but several facts about hunting and its effects on the monkeys have already emerged. One major factor that determines the outcome of a hunt in Gombe is the number of male

chimps involved. (Although females also hunt, the males are responsible for more than 90 percent of all colobus kills.) Red colobus males launch a courageous counterattack in response to their chimpanzee predators, but their ability to defend their group is directly proportional to the number of attackers and does not seem to be related to the number of defenders. The outcome of a hunt is thus almost always in the hands of the chimps, and in most instances, the best the monkeys can hope to do is limit the damage to a single group member rather than several. Chimpanzees have a highly fluid social grouping pattern in which males tend to travel together while females travel alone with their infants. At times, however, twenty or more male and female chimpanzees forage together. When ten or more male chimps hunt together, they are successful nine times out of ten, and the colobus have little hope of escape.

Hunting success depends on other factors as well. Unlike the shy red-tailed and blue monkeys with which they share the forest (and which are rarely hunted by the chimps), red colobus do not flee the moment they hear or see chimps approaching. Instead, the red colobus give alarm calls and adopt a vigilant wait-and-see strategy, with males positioned nearest the potential attackers. The alarm calls increase in frequency and intensity as the chimpanzees draw closer and cease only when the chimps are sighted beneath the tree. Then, the colobus sit quietly, watching intently, and only if the chimps decide to hunt do the colobus males launch a counterattack. The monkeys' decision to stand and fight rather than flee may seem maladaptive given their low rate of successful defense. I observed, however, that when the monkeys scatter or try to flee, the chimps nearly always pursue and catch one or more of them.

Fleeing red colobus monkeys are most likely to be caught when they have been feeding on the tasty new leaves of the tallest trees, the "emergents," which rise above the canopy. When these trees are surrounded by low plant growth, they frequently become death traps because the only way colobus can escape from attacking chimps is to leap out of the

tree—often into the waiting arms of more chimpanzees on the ground below.

One of my primary goals has been to learn why a party of chimps will eagerly hunt a colobus group one day while ignoring the same group under seemingly identical circumstances on another. One determinant is the number of males in the chimp party: the more males, the more likely the group will hunt. Hunts are also undertaken mainly when a mother colobus carrying a small infant is visible, probably because of the Gombe chimps' preference for baby red colobus, which make up 75 percent of all kills. The situation is quite different in the Taï forest, where half of the chimp kills are adult colobus males (*see* "Dim Forest, Bright Chimps," *Natural History*, September 1991). Christophe and Hedwige Boesch have shown that the Taï chimps hunt cooperatively, perhaps because red colobus monkeys are harder to catch in the much taller canopy of the Taï rainforest. Successful Taï chimp hunters also regularly share the spoils. In contrast, each chimp in Gombe appears to have his own hunting strategy.

The single best predictor of when Gombe chimps will hunt is the presence of one or more estrous females in the party. This finding, together with the earlier observation by Geza Teleki (formerly of George Washington University) that male hunters tend to give meat preferentially to swollen females traveling with the group, indicates that Gombe chimps sometimes hunt in order to obtain meat to offer a sexually receptive female. Since hunts also occur when no estrous females are present, this trade of sex for meat cannot be the exclusive explanation, but the implications are nonetheless intriguing. Gombe chimps use meat not only for nutrition; they also share it with their allies and withhold it from their rivals. Meat is thus a social, political, and even reproductive tool. These "selfish" goals may help explain why the Gombe chimps do not cooperate during a hunt as often as do Taï chimps.

Whatever the chimps want the monkey meat for, their predation has a severe effect on the red colobus population. Part of my work involves taking repeated censuses of the red colobus groups living in the different valleys that form the hunting range of our chimpanzees. In the core area of the range, where hunting is most intense, predation by chimps is certainly the limiting factor on colobus population growth: red colobus group size in this area is half that at the periphery of the chimps' hunting range. The number of infant and juvenile red colobus monkeys is particularly low in the core area; most of the babies there are destined to become chimpanzee food.

The proportion of the red colobus population eaten by chimps appears to fluctuate greatly from year to year, and probably from decade to decade, as the number of male hunters in the chimpanzee community changes. In the early 1980s, for instance, there were five adult and adolescent males in the Kasakela chimp community, while today there are eleven; the number of colobus kills per year has risen as the number of hunters in the community has grown.

Furthermore, a single avid hunter may have a dramatic effect. I estimate that Frodo has single-handedly killed up to 10 percent of the entire red colobus population within his hunting range. I now want to learn if chimps living in forests elsewhere in Africa are also taking a heavy toll of red colobus monkeys. If they are, then they will add support to the theory that predation is an important limiting factor on wild primate populations and may also influence some aspects of behavior. Meanwhile, I will continue to watch in awe as Frodo and his fellow hunters attack my colobus monkeys and to marvel at the courageousness of the colobus males that risk their lives to protect the other members of their group.

Craig B. Stanford is an assistant professor of anthropology at the University of Southern California. His first fieldwork on primates was in Peru, where he studied tamarins. For his Ph.D. at the University of California, Berkeley, Stanford traveled to India and Bangladesh to investigate ecological influences on social behavior in capped langur monkeys. Stanford hopes to expand his research to the evolution of hunting behavior in primates, including humans.

Reprinted with permission from *Natural History*, January 1995, pp. 48–54. © 1995 by the American Museum of Natural History.

[handwritten notes:]
Most males hunt
Target - infant colubus 75%
They do not shon
next for TOY

Coping with CROWDING

A persistent and popular view holds that high population density inevitably leads to violence. This myth, which is based on rat research, applies neither to us nor to other primates

by Frans B. M. de Waal, Filippo Aureli and Peter G. Judge

In 1962 this magazine published a seminal paper by experimental psychologist John B. Calhoun entitled "Population Density and Social Pathology." The article opened dramatically with an observation by the late 18th-century English demographer Thomas Malthus that human population growth is automatically followed by increased vice and misery. Calhoun went on to note that although we know overpopulation causes disease and food shortage, we understand virtually nothing about its behavioral impact.

This reflection had inspired Calhoun to conduct a nightmarish experiment. He placed an expanding rat population in a crammed room and observed that the rats soon set about killing, sexually assaulting and, eventually, cannibalizing one another. Much of this activity happened among the occupants of a central feeding section. Despite the presence of food elsewhere in the room, the rats were irresistibly drawn to the social stimulation— even though many of them could not reach the central food dispensers. This pathological togetherness, as Calhoun described it, as well as the attendant chaos and behavioral deviancy, led him to coin the phrase "behavioral sink."

In no time, popularizers were comparing politically motivated street riots to rat packs, inner cities to behavioral sinks and urban areas to zoos. Warning that society was heading for either anarchy or dictatorship, Robert Ardrey, an American science journalist, remarked in 1970 on the voluntary nature of human crowding: "Just as Calhoun's rats freely chose to eat in the middle pens, we freely enter the city." Calhoun's views soon became a central tenet of the voluminous literature on aggression.

In extrapolating from rodents to people, however, these thinkers and writers were making a gigantic leap of faith. A look at human populations suggests why such a simple extrapolation is so problematic. Compare, for instance, per capita murder rates with the number of people per square kilometer in different nations—as we did, using data from the United Nations' *1996 Demographic Yearbook*. If things were straightforward, the two ought to vary in tandem. Instead there is no statistically meaningful relation.

But, one could argue, perhaps such a relation is obscured by variation in national income level, political organization or some other variable. Apparently not, at least for income. We divided the nations into three categories—free-market, former East Block and Third World—and did the analysis again. This time we did find one significant correlation, but it was in the other direction: it showed more violent crime in the least crowded countries of the former East Block. A similar trend existed for free-market nations, among which the U.S. had by far the highest homicide rate despite its low overall population density. The Netherlands had a population density 13 times as high, but its homicide rate was eight times lower.

Knowing that crime is generally more common in urban areas than it is in the countryside, we factored in the proportion of each nation's population that lives in large cities and controlled for it. But this correction did nothing to bring about a positive correlation between population density and homicide. Perhaps because of the overriding effects of history and culture, the link between available space and human aggression— if it exists at all—is decidedly not clear-cut.

Even if we look at small-scale human experiments, we find no supporting evidence. Crowding of children and college students, for instance, sometimes produced irritation and mild aggression, but in general, people seemed adept at avoiding conflict. Andrew S. Baum and his co-workers in the psychiatry department at the Uniformed Services University found that dormitory residents who shared facilities with many people spent less time socializing and kept the doors to their rooms closed more often than did students who had more space. Baum concluded that the effects of crowding are not nearly as overwhelming as originally presumed. Published in the 1980s, these and other findings began to undermine, at least in the scientific community, the idea that people and rats react in the same ways to being packed together. In modern society, people commonly assemble in large masses—during their daily commute to work or during holiday-season shopping expeditions—and most of the time they control their behavior extraordinarily well.

A quick many studies attentively reviews to it RD, [handwritten]

Studies that proved calhorew point was not controlled well-betw control lead to a bluries line. [handwritten]

RHESUS MONKEYS from three different settings show different rates of grooming—that is, of calming one another. The monkeys seem to adapt to crowded conditions by grooming more frequently. Among the males, grooming of each other and of females was more common when they lived in crowded conditions than when they lived in more spacious quarters. Among female non-kin, aggression was common and increased further with crowding but was accompanied by increased grooming, which served to reduce conflicts.

Calhoun's model, we must conclude, does not generally apply to human behavior. Is this because our culture and intelligence makes us unique, or is the management of crowding part of an older heritage? To answer this question, we turn to the primates.

PRIMATES ARE NOT RATS

Primate research initially appeared to support the harrowing scenario that had been presented for rats. In the 1960s scientists reported that city-dwelling monkeys in India were more aggressive than were those living in forests. Others claimed that monkeys in zoos were excessively violent. Those monkeys were apparently ruled by terrifying bullies who dominated a social hierarchy that was considered an artifact of captivity—in other words, in the wild, peace and egalitarianism prevailed. Borrowing from the hyperbole of popularizers, one study of crowding in small captive groups of baboons even went so far as to report a "ghetto riot."

ding ding [handwritten] As research progressed, however, conflicting evidence accumulated. Higher population density seemed to increase aggression occasionally—but the opposite was also true. One report, for instance, described intense fighting and killing when a group of macaques were released into a corral 73 times *larger* than their previous quarters had been. Then, after two and a half years in the corral, a similar increase in aggression occurred when the monkeys were crowded back into a small pen.

Whereas the macaque study manipulated population density through environmental change, other early research did so by adding new monkeys to existing groups. Given the xenophobic nature of monkeys, these tests mainly measured their hostile attitude toward strangers, which is quite different from the effect of density. The better controlled the studies became, the less clear-cut the picture turned out to be. Increased population density led to increased aggression in only 11 of the 17 best-designed studies of the past few decades.

In the meantime, the view of wild primates was changing. They were no longer the purely peaceful, egalitarian creatures people had presumed them to be. In the 1970s field-workers began reporting sporadic but lethal violence in a wide range of species—from macaques to chimpanzees—as well as strict and well-defined hierarchies that remained stable for decades. This view of an often anxiety-filled existence was confirmed when researchers found high levels of the stress hormone cortisol in the blood of wild monkeys [see "Stress in the Wild," by Robert M. Sapolsky; SCIENTIFIC AMERICAN, JANUARY 1990].

As the view of primates became more complex, and as the rat scenario was weakened by counterexamples, researchers began to wonder whether primates had developed a means to reduce conflict in crowded situations. We saw the first hint of this possibility in a study of the world's largest zoo colony of chimpanzees in Arnhem, the Netherlands. The apes lived on a spacious, forested island in the summer but were packed together in a heated building during the winter. Despite a 20-fold reduction in space, aggression increased only slightly. In fact, the effect of crowding was not entirely negative: friendly grooming and greetings, such as kissing and submissive bowing, increased as well.

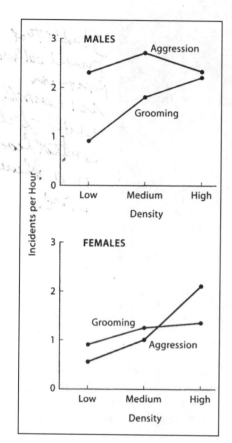

BRYAN CHRISTIE

SOURCE: Peter G. Judge and Frans B.M. de Waal

We wondered if this conciliatory behavior mitigated tension and proposed a way to test this possibility. Without ignoring the fact that crowding increases the potential for conflict, we predicted that primates employ counterstrategies—including avoiding potential aggressors and offering appeasement or reassuring body contact. Because some of the skills involved are probably acquired, the most effective coping responses would be expected in animals who have experienced high density for a long time. Perhaps they develop a different "social culture" in the same way that people in different places have varying standards of privacy and interpersonal comfort zones. For example, studies show that white North Americans and the British keep greater distances from others during conversations than Latin Americans and Arabs do.

FRANS B. M. DE WAAL

CHIMPANZEES IN THE WILD have hostile territorial relations with other groups, and in captivity they are bothered by the presence of noisy neighboring chimps. By examining apes under three conditions—those living in a crowded space and able to hear their neighbors, those living in a crowded space without such worrisome sounds, and those living in isolated large compounds (photograph right)—we were able to measure the association between aggression, space and stress. Aggression (photograph above) remained the same, but stress varied with neighbors' noise. Chimpanzees in small spaces exposed to vocalizations from other groups showed the highest levels of the stress hormone cortisol.

COPING CULTURE

We set about finding several populations of monkeys that were of the same species but that had been living in different conditions to see if their behavior varied in discernible ways. We collected detailed data on 122 individual rhesus monkeys at three different sites in the U.S.: in relatively cramped outdoor pens at the Wisconsin primate center in Madison, in large open corrals at the Yerkes primate center in Atlanta and on Morgan Island off the coast of South Carolina. These last monkeys had approximately 2,000 times more space per individual than the highest-density groups. All three groups had lived together for many years, often for generations, and included individuals of both sexes. All the groups had also been in human care, receiving food and veterinary treatment, making them comparable in that regard as well.

Rhesus society typically consists of a number of subgroups, known as matrilines, of related females and their offspring. Females remain together for life, whereas males leave their natal group at puberty. Rhesus monkeys make a sharp distinction between kin and non-kin: by far the most friendly contact, such as groom-

FRANS B.M. DE WAAL

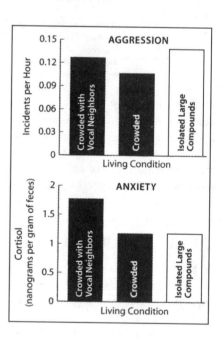

BRYAN CHRISTIE

ing, takes place within the matrilines. Females of one matriline also fiercely support one another in fights against other matrilines. Because of their strict hierarchy and pugnacious temperament, rhesus seemed to be ideal subjects. We figured that if this aggressive primate showed coping responses, our hypothesis would have withstood its most rigorous test.

Our first finding was, surprisingly, that density did not affect male aggressiveness. Adult males increasingly engaged in friendly contact under crowded conditions. They groomed females more, and likewise the females groomed the males more frequently. (Grooming is a calming behavior. In another study, we demonstrated that a monkey's heart rate slows down when it is being groomed.) Females also bared their teeth more often to the males—the rhesus way of communicating low status and appeasing potentially aggressive dominant monkeys.

Females showed a different response with other females, however. Within their own matrilines they fought more but did not change the already high level of friendly interaction. In their dealings with other matrilines, they also showed more aggression—but here it was coupled with more grooming and submissive grinning.

These findings make sense in light of the differences between kin and non-kin relationships. Related females—such as sisters and mothers and daughters—are so strongly bonded that their relationships are unlikely to be disrupted by antagonism. Rhesus monkeys are used to managing intrafamilial conflict, cycling through fights and reconciliations, followed by comforting contact. Crowding does little to change this, except that they may have to repair frayed family ties more often. Between matrilines, on the other hand, crowding poses a serious challenge. Normally, friendly contact between matrilines is rare and antagonism common. But reduced escape opportunities make the risk of escalated conflict greater in a confined space. And our data indicated that female rhesus monkeys make a concerted effort at improving these potentially volatile relationships.

EMOTIONS IN CHECK

In a second project, we turned our attention to chimpanzees. As our closest animal relatives, chimpanzees resemble us in appearance, psychology and cognition. Their social organization is also humanlike, with well-developed male bonding—which is rare in nature—reciprocal exchange and a long dependency of offspring on the mother. In the wild, male chimpanzees are extremely territorial, sometimes invading neighboring territories and killing enemy males. In captivity such encounters are, of course, prevented.

We collected data on more than 100 chimpanzees in various groups at the Yerkes primate center. Although some groups had only a tenth the space of others, cramped quarters had no measurable impact on aggression. In contrast to the monkeys, chimpanzees maintained their grooming and appeasement behavior—no matter the situation. If crowding did induce social tensions, our chimpanzees seemed to control them directly.

We usually do not think of animals as holding in their emotions, but chimpanzees may be different. These apes are known for deceptive behavior—for instance, they will hide hostile intentions behind a friendly face until an adversary has come within reach. In our study, emotional control was reflected in the way chimpanzees responded to the vocalizations of neighboring groups. Such noises commonly provoke hooting and charging displays, which in wild chimpanzees serve to ward off territorial intrusion.

In a confined space, however, excited reactions trigger turmoil within the group. We found that chimpanzees in the most crowded situations had a three times *lower* tendency to react to neighbors' vocalizations than chimpanzees with more space did. Chimpanzees may be smart enough to suppress responses to external stimuli if those tend to get them into trouble. Indeed, field-workers report that chimpanzee males on territorial patrol suppress all noise if being detected by their neighbors is to their disadvantage.

The inhibition of natural responses is not without cost. We know that continuous stress has the potential to suppress the immune system and therefore has important implications for health and longevity. We developed two noninvasive techniques to measure stress in our chimpanzees. One was to record the rate of self-scratching. Just as with college students who scratch their heads when faced with a tough exam question, self-scratching indicates anxiety in other primates. Our second technique was to collect fecal samples and analyze them for cortisol.

Both measures showed that groups of chimpanzees who had little space and heard neighbors' vocalizations experienced more stress. Space by itself was not a negative factor, because in the absence of noisy neighbors, chimpanzees in small spaces showed the same stress level as those with a good deal of space.

So even though chimpanzees fail to show a rise in aggression when crowded, this does not necessarily mean that they are happy and relaxed. They may be working hard to maintain the peace. Given a choice, they would prefer more room. Every spring, when the chimpanzees at the Arnhem zoo hear the door to their outdoor island being opened for the first time, they fill the building with a chorus of ecstasy. They then rush outside to engage in a pandemonium in which all of the apes, young and old, embrace and kiss and thump one another excitedly on the back.

The picture is even more complex if we also consider short periods of acute crowding. This is a daily experience in human society, whether we find ourselves on a city bus or in a movie theater. During acute crowding, rhesus monkeys show a rise in mild aggression, such as threats, but not violence. Threats serve to keep others at a distance, forestalling unwanted contact. The monkeys also avoid one another and limit active social engagement, as if they are trying to stay out of trouble by lying low.

Chimpanzees take this withdrawal tactic one step further: they are actually less aggressive when briefly crowded. Again, this reflects greater emotional restraint. Their reaction is reminiscent of people on an elevator, who reduce frictions by minimizing large body movements, eye contact and loud verbalizations. We speak of the elevator effect, therefore, as a way in which both people and other primates handle the risks of temporary closeness.

Our research leads us to conclude that we come from a long lineage of social animals capable of flexibly adjusting to all kinds of conditions, including unnatural ones such as crowded pens and city streets. The adjustment may not be without cost, but it is certainly preferable to the frightening alternative predicted on the basis of rodent studies.

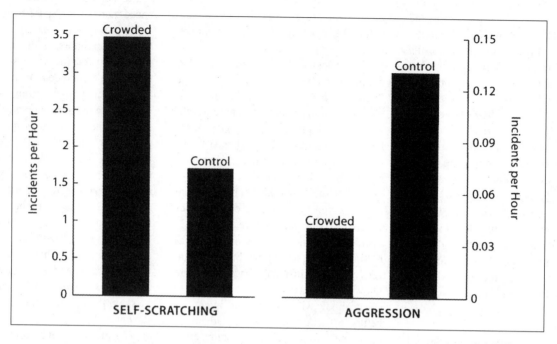

BRYAN CHRISTIE

During brief periods of crowding, people often limit social interaction—a way of avoiding any conflict. Chimpanzees do the same, reducing their aggressive interacions. This doesn't mean that crowded situations do not induce anxiety. Chimpanzees packed together tend to scratch themselves more often—a sign of stress.

We should add, though, that even the behavioral sink of Calhoun's rats may not have been entirely the product of crowding. Food competition seemed to play a role as well. This possibility contains a serious warning for our own species in an ever more populous world: the doomsayers who predict that crowding will inevitably rip the social fabric may have the wrong variable in mind. We have a natural, underappreciated talent to deal with crowding, but crowding combined with scarcity of resources is something else.

FURTHER INFORMATION

THE HIDDEN DIMENSION. E. T. Hall. Doubleday, 1966.

CROWDING. A. Baum in *Handbook of Environmental Psychology*, Vol. 1. Edited by D. Stokols and I. Altman. Wiley, 1987.

THE MYTH OF A SIMPLE RELATION BETWEEN SPACE AND AGGRESSION IN CAPTIVE PRIMATES. F. B. M. de Waal in *Zoo Biology* supplement, Vol. 1, pages 141–148; 1989.

INHIBITION OF SOCIAL BEHAVIOR IN CHIMPANZEES UNDER HIGH-DENSITY CONDITIONS. F. Aureli and F. B. M. de Waal in *American Journal of Primatology*, Vol. 41, No. 3, pages 213–228; March 1997.

RHESUS MONKEY BEHAVIOUR UNDER DIVERSE POPULATION DENSITIES: COPING WITH LONG-TERM CROWDING. P. G. Judge and F. B. M. de Waal in *Animal Behaviour*, Vol. 54, no. 3, pages 643–662; September 1997.

FRANS B. M. DE WAAL, FILIPPO AURELI and PETER G. JUDGE share a research interest in the social relationships and behavioral strategies of nonhuman primates. Their work on aspects of this topic will appear in Natural Conflict Resolution, *to be published by the University of California Press. De Waal, author of* Chimpanzee Politics *and* Good Natured, *worked for many years at the Arnhem zoo in the Netherlands before coming to the U.S., where he is now director of the Living Links Center at the Yerkes Regional Primate Research Center in Atlanta and professor of psychology at Emory University. Aureli is a senior lecturer in biological and earth sciences at Liverpool John Moores University in England. Judge is an assistant professor at Bloomsburg University in Pennsylvania and a research associate at Yerkes.*

Aping Language

New studies suggest that the brains of chimps possess the same structures for syntax and meaning that ours do.

By Sharon Begley

THESE ARE AMONG THE THINGS KANZI, a bonobo or "pygmy" chimp, can do. When he hears "give the dog a shot," he grabs a syringe from a mess of objects on the floor, yanks off the cap and injects his stuffed dog. He understands the difference between "take the potato outdoors" and "go outdoors and get the potato," and between "put the water in the raisins" and "put the raisins in the water." Kanzi, now 17, also combines words (actually, shapes called lexigrams on a keyboard) in the appropriate order to produce "grab Matata," meaning that the chimp Matata was grabbed, but "Matata bite" to mean Matata did the biting.

Impressive, yes. But is it evidence that Kanzi has command of the skill that linguists, beginning with Noam Chomsky, have argued distinguishes mere communication from true language—and thus humans from other animals? That skill is the aspect of grammar called syntax, or the use of word order to impart meaning, as in the raisins-and-water phrases. To Sue Savage-Rumbaugh of Georgia State University, who directs the research on Kanzi and other chimps, their language abilities suggest that apes are capable of "proto-grammar ... as complex as [that] used by human 2-year-olds." But to others, apes fall short: if combinations like "Lana tomorrow scare snake river monster" are language, they say, then toddlers are Shakespeare.

It's been a bitter standoff, but last week scientists announced the first results of a radical new approach that may help resolve the feud: innovative studies that probe apes' brains for structures and patterns of activity that, in humans, produce language. At Mount Sinai School of Medicine in New York, neurobiologist Patrick Gannon and colleagues examined the preserved brains of chimps that had died natural deaths in zoos or labs. The team was looking for a little bump of gray matter similar to one that the human brain uses to understand and generate language—both spoken and, in the case of the deaf, signed. The structure, called the planum temporale (PT), is nestled in the auditory-association cortex, which receives sounds and attaches meaning to them. In 17 of 18 chimps, the PT was larger on the left side of the brain than the right. That is also the pattern in most people. Such "lateralization" implies that the structure has developed a special function. Writing in the journal Science, the researchers conclude that "chimpanzees possess the anatomic neural substrate for 'language' ... essentially identical to that of humans."

That discovery, and others in the research pipeline, promise to jump-start the debate over ape language. In the 1960s psychologists began teaching chimps either American Sign Language or a system of plastic tokens or geometric shapes that stand for words, or even

spoken English. The early results were hugely controversial. The chimps' enthusiastic trainers described how the animals coined new phrases (such as "water bird" for swan, "banana which is green" for cucumber and "cookie rock" for a stale danish) that seemed to indicate true comprehension. They claimed that the animals understood syntax, inferring meaning from the order of words such as "please carry the cooler to Penny" (rather than Penny to the cooler). But on closer examination, critics charged, the animals were doing nothing more than imitating, or producing so many repetitive strings of words ("me banana you banana me you give") that a novel utterance was as inevitable as it was meaningless. And a chimp does not need syntax to realize that it makes more sense to carry an object like a cooler to a person than to lug a human over to an object. The criticism practically shut down research on ape language.

The rationale for moving beyond studies of chimps' behavior to probes of the structure and activity of their brains is simple. If the animals are doing something that looks like language, and if they are doing it with the same structures in their brain that humans tap when they use language, it will be increasingly difficult to argue that chimps do not have at least a proto-language. "What else could it be?" asks Duane Rumbaugh (Savage-

SIGNS OF INTELLIGENT LIFE

Pygmy chimpanzees have learned to communicate using a keyboard with special symbols called lexigrams.

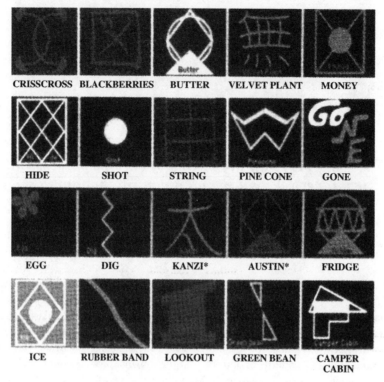

CRISSCROSS BLACKBERRIES BUTTER VELVET PLANT MONEY

HIDE SHOT STRING PINE CONE GONE

EGG DIG KANZI* AUSTIN* FRIDGE

ICE RUBBER BAND LOOKOUT GREEN BEAN CAMPER CABIN

*NAMES OF CHIMPS. SOURCE: LANGUAGE RESEARCH CENTER, GEORGIA STATE UNIVERSITY

Rumbaugh's husband) of Georgia State, a founder of ape-language studies.

Part of the answer may come from the apes and monkeys that researchers have been bundling into a van under cover of darkness and driving to the MRI facility at an Atlanta hospital. Led by William Hopkins of the Yerkes Regional Primate Research Center, the scientists lightly sedate the animals and slip them into the deafening brain-scan machine. The MRI snaps image after image of the primates' gray matter. In an upcoming paper, Hopkins describes finding in living brains exactly what his competitors at Mount Sinai did in cadaver brains: the language-controlling PT is larger on the left side of chimps' brains than on the right. But it is not lateralized in monkeys, which are less closely related to humans than apes are. That suggests that the feature is not some general aspect of primate brains but, perhaps, something more meaningful. The discovery, says Gannon, "could overturn long-held assumptions about the uniqueness of this

region [and] stimulate a reappraisal of existing dogma."

That dogma holds that apes do not and cannot use language. Yet apes have come a long way from the much-criticized studies of the 1970s and 1980s. Kanzi was the first chimp to pick up language "naturally": he observed trainers try (and fail) to teach it to his adoptive mother. The Georgia team claims that Kanzi deduces meaning from syntactical structure and even goes beyond the literal meaning of a sentence. For instance, when asked to "go to the potty and get the sparklers," he retrieves the sparklers from the potty rather than first using the potty and then getting them, as a word-by-word decoding of the sentence would mean. Panbanisha, a bonobo, and Panzee, a common chimp, are also learning language through immersion, as a child does. That they make sense of spoken words and acquire "a primitive grammar," says Savage-Rumbaugh, "suggests that the basic cognitive substrates for language are present in apes."

To test that suggestion, her team has been PET-scanning the chimps Lana and Panzee. The idea is to see whether areas corresponding to humans' language circuits turn on when Lana uses lexigrams and Panzee responds to speech. The scans should be more informative than scans of brain structure. That's because, as psychologist Steven Pinker of MIT argues, "just because two computer chips are the same size and have 16 wires coming out of them doesn't mean they perform the same function. To know that, you'd have to look at the wiring diagram inside." It is possible, for instance, that although the job of the planum temporale in humans is language, in chimps it might simply process and recognize calls, which do not rise to the level of language. All Duane Rumbaugh will say about the PET scans at this point is that "we're getting very, very interesting results." If the scans show doing a linguistic task activates circuits that mere hearing or remembering do not, says Pinker, one of the more incisive critics of

MAYBE A NICE CONDO?

After a life's work, lab chimps hanker for a life of ease.
But finding a retirement village isn't so easy.

THEY WERE THE ANIMAL elite. They flew in space. They were taught American Sign Language (ASL). They fought in the early battles against AIDS. But now they've been downsized, or aged out of their jobs, or watched helplessly as they've been replaced by robots. What's to be done with the chimps who are ready to be put out to pasture?

It's a real, if unusual, ethical and practical problem. Other lab animals are cheap to keep or dispose of: no one worries much about the fate of lab mice. But chimps, which are genetically so close to humans, are a breed apart. They cost $10,000 a year to keep, and, like humans, they have complicated social structures and emotional lives. "We have a moral obligation to meet the needs of whatever animal we're using," says Lilly-Marlene Russow, who teaches philosophy at Purdue. "But we need to do more for a chimpanzee than a rat."

About 1,600 chimpanzees are kept in laboratories in the United States; up to 200 of them are probably not needed. In the mid-1980s, researchers were scrambling to understand AIDS. By the time scientists finally realized chimps weren't perfect subjects for experiment (they don't get AIDS), they'd bred far too many. Combine those with other chimps no longer considered useful for research, and you've got a bunch of underemployed animals with long life spans—chimps can live to 60. "A number of animals have already done their service for research, and they are ready to be retired," says Dr. Dani Bolognesi, chair of a National Research Council committee that last summer recommended creating sanctuaries for the retiring chimpanzees.

Nearly half of the research chimps in the United States are currently housed in the Coulston Foundation's multipurpose research facility in Alamogordo, N.M. The foundation's controversial 83-year-old chief, Frederick Coulston, says he doesn't think there are too many chimpanzees; in fact, he wants more. At no point, Coulston says, does a chimpanzee stop being useful. Study their aging, he suggests. "I'm not against sanctuaries if [the chimps] were there to do some good," he says.

Researchers in other facilities, however, say chimps are overbred. Roger Fouts would rather they got some rest. "Sanctuaries are the best life we can possibly give them," says Fouts, author of "Next of Kin," who has spent the last 30 years teaching chimpanzees ASL. Sanctuaries would provide large indoor and outdoor spaces, and would allow chimpanzees to socialize freely. This would be expensive.

Returning the chimps to the wild, though, is pretty much unthinkable. Domesticated chimps lack the right survival skills. Lucy, the world-famous ASL-speaking chimpanzee raised as a "middle-class Oklahoman," was sent into the Gambian jungle in 1977. Friendly to every human who approached her, in 1988 poachers easily killed and skinned Lucy, her hands and feet taken as trophies.

THEODORE GIDEONSE

ape language, "that would be interesting."

And not only for what it would say about the differences between chimps and humans, in whom 99 percent of the genetic material is identical. If chimps possess language structures and activate them when using language, it would suggest that the last common ancestor of chimps and humans had and used these structures, too. (The alternative would be that chimps and humans developed the structures independently, which rarely happens in evolution.) In that case, early humans like australopithecines and Homo erectus might have had rudimentary language. The very possibility is, for now, wildly controversial. Still, as the ape-language believers say, in learning about chimps we may also learn more about ourselves.

COMMENTARY

Are We in Anthropodenial?

[handwritten: Loaded Term]

By Frans De Waal

WHEN GUESTS ARRIVE AT THE Yerkes Regional Primate Research Center in Georgia, where I work, they usually pay a visit to the chimpanzees. And often, when she sees them approaching the compound, an adult female chimpanzee named Georgia will hurry to the spigot to collect a mouthful of water. She'll then casually mingle with the rest of the colony behind the mesh fence, and not even the sharpest observer will notice anything unusual. If necessary, Georgia will wait minutes, with her lips closed, until the visitors come near. Then there will be shrieks, laughs, jumps—and sometimes falls—when she suddenly sprays them.

I have known quite a few apes that are good at surprising people, naive and otherwise. Heini Hediger, the great Swiss zoo biologist, recounts how he—being prepared to meet the challenge and paying attention to the ape's every move—got drenched by an experienced chimpanzee. I once found myself in a similar situation with Georgia; she had taken a drink from the spigot and was sneaking up to me. I looked her straight in the eye and pointed my finger at her, warning in Dutch, "I have seen you!" She immediately stepped back, let some of the water dribble from her mouth, and swallowed the rest. I certainly do not wish to claim that she understands Dutch, but she must have sensed that I knew what she was up to, and that I was not going to be an easy target.

[handwritten: Oh really]

> *To endow animals with human emotions has long been a scientific taboo. But if we do not, we risk missing something fundamental, about both animals and us.*

Now, no doubt even a casual reader will have noticed that in describing Georgia's actions, I've implied human qualities such as intentions, the ability to interpret my own awareness, and a tendency toward mischief. Yet scientific tradition says I should avoid such language—I am committing the sin of anthropomorphism, of turning nonhumans into humans. The word comes from the Greek, meaning "human form," and it was the ancient Greeks who first gave the practice a bad reputation. They did not have chimpanzees in mind: the philosopher Xenophanes objected to Homer's poetry because it treated Zeus and the other gods as if they were people. How could we be so arrogant, Xenophanes asked, as to think that the gods should look like us? If horses could draw pictures, he suggested mockingly, they would no doubt make their gods look like horses.

Nowadays the intellectual descendants of Xenophanes warn against perceiving animals to be like ourselves. There are, for example, the behaviorists, who follow psychologist B. F. Skinner in viewing the actions of animals as responses shaped by rewards and punishments rather than the result of internal decision making, emotions, or intentions. They would say that Georgia was not "up to" anything when she sprayed water on her victims. Far from planning and executing a naughty plot, Georgia merely fell for the irresistible reward of human surprise and annoyance. Whereas any person acting like her would be scolded, arrested, or held accountable, Georgia is somehow innocent.

Behaviorists are not the only scientists who have avoided thinking about the inner life of animals. Some sociobiologists—researchers who look for the roots of behavior in evolution—depict animals as "survival machines" and "pre-programmed robots" put on Earth to serve their "selfish" genes. There is a certain metaphorical value to these concepts, but is has been negated by the misunderstanding they've created. Such language can give the impression that only genes are entitled to an inner life. No more delusively anthropomorphizing idea has been put forward since the pet-rock craze of the 1970s. In fact, during evolution, genes—a mere batch of molecules—simply multiply at different rates, depending on the traits they produce in an individual. To say that genes are selfish is like saying a snowball growing in size as it rolls down a hill is greedy for snow.

Logically, these agnostic attitudes toward a mental life in animals can be valid only if they're applied to our own species as well. Yet it's uncommon to find researchers who try to study human behavior as purely a matter of reward and punishment. Describe a person as having intentions, feelings, and thoughts and you most likely won't encounter much resistance. Our own familiarity with our inner lives overrules whatever some school of thought might claim about us. Yet despite this double standard toward behavior in humans and animals, modern biology leaves us no choice other than to conclude that we *are* animals. In terms of anatomy, physiology, and neurology we are really no more exceptional than, say, an elephant or a platypus is in its own way. Even such presumed hallmarks of humanity as warfare, politics, culture, morality, and language may not be completely unprecedented. For example, different groups of wild chimpanzees employ different technologies—some fish for termites with sticks, others crack nuts with stones—that are transmitted from one generation to the next through a process reminiscent of human culture.

Given these discoveries, we must be very careful not to exaggerate the uniqueness of our species. The ancients apparently never gave much thought to this practice, the opposite of anthropomorphism, and so we lack a word for it. I will call it anthropodenial: a blindness to the human-like characteristics of other animals, or the animal-like characteristics of ourselves.

Those who are in anthropodenial try to build a brick wall to separate humans from the rest of the animal kingdom. They carry on the tradition of René Descartes, who declared that while humans possessed souls, animals were mere automatons. This produced a serious dilemma when Charles Darwin came along: If we descended from such automatons, were we not automatons ourselves? If not, how did we get to be so different?

Each time we must ask such a question, another brick is pulled out of the dividing wall, and to me this wall is beginning to look like a slice of Swiss cheese. I work on a daily basis with animals from which it is about as hard to distance yourself as from "Lucy," the famed 3.2-million-year-old fossil australopithecine. If we owe Lucy the respect of an ancestor, does this not force a different look at the apes? After all, as far as we can tell, the most significant difference between Lucy and modern chimpanzees is found in their hips, not their craniums.

AS SOON AS WE ADMIT THAT ANIMALS are far more like our relatives than like machines, then anthropodenial becomes impossible and anthropomorphism becomes inevitable—and scientifically acceptable. But not *all* forms of anthropomorphism, of course. Popular culture bombards us with examples of animals being humanized for all sorts of purposes, ranging from education to entertainment to satire to propaganda. Walt Disney, for example, made us forget that Mickey is a mouse, and Donald a duck. George Orwell laid a cover of human societal ills over a population of livestock. I was once struck by an advertisement for an oil company that claimed its propane saved the environment, in which a grizzly bear enjoying a pristine landscape had his arm around his mate's shoulders. In fact, bears are nearsighted and do not form pair-bonds, so the image says more about our own behavior than theirs.

Perhaps that was the intent. The problem is, we do not always remember that, when used in this way, anthropomorphism can provide insight only into human affairs and not into the affairs of animals. When my book *Chimpanzee Politics* came out in France, in 1987, my publisher decided (unbeknownst to me) to put François Mitterrand and Jacques Chirac on the cover with a chimpanzee between them. I can only assume he wanted to imply that these politicians acted like "mere" apes. Yet by doing so he went completely against the whole point of my book, which was not to ridicule people but to show that chimpanzees live in complex societies full of alliances and power plays that in some ways mirror our own.

You can often hear similar attempts at anthropomorphic humor in the crowds that form around the monkey exhibit at a typical zoo. Isn't it interesting that antelopes, lions, and giraffes rarely elicit hilarity? But people who watch primates end up hooting and yelling, scratching themselves in exaggeration, and pointing at the animals while shouting, "I had to look twice, Larry. I thought it was you!" In my mind, the laughter reflects anthropodenial: it is a nervous reaction caused by an uncomfortable resemblance.

That very resemblance, however, can allow us to make better use of anthropomorphism, but for this we must view it as a means rather than an end. It should not be our goal to find some quality in an animal that is precisely equivalent to an aspect of our own inner lives. Rather, we should use the fact that we are similar to animals to develop ideas we can test. For example, after observing a group of chimpanzees at length, we begin to suspect that some individuals are attempting to "deceive" others—by giving false alarms to distract unwanted attention from the theft of food or from forbidden sexual activity. Once we frame the observation in such terms, we can devise testable predictions. We can figure out just what it would take to demonstrate deception on the part of chimpanzees. In this way, a speculation is turned into a challenge.

Naturally, we must always be on guard. To avoid making silly interpretations based on anthropomorphism, one must always interpret animal behavior in the wider context of a species' habits and natural history. Without experience with primates, one could imagine that a grinning rhesus monkey must be delighted, or that a chimpanzee running toward another with loud grunts must be in an aggressive mood. But primatologists know from many hours of observation that rhesus monkeys bare their teeth when intimidated, and that chimpanzees often grunt when they meet and embrace. other words, a grinning rhesus mo signals submission, and a chimp grunting often serves as a gr careful observer may thus ar formed anthropomorphis odds with extrapolations from human behavior.

One must also always be aware that some animals are more like ourselves than others. The problem of sharing the experiences of organisms that rely on different senses is a profound one. It was expressed most famously by the philosopher Thomas Nagel when he asked, "What is it like to be a bat?" A bat perceives its world in pulses of reflected sound, something we creatures of vision would have a hard time imagining. Perhaps even more alien would be the experience of an animal such as the star-nosed mole. With 22 pink, writhing tentacles around its nostrils, it is able to feel microscopic textures on small objects in the mud with the keenest sense of touch of any animal on Earth.

Humans can barely imagine a star-nosed mole's *Umwelt*—a German term for the environment as perceived by the animal. Obviously, the closer a species is to us, the easier it is to enter its *Umwelt*. This is why anthropomorphism is not only tempting in the case of apes but also hard to reject on the grounds that we cannot know how they perceive the world. Their sensory systems are essentially the same as ours.

LAST SUMMER, AN APE SAVED A three-year-old boy. The child, who had fallen 20 feet into the primate exhibit at Chicago's Brookfield Zoo, was scooped up and carried to safety by Binti Jua, an eight-year-old western lowland female gorilla. The gorilla sat down on a log in a stream, cradling the boy in her lap and patting his back, and then carried him to one of the exhibit doorways before laying him down and continuing on her way.

Binti became a celebrity overnight, figuring in the speeches of leading politicians who held her up as an example of much-needed compassion. Some scientists were less lyrical, however. They cautioned that Binti's motives might have been less noble than they appeared, pointing out that this gorilla had been

raised by people and had been taught parental skills with a stuffed animal. The whole affair might have been one of a confused maternal instinct, they claimed.

> *Bonobos have been known to assist companions new to their quarters in zoos, taking them by the hand to guide them through the maze of corridors connecting parts of their building.*

The intriguing thing about this flurry of alternative explanations was that nobody would think of raising similar doubts when a person saves a dog hit by a car. The rescuer might have grown up around a kennel, have been praised for being kind to animals, have a nurturing personality, yet we would still see his behavior as an act of caring. Whey then, in Binti's case, was her background held against her? I am not saying that I know what went through Binti's head, but I do know that no one had prepared her for this kind of emergency and that it is unlikely that, with her own 17-month-old infant on her back, she was "maternally confused." How in the world could such a highly intelligent animal mistake a blond boy in sneakers and a red T-shirt for a juvenile gorilla? Actually, the biggest surprise was how surprised most people were. Students of ape behavior did not feel that Binti had done anything unusual. Jörg Hess, a Swiss gorilla expert, put it most bluntly, "The incident can be sensational only for people who don't know a thing about gorillas."

Binti's action made a deep impression mainly because it benefited a member of our own species, but in my work on the evolution of morality and empathy, I have encountered numerous instances of animals caring for one another. For example, a chimpanzee consoles a victim after a violent attack, placing an arm around him and patting his back. And

bonobos (or pygmy chimpanzees) have been known to assist companions new to their quarters in zoos, taking them by the hand to guide them through the maze of corridors connecting parts of their building. These kinds of cases don't reach the newspapers but are consistent with Binti's assistance to the unfortunate boy and the idea that apes have a capacity for sympathy.

The traditional bulwark against this sort of cognitive interpretation is the principle of parsimony—that we must make as few assumptions as possible when trying to construct a scientific explanation, and that assuming an ape is capable of something like sympathy is too great a leap. But doesn't that same principle of parsimony argue against assuming a huge cognitive gap when the evolutionary distance between humans and apes is so small? If two closely related species act in the same manner, their underlying mental processes are probably the same, too. The incident at the Brookfield Zoo shows how hard it is to avoid anthropodenial and anthropomorphism at the same time: in trying to avoid thinking of Binti as a human being, we run straight into the realization that Binti's actions make little sense if we refuse to assume intentions and feelings.

In the end we must ask: What kind of risk we are willing to take—the risk of underestimating animal mental life or the risk of overestimating it? There is no simple answer. But from an evolutionary perspective, Binti's kindness, like Georgia's mischief, is most parsimoniously explained in the same way we explain our own behavior—as the result of a complex, and familiar, inner life.

FRANS DE WAAL is a professor of psychology at Emory University and research professor at the Yerkes Regional Primate Research Center in Atlanta. He is the author of several books, including Chimpanzee Politics *and* Good Natured: The Origins of Right and Wrong in Humans and Other Animals. *His latest book, in collaboration with acclaimed wildlife photographer Frans Lanting, is* Bonobo: The Forgotten Ape, *published by the University of California Press (1997).*

UNIT 3
Sex and Society

Unit Selections

Key Points to Consider

- How can the muriqui monkeys be sexually competitive and yet gregarious and cooperative?

- How involved should fathers be in the care of their children?

- Why do women live longer than men?

- How does human sexuality differ from that of other creatures?

- What implications does bonobo sexual behavior have for understanding human evolution?

- Why do human females experience menopause?

- Why do cultures the world over treat menstruating women as taboo?

- How do social bonds provide females with protection against abusive males?

 **Links: www.dushkin.com/online/**
These sites are annotated in the World Wide Web pages.

American Anthropologist
http://www.aaanet.org/aa/index.htm
American Scientist
http://www.amsci.org/amsci/amsci.html
Bonobo Sex and Society
http://songweaver.com/info/bonobos.html

Any account of hominid evolution would be remiss if it did not at least attempt to explain that most mystifying of all human experiences—our sexuality.

No other aspect of our humanity—whether it be upright posture, tool-making ability, or intelligence in general—seems to elude our intellectual grasp at least as much as it dominates our subjective consciousness. While we are a long way from reaching a consensus as to why it arose and what it is all about, there is widespread agreement that our very preoccupation with sex is in itself one of the hallmarks of being human. Even as we experience it and analyze it, we exalt it and condemn it. Beyond seemingly irrational fixations, however, there is the further tendency to project our own values upon the observations we make and the data we collect.

There are many who argue quite reasonably that the human bias has been more male- than female-oriented and that the recent "feminization" of anthropology has resulted in new kinds of research and new theoretical perspectives. (See "The Myth of the Coy Female" by Carol Tavris, "A Woman's Curse?" by Meredith Small, and "Why Women Change" by Jared Diamond.) Not only should we consider the source when evaluating the old theories, so goes the reasoning, but we should also welcome the source when considering the new. To take one example, traditional theory would have predicted that the reproductive competitiveness of muriqui monkeys, as described in "These Are Real Swinging Primates" by Shannon Brownlee, would be associated with greater size and aggression among males. That this is not so, that making love can be more important than making war, and that females do not necessarily have to live in fear of competitive males, just goes to show that, even among monkeys, nothing can be taken for granted. The very idea that females are helpless in the face of male aggression is called into question by Barbara Smuts in "Apes of Wrath."

Finally, there is the question of the social significance of sexuality in humans. In "Mothers and Others," Sarah Blaffer Hrdy points out that reproductive success often depends upon how much assistance the mother gets from others, including males. As if there is some sort of poetic justice involved, John Allman tells us, in "Big Brains and Parenting," that whoever takes on the role of primary caretaker—and it usually is the mother—lives longer! In "What's Love Got to Do With It?" Meredith Small shows that the chimp-like bonobos of Zaire use sex to reduce tensions and cement social relations and, in so doing, have achieved a high degree of equality between the sexes. Whether we see parallels in the human species, says Small, depends on our willingness to interpret bonobo behavior as a "modern version of our own ancestors' sex play," and this, in turn, may depend on our prior theoretical commitments.

These Are Real Swinging Primates

There's a good evolutionary reason why the rare muriqui of Brazil should heed the dictum 'Make love, not war'

Shannon Brownlee

When I first heard of the muriqui four years ago, I knew right away that I had to see one. This is an unusual monkey, to say the least. To begin with, it's the largest primate in South America; beyond that, the males have very large testicles. We're talking gigantic, the size of billiard balls, which means that the 30-pound muriqui has *cojones* that would look more fitting on a 400-pound gorilla.

But it wasn't prurience that lured me to Brazil. My interest in the muriqui was intellectual, because more than this monkey's anatomy is extraordinary. Muriqui society is untroubled by conflict: troops have no obvious pecking order; males don't compete overtly for females; and, most un-monkeylike, these monkeys almost never fight.

The muriqui is also one of the rarest monkeys in the world. It lives in a single habitat, the Atlantic forest of southeastern Brazil. This mountainous region was once blanketed with forest from São Paulo to Salvador (*see map*), but several centuries of slash-and-burn agriculture have reduced it to fragments.

In 1969 Brazilian conservationist Alvaro Coutinho Aguirre surveyed the remaining pockets of forest and estimated that 2,000 to 3,000 muriquis survived. His data were all but ignored until Russell Mittermeier, a biologist, trained his sights on the muriquis ten years later.

Known as Russell of the Apes to his colleagues, Mittermeier, an American, directs the primate program for the World Wildlife Fund. He hopscotches from forest to forest around the world looking for monkeys in trouble and setting up conservation plans for them. In 1979 he and Brazilian zoologist Celio Valle retraced Aguirre's steps and found even fewer muriquis. Today only 350 to 500 are left, scattered among four state and national parks and six other privately held plots.

In 1981 Karen Strier, then a graduate student at Harvard, approached Mittermeier for help in getting permission to observe the muriqui. He took her to a coffee plantation called Montes Claros, near the town of Caratinga, 250 miles north of Rio de Janeiro. Over the next four years she studied the social behavior of the muriqui there—and came up with a provocative theory about how the monkey's unconventional behavior, as well as its colossal testicles, evolved. She reasoned that the evolution of both could be explained, at least in part, by the muriquis' need to avoid falling out of trees.

Last June I joined Strier, now a professor at Beloit (Wis.) College, on one of her periodic journeys to Montes Claros—clear mountains, in Portuguese. We arrived there after a disagreeable overnight bus trip over bad roads. As we neared the plantation, I found it difficult to believe there was a forest—much less a monkey—within miles. Through the grimy windows of the bus I saw hillsides stripped down to russet dirt and dotted with spindly coffee plants and stucco farmhouses. There wasn't anything taller than a banana tree in sight. As the bus lurched around the last curve before our stop the forest finally appeared, an island of green amid thousands of acres of coffee trees and brown pastures.

Strier was eager to start looking for the muriquis—"There's a chance we won't see them the whole four days you're here," she said—so no sooner had we dropped our bags off at a cottage on the plantation than we set out along a dirt road into the forest. The trees closed around us—and above us, where they gracefully arched to form a vault of green filigree. Parrots screeched; leaves rustled; a large butterfly flew erratically by on transparent wings. By this time Strier had guided me onto a steep trail, along which she stopped from time to time to listen for the monkeys.

They appeared soon enough, but our first meeting was less than felicitous. After we had climbed half a mile, Strier motioned for me to stop. A muffled sound, like that of a small pig grunting contentedly, came from up ahead. We moved forward a hundred yards. Putting a finger to her lips, Strier sank to her haunches and looked up.

I did the same; twelve round black eyes stared back at me. A group of six muriquis squatted, silent, 15 feet above in the branches, watching us intently. They began to grunt again. A sharp smell with undertones of cinnamon permeated the air. A light rain began to fall. I held out my palm to catch a drop. It was warm.

"Hey, this isn't rain!" I said.

Strier grinned and pointed to her head. "That's why I wear a hat," she said.

My enthusiasm for the muriquis waned slightly after that. We left them at dusk and retired to the cottage, where Strier described her arrival at Montes Claros four years earlier. Mittermeier acted as guide and interpreter during the first few days of her pilot study. He introduced her to the owner of the 5,000-acre plantation, Feliciano Miguel Abdala, then 73, who had preserved the 2,000-acre forest for more than 40 years. His is one of the only remaining tracts of Atlantic forest, and he agreed to let Strier use it as the site of her study. Then Mittermeier introduced her to the muriquis, assuring her they would be easy to see.

They weren't, and observing them closely is a little like stargazing on a rainy night: not only do you run the risk of getting wet, but you can also spend a lot of time looking up and never see a thing. Mittermeier was adept at spotting the monkeys in the forest, and helped Strier acquire this skill.

But brief glimpses of the monkeys weren't enough. "My strategy was to treat them like baboons, the only other species I'd ever studied," she says. "I thought I couldn't let them out of my sight." She tried to follow on the ground as they swung along in the trees. "They went berserk," she says. They threw branches, shrieked, urinated on her—or worse—and fled.

Even after the muriquis grew accustomed to her, keeping up with them wasn't easy. They travel as much as two miles a day, which is tough for someone picking her way through thick growth on the forest floor. As Strier and a Brazilian assistant learned the muriquis' habitual routes and daily patterns, they cleared trails. These helped, but the muriquis could still travel much faster than she

could. "I've often thought the thing to have would be a jet pack," Strier says. "It would revolutionize primatology. Your National Science Foundation grant would include binoculars, pencils, and a jet pack."

The monkeys move by brachiating, swinging hand over hand from branch to branch, much like a child on a jungle gym. Only one other group of monkeys brachiates; the rest clamber along branches on all fours. The muriquis' closest relatives are two other Latin American genera, the woolly monkeys and the spider monkeys—hence woolly spider monkey, its English name. But the muriqui is so unlike them that it has its own genus, *Brachyteles*, which refers to its diminutive thumb, an adaptation for swinging through the trees. Its species name is *arachnoides*, from the Greek for spider, which the muriqui resembles when its long arms, legs, and tail are outstretched.

Brachiating is a specialization that's thought to have evolved because it enables primates to range widely to feed on fruit. Curiously, though, muriquis have a stomach designed for digesting leaves. Strier found that their diet consists of a combination of the two foods. They eat mostly foliage, low-quality food for a monkey, but prefer flowers and fruits, like figs and the *caja manga*, which is similar to the mango. Year after year they return to certain trees when they bloom and bear fruit. The rest of the time the muriquis survive on leaves by passing huge quantities of them through their elongated guts, which contain special bacteria to help them digest the foliage. By the end of the day their bellies are so distended with greenery that even the males look pregnant.

We returned to the trail the next morning just after dawn. Condensation trickled from leaves; howler monkeys roared and capuchins cooed and squeaked; a bird sang with the sweet, piercing voice of a piccolo. Then Strier had to mention snakes. "Watch out for snakes," she said blithely, scrambling on all fours up a steep bank. I followed her, treading cautiously.

The muriqui weren't where we had left them the day before. Strier led me along a ridge through a stand of bamboo, where a whisper of movement drifted up

from the slope below. Maybe it was just the wind, but she thought it was the muriquis, so we sat down to wait. After a couple of hours, she confessed, "This part of research can get kind of boring."

By noon the faint noise became a distinct crashing. "That's definitely them," she said. "It's a good thing they're so noisy, or I'd never be able to find them." The monkeys, perhaps a dozen of them, swarmed uphill, breaking branches, chattering, uttering their porcine grunts as they swung along. At the crest of the ridge they paused, teetering in indecision while they peered back and forth before settling in some legume trees on the ridgetop. We crept down out of the bamboo to within a few feet of them, so close I noticed the cinnamon scent again— only this time I kept out of range.

Each monkey had its own feeding style. One hung upside down by its tail and drew the tip of a branch to its mouth; it delicately plucked the tenderest shoots with its rubbery lips. Another sat upright, grabbing leaves by the handful and stuffing its face. A female with twins— "Twins have never been seen in this species," Strier whispered as she excitedly scribbled notes—ate with one hand while hanging by the other and her tail. Her babies clung to the fur on her belly.

I had no trouble spotting the males. Their nether parts bulged unmistakably— blue-black or pink-freckled, absurd-looking monuments to monkey virility. I asked Strier what sort of obscene joke evolution was playing on the muriquis when it endowed them thus.

We were about to consider this question when a high-pitched whinnying began a few hundred yards away. Immediately a monkey just overhead pulled itself erect and let out an ear-splitting shriek, which set the entire troop to neighing like a herd of nervous horses. Then they took off down into the valley.

Strier and I had to plunge pell-mell into the underbrush or risk losing them for the rest of the day. "They're chasing the other troop," she said as we galloped downhill. A group of muriquis living on the opposite side of the forest had made a rare foray across the valley.

The monkeys we were observing swung effortlessly from tree to tree; we wrestled with thorny vines, and fell farther and farther behind. An impenetrable thicket forced us to backtrack in search of another route. By the time we caught up to the muriquis, they were lounging in a tree, chewing on unripe fruit and chuckling in a self-satisfied sort of way. The intruding troop was nowhere to be seen. "They must have scared the hell out of those other guys," said Strier, laughing.

Such confrontations occur infrequently; muriquis ordinarily tolerate another troop's incursions. Strier thinks they challenge intruders only when there's a valuable resource to defend—like the fruit tree they were sitting in.

Tolerance of another troop is odd behavior for monkeys, but not as odd as the fact that members of a muriqui troop never fight among themselves. "They're remarkably placid," said Strier. "They wait in line to dip their hands into water collected in the bole of a tree. They have no apparent pecking order or dominance hierarchy. Males and females are equal in status, and males don't squabble over females." No other primate society is known to be so free of competition, not even that of gorillas, which have lately gained a reputation for being the gentle giants of the primate world.

Strier's portrayal of the muriqui brought to mind a bizarre episode that Katharine Milton, an anthropologist at the University of California at Berkeley, once described. While studying a troop of muriquis in another patch of the Atlantic forest, she observed a female mating with a half a dozen males in succession; that a female monkey would entertain so many suitors came as no surprise, but Milton was astonished at the sight of the males lining up behind the female "like a choo-choo train" and politely taking turns copulating. They continued in this manner for two days, stopping only to rest and eat, and never even so much as bared their teeth.

Primates aren't known for their graciousness in such matters, and I found Milton's report almost unbelievable. But Strier confirms it. She says that female muriquis come into heat about every two and a half years, after weaning their latest offspring, and repeatedly copulate during that five- to seven-day period with a number of males. Copulations, "cops" in animal-behavior lingo, last as long as 18 minutes, and average six,

which for most primates (including the genus *Homo*, if Masters and Johnson are correct) would be a marathon. Yet no matter how long a male muriqui takes, he's never harassed by suitors-in-waiting.

Strier has a theory to explain the muriqui's benignity, based on a paper published in 1980 by Richard Wrangham, a primatologist at the University of Michigan. He proposed that the social behavior of primates could in large part be predicted by what the females eat.

This isn't a completely new idea. For years primatologists sought correlations between ecological conditions and social structure, but few patterns emerged—until Wrangham's ingenious insight that environment constrains the behavior of each sex differently. Specifically, food affects the sociability of females more than males.

Wrangham started with the generally accepted premise that both sexes in every species have a common aim: to leave as many offspring as possible. But each sex pursues this goal in its own way. The best strategy for a male primate is to impregnate as many females as he can. All he needs, as Wrangham points out, is plenty of sperm and plenty of females. As for the female, no matter how promiscuous she is, she can't match a male's fecundity. On average, she's able to give birth to only one offspring every two years, and her success in bearing and rearing it depends in part upon the quality of food she eats. Therefore, all other things being equal, male primates will spend their time cruising for babes, while females will look for something good to eat.

Wrangham perceived that the distribution of food—that is, whether it's plentiful or scarce, clumped or evenly dispersed—will determine how gregarious the females of a particular species are. He looked at the behavior of 28 species and found that, in general, females forage together when food is plentiful and found in large clumps—conditions under which there's enough for all the members of the group and the clumps can be defended against outsiders. When clumps become temporarily depleted, the females supplement their diet with what Wrangham calls subsistence foods. He suggests that female savanna baboons, for example, live in groups be-

cause their favorite foods, fruits and flowers, grow in large clumps that are easy to defend. When these are exhausted they switch to seeds, insects, and grasses. The females form long-lasting relationships within their groups, and establish stable dominance hierarchies.

Chimpanzees provide an illustration of how females behave when their food isn't in clumps big enough to feed everybody. Female chimps eat flowers, shoots, leaves, and insects, but their diet is composed largely of fruits that are widely scattered and often not very plentiful. They may occasionally gather at a particularly abundant fruit tree, but when the fruit is gone they disperse to forage individually for other foods. Members of the troop are constantly meeting at fruit trees, splitting up, and gathering again.

These two types of female groups, the "bonded" savanna baboons and "fissioning" chimps, as Wrangham calls them, pose very different mating opportunities for the males of their species. As a consequence, the social behavior of the two species is different. For a male baboon, groups of females represent the perfect opportunity for him to get cops. All he has to do is exclude other males. A baboon troop includes a clan of females accompanied by a number of males, which compete fiercely for access to them. For baboons there are few advantages to fraternal cooperation, and many to competition.

Male chimpanzees fight far less over females than male baboons do, principally because there's little point—the females don't stick together. Instead, the males form strong alliances with their fellows. They roam in gangs looking for females in heat, and patrol their troop's borders against male interlopers.

Wrangham's theory made so much sense, Strier says, that it inspired researchers to go back into the field with a new perspective. She saw the muriqui as an excellent species for evaluating the model, since Wrangham had constructed it before anyone knew the first thing about this monkey. His idea would seem all the more reasonable if it could predict the muriqui's behavior.

It couldn't, at least not entirely. Strier has found that the females fit Wrangham's predictions: they stick together and

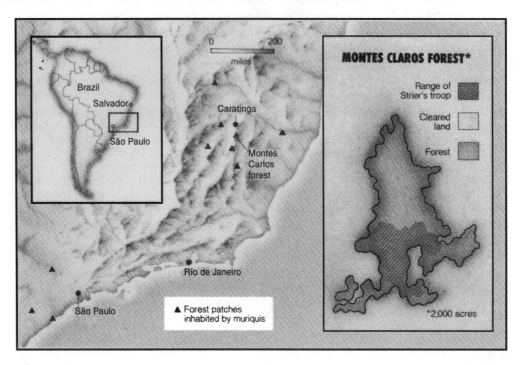

The 350 to 500 surviving muriquis live in ten patches of the Atlantic forest of southeastern Brazil.

eat a combination of preferred and subsistence foods, defending the preferred from other troops. But the males don't conform to the theory. "Considering that the females are foraging together, there should be relatively low pressure on the males to cooperate," she says. "It's odd: the males should compete, but they don't."

She thinks that limitations on male competition may explain muriqui behavior. First, the muriquis are too big to fight in trees. "I think these monkeys are at about the limit of size for rapid brachiation," she says. "If they were bigger, they couldn't travel rapidly through the trees. They fall a lot as it is, and it really shakes them up. I've seen an adult fall about sixty feet, nearly to the ground, before catching hold of a branch. That means that whatever they fight about has got to be worth the risk of falling out of a tree."

Moreover, fighting may require more energy than the muriquis can afford. Milton has estimated the caloric value of the food eaten by a muriqui each day and compared it to the amount of energy she would expect a monkey of that size to need. She concluded that the muriqui had little excess energy to burn on combat.

The restriction that rapid brachiation sets on the muriqui's size discourages competition in more subtle ways, as well. Given that muriquis are polygynous, the male should be bigger than the female, as is almost invariably the case among other polygynous species—but he's not. The link between larger males and polygyny is created by sexual selection, an evolutionary force that Darwin first recognized, and which he distinguished from natural selection by the fact that it acts exclusively on one sex. Sexual selection is responsible for the manes of male lions, for instance, and for the large canines of male baboons.

In a polygynous society, the advantages to being a large male are obvious: he who's biggest is most likely to win the battles over females—and pass on his genes for size. But sexual selections' push toward large males has been thwarted in the muriqui, says Strier. Any competitive benefits greater size might bring a male would be offset in part by the excessive demands on his energy and the costs of falling out of trees.

She believes that the constraints on the males' size have had a profound effect on the muriquis' social behavior. Most important, says Strier, with males and females being the same size, the females can't be dominated, which means they can pick their mates. Most female pri-

mates aren't so fortunate: if they copulate with subordinate males, they risk being attacked by dominant ones. But a female muriqui in heat can easily refuse a suitor, simply by sitting down or by moving away. Fighting not only doesn't help the male muriqui in his quest for cops; it may even harm his chances, since females can shun an aggressive male. Strier believes that females may also be responsible for the male muriquis' canine teeth not being oversized. As a rule, the male's canines are the same size as the female's only in monogamous primate species, but over the generations female muriquis may have mated more readily with males whose teeth were no bigger than their own. In sum, Strier thinks, for a male muriqui the costs of competing are far outweighted by the benefits of avoiding it.

But he has the means to vie for reproductive success and still come across as Mr. Nice Guy: his sperm. Sperm competition, as it's called, is a hot new idea in sociobiology, originally proposed to explain male bonding in chimpanzees, and, as Milton was the first to suggest, it may explain why the muriqui has such enormous testicles.

The competition is something like a game of chance. Imagine a bucket with a hole in the bottom just big enough for a marble to pass through. People gather round, each with a handful of marbles. They drop their marbles in the bucket, mix them up, and one comes out the bottom. Whoever owns that marble is the winner.

In the sperm competition among male muriquis, the bucket is a female, the marbles are sperm, and winning means becoming a father. No male can be sure it will be his sperm that impregnates a female, since she mates with a number of his fellows. His chances are further complicated by the fact that the female muriqui, like all New World monkeys, gives no visible indication of ovulation; there may be nothing that signals the male (or the female) when during her heat that occurs. So it's to the male's advantage to continue mating as often as the female will have him.

This may sound like monkey heaven, but it puts the male on the horns of a dilemma. If he copulates as often as possible, he could run low on sperm just when the female is ovulating. On the other hand, if he refrains from copulating to save sperm, he may miss his chance at procreating altogether. Selection may have come to his aid, Strier reasons, by acting on his testicles.

Here's a plausible scenario. Suppose a male came along that could produce more sperm than the average muriqui because his testicles were bigger than average. That male would clean up in the reproductive arena. The ratio of testicle size to body weight has been correlated with high sperm count and repeated copulation over a short period in other mammals, and bigger testicles probably also increase the percentage of viable and motile sperm.

If the muriqui's testicles are anything like those of other species, then a male with extra big ones has a slight reproductive advantage. Like a player with more marbles to put in the bucket, a male that can produce more and better sperm has a better than average chance of impregnating females and passing on this advantageous trait to his sons. Just as important, the outsized organs probably don't cost him much in metabolic energy. Thus,

over generations, the muriqui's testicles have grown larger and larger.

Strier's theory has five years of data behind it, and it's the kind of theory that will stimulate researchers to reexamine their ideas about other species. Yet it isn't her only concern; she concentrates equally on the muriqui's uncertain future. On our last day in the forest we watched the monkeys cross a six-foot gap in the canopy 60 feet above us. One by one they stood poised for a moment on the end of a branch before launching themselves. Strier counted them as they appeared in silhouette against a grey sky. The total was 33, including the twins. "They're up from twenty-two in 1982," she said. "That's a very fast increase."

The muriquis at Montes Claros make up almost one-tenth of the total population of the species, and they're critical to its survival—as are all the other isolated and widely separated troops. Each groups's genetic pool is limited, and eventually the troops could suffer inbreeding depression, a decline in fecundity that often appears in populations with little genetic variability.

Strier and Mittermeier predict that one day muriquis will have to be managed, the way game species are in the U.S. They may be transported between patches of forest to provide some gene flow. But that's a dangerous proposition now. There are too few muriquis to risk it, and none has ever bred or survived for long in captivity. "Before my study, conservationists would probably have moved males between forests," Strier says. "That would've been a mistake. I have tentative evidence that in a natural situation the females may be the ones that do the transferring between groups."

For now, though, she thinks the biggest concern isn't managing the monkeys but preventing their habitat from disappearing. Preserving what remains of the Atlantic forest won't be easy, and no one knows this better than Feliciano Miguel Abdala, the man responsible for there being any forest at all at Montes Claros.

Abdala has little formal education, but he's rich; he owns nine plantations beside

Montes Claros. His family lives in relative splendor in Caratinga, but he likes to spend the weekdays here. His house is just beyond the edge of the forest, and sunlight filters through the bougainvillea vine entwining the front porch. Chickens can be seen through the cracks in the floorboards, scratching in the dirt under the house. Electric cords are strung crazily from the rafters, and a bare bulb dangles in the center of his office. Abdala removes his straw hat decorously and places it on a chair before sitting at his desk.

Abdala bought the 5,000 acres of Montes Claros in 1944. The region was barely settled then, and smoke still rose from the great burning heaps of slash left from clearing the forest. Abdala's land included one of the last stands of trees. I ask him why he saved it. "I am a conservationist," he says. "For a long time the local people thought I was crazy because I wouldn't cut the forest. I told them not to shoot the monkeys, and they stopped. Now all my workers are crazy, too."

I ask Abdala about his plans for his forest. He rubs his head distractedly and says, vaguely. "I hope it will continue."

Abdala believes the government should buy Montes Claros—plantation and rain forest—to create a nature reserve. He'll probably maintain the forest as long as he lives, but the land is quite valuable, and his heirs might not share his lofty sentiments.

As important as the muriquis have become to understanding social systems, and as much as U.S. conservationists may wish to see these monkeys preserved, Strier thinks that in the end it's up to the Brazilians to save them. She's expecting a three-year grant from the National Science Foundation; part of the money will go toward allowing her to observe the monkeys in other forest patches, watching for variation in their behavior as a test of her ideas. Studies like hers will be critical not only for proving theories but also for ensuring that plans for managing the muriquis will work. The rest of the money will permit her to train seven Brazilian graduate students, because she says, "the future of the muriqui lies with the Brazilians."

Reprinted with permission from *Discover* magazine, April 1987, pp. 67–68, 70, 77. © 1987 by The Walt Disney Company.

The Myth of the Coy Female

Carol Tavris

[Thus] we arrived at the important conclusion that polygamy is the natural order among human beings, just as it is in most species of the animal kingdom... monogamy is responsible for the high incidence of divorce and female grievances in modern society, as well as the genetic deevolution and behavioral degeneration of civilization as a whole.... Culture is to blame, and fortunately *culture can be changed*. Mating is the key. [Emphasis in original.]

—Sam Kash Kachigan,
The Sexual Matrix

Sam Kash Kachigan is not a social scientist; he's just a regular fellow who thinks that the theories of sociobiology offer the best hope of improving relations between women and men. "Mating is the key," he argues. The mating he has in mind, it turns out, would (if we were truly to follow our evolutionary heritage) occur between rich old men and beautiful young girls. Among the annoying contemporary practices that Kachigan laments is the habit of beautiful young girls marrying boys their own age. To Kachigan, in any truly civilized society—that is, one in which our practices fit our sociobiological natures—girls would marry men who were old enough to demonstrate their "true potential":

In every respect, then, it makes much more sense for young women to mate with *older* men, who will have *proven* their genetic endowment as well as their financial and emotional capacity for

raising children. [Emphasis in original.]

Why do I suspect that Kachigan is such a man?

The basic ideas behind sociobiology date back to Charles Darwin, who in 1871 described what he considered to be a basic dichotomy in the sexual natures of males and females of all species. Males actively pursue females; they are promiscuous; and those who are strongest, most fit in evolutionary terms, succeed in their sexual conquest. Females, said Darwin, are "comparatively passive"; they may choose their preferred suitor, but then remain monogamous and faithful. That this dichotomy conveniently fit Victorian dating and mating patterns was, naturally, pure coincidence.

For a century after Darwin, research on sexual selection and sexual behavior was based on the belief that males are passionate and undiscriminating (any female in a storm will do), whereas females are restrained, cautious, and highly discriminating in their choice of partner (only a male who meets her shopping list of qualifications will do). According to primatologist Sarah Blaffer Hrdy, this stereotype of "the coy female" has persisted in the public mind—and she adds a phrase that by now should be familiar to us—"*despite the accumulation of abundant openly available evidence contradicting it*" [my emphasis].

The stereotype of the coy female got a major boost in an important paper published in 1948 by Angus John Bateman. Bateman was a distinguished plant geneticist who did dozens of experiments with Drosophila, the tiny fruit fly that

many people remember from science experiments in junior high school. Bateman found that successful male fruit flies could, with multiple matings, produce nearly three times as many offspring as the most reproductively successful female. As Hrdy explains, "whereas a male could always gain by mating just one more time, and hence benefit from a nature that made him undiscriminatingly eager to mate, a female, already breeding near capacity after just one copulation, could gain little from multiple mating and should be quite uninterested in mating more than once or twice."

What, you may ask, does a human man have in common with a fruit fly? When it comes to sexual strategies, said Bateman, the answer is everything. Generalizing from his sixty-four experiments with Drosophila to all species, Bateman concluded that there is a universally lopsided division in the sexual natures of all creatures, apart from "a few very primitive organisms." Quite simply, males profit, evolutionarily speaking, from frequent mating, and females do not. This is why, said Bateman, "there is nearly always a combination of an undiscriminating eagerness in the males and a discriminating passivity in the females."

The modern field of sociobiology took this idea still further, attempting to account for complex human social arrangements and customs—warfare and corporate raiding, feeding infants and giving children karate lessons—in terms of the individual's basic need to reproduce his or her genes. Women and men, sociobiologists believe, adopt highly different strategies in order to do this. Males compete with other males for access to desirable females, and their goal is to inseminate as many females as possible. Females, in contrast, are motivated to attach themselves to genetically "superior" males because of the female's greater "investment" in terms of time and energy in her offspring; this, according to sociobiologists, is why females are more faithful and nurturant than males. As biologist Ruth Hubbard observes, "Thus, from the seemingly innocent asymetries between eggs and sperm [say the sociobiologists] flow such major social consequences as female fidelity, male promiscuity, women's disproportional contribution to the care of children, and the unequal distribution of labor by sex."

Sociobiological explanations of competitive, promiscuous men and choosy, inhibited but flirtatious women fit right in with many elements within the popular culture. "And so it was," Hrdy says, "that 'coyness' came to be the single most commonly mentioned attribute of females in the literature on sociobiology."

It all seems a cruel joke of nature. Certainly many people are convinced, as the King of Siam sings in *The King and I*, that the male is like the honeybee, flitting from flower to flower, "gathering all he can," whereas the female has "honey for just one man." But notice that it is the King who sings that song; until relatively recently, no one was asking Queens for their view of things. Nor were male observers asking why, if human females were so naturally chaste, coy, and monogamous, social taboos from ostracism to death had to be placed on females who indulged in forbidden sexual relationships. For that matter, why did non-marital affairs need to be forbidden anyway, if females have "honey for just one man"?

Sociobiologists attempt to explain human social customs by drawing on research on nonhuman animals, from the fields of primatology, evolutionary biology, anthropology, and related disciplines. In the last two decades, however, there has been an explosion of new research that casts doubt on many sociobiological assumptions, a change that is largely a result of the growing numbers of women who have entered these fields. Most of the women saw animal behavior

in a different light from most of the male observers who had preceded them. Male primatologists, for example, had tended to observe and emphasize male-male competition and the number of times the male animals "got lucky"; the female animals, to the human men observing them, seemed mysterious and unpredictable. This is not unlike the ways in which human females have seemed mysterious and unpredictable to the human males who have observed *them*.

At first, women who went into these research fields saw the world as they had been taught to see it, through the academic perspective of their mentors. But after a while, they began to ask different questions and to bring different expectations to their observations. Hrdy recalls her own first glimpse of a female langur

… moving away from her natal group to approach and solicit males in an all-male band. At the time, I had no context for interpreting behavior that merely seemed strange and incomprehensible to my Harvard-trained eyes. Only in time, did I come to realize that such wandering and such seemingly "wanton" behavior were recurring events in the lives of langurs.

Eventually, Hrdy learned that female langurs often leave their troops to join up with bands of males; and she also found that often a female, for reasons unknown, "simply takes a shine to the resident male of a neighboring troop." In fact, female langurs (and many other primate species) are able to shift from being in heat once a month to being continuously receptive for weeks at a time, a state not unlike the first phase of (human) love. In many primates, female receptivity is often *situation specific*, rather than being dependent exclusively on cyclical periods of being in heat.

As a result of the efforts of many pioneers like Hrdy, we now know that the females of many animal species do not behave like the patient, coy fruit fly. On the contrary, the females are sexually ardent and can even be called polyandrous (having many male partners). Further, their sexual behavior does not depend

simply on the goal of being fertilized by the male, because in many cases females actively solicit males when they are not ovulating, and even when they are already pregnant. Here are a few illustrations from hundreds of research studies:

- Many species of female birds are promiscuous. In one study, researchers vasectomized the "master" of a blackbird harem… but the females nevertheless conceived.

- Many species of female fish are promiscuous. A female shiner perch who is not ovulating will nevertheless mate with many males, collecting sperm and storing them internally until she is ready to ovulate.

- Many species of female cats, notably leopards, lions, and pumas, are promiscuous. A lioness may mate dozens of times with many different partners during the week she is in estrus.

- Many species of female primates are promiscuous. Among savanna baboons and Barbary macaques, females initiate many different brief sexual encounters. Among chimpanzees, Hrdy reports, some females form partnerships with one male, but others engage in communal mating with all males in the vicinity. And among wild tamarin monkeys, a species long thought to be monogamous (at least in captivity), supposedly faithful females will mate with several males. So do female Hanuman langurs, blue monkeys, and redtail monkeys, all primates that were formerly believed to be one-man women. The old notion that primate females typically form "one-male breeding units," as primatologists would say, is now seriously called into question.

In spite of rapidly accumulating evidence that females of many different and varied species do mate "promiscuously" (a word that itself has evaluative overtones), it was not until 1980 or so that researchers realized that this fact threw, well, a monkey wrench into traditional evolutionary theories. Why would females have more copulations than are necessary for conception? Why would they go off with some guy from a neighboring town, whom none of her friends approves of? Why risk losing the genetic father's support by joining the baboon equivalent of Hell's Angels? And the brooding question over all of them, why did female primates develop continuous sexual receptivity?

These questions stimulated a flurry of new theories to explain why female philandering would make as much survival sense as its male counterpart. Most of these new explanations directly resulted from considering the world from the female's point of view. Traditional theories of sexual selection, after all, were based exclusively on the perspective of the male: Males compete for *access* to the female, who apparently is just hanging around waiting to go out and party with the winner. And it's only from a male point of view that multiple female matings can be considered "excessive," or that female sexual interest is even described as her time of "receptivity." Is she passively "receptive" to the active intentions of the male? The word implies that she's just putting up with his annoying lustfulness yet again.

New hypotheses argue that there are genetic benefits for the offspring of sexually adventurous mothers. According to Hrdy's review of these explanations, the "fertility backup" hypothesis assumes that females need sperm from a number of males in order to assure conception by the healthiest sperm. The "inferior cuckold" hypothesis suggests that a female who has a genetically inferior mate will sneak off with a genetically superior male when she is likely to conceive. (I suppose she knows this by the size of his income.) And the "diverse paternity" hypothesis argues that when the environment is unpredictable, females diversify. Over a reproductive lifetime, females who have numerous partners, and thus different fathers for their offspring, improve their offspring's chances for survival.

Other theories look for the social and environmental benefits of female promiscuity to the mother and her infants. The "therapeutic hypothesis" suggests that having lots of partners and multiple orgasms (in some species) makes intercourse and conception more pleasurable, and therefore more likely to occur. The "keep 'em around" hypothesis maintains that females actively solicit lower-status males (with the tacit approval of dominant males), a behavior that prevents weaker males from leaving the group. Hrdy's own favored theory is what she calls the "manipulation hypothesis," the idea that females mate with numerous males precisely because paternity becomes uncertain. The result is that male partners will be more invested in, and tolerant of, the female's infants. This idea, Hrdy explains,

grew out of a dawning awareness that, first of all, individual females could do a great deal that would affect the survival of their offspring, and second, that males, far from mere dispensers of sperm, were critical features on the landscape where infants died or survived. That is, females were more political, males more nurturing (or at least not neutral), than some earlier versions of sexual selection theory would lead us to suppose.

Both of these points are essential: Not only are females more than passive receptacles of sperm, but also males are more than "mere dispensers of sperm." They don't just mate and run. They have a key role in determining whether infants survive or die. Among primates, there is enormous variation in the extent to which males nurture and protect offspring:

- Among the ruffed lemur, the male tends the nest while the female forages for food.
- Among New World monkeys, males directly care for offspring in half of all species; often, the male is the primary caretaker, carrying the infant on his back, sharing food with it.
- In a rare study of a monogamous species of night money, an observer found that during one infant's first week of life, the mother carried it 33 percent of the time, the father 51 percent of the time, and a juvenile member of the troop the remaining time.
- Among baboons, males do not have much direct contact with infants, but they hover nearby protectively and offer what Hrdy calls "quality" time in a very real sense: They increase the infant's chances of survival. They discourage attacks on the infant from males who are unknown, in both the literal and the Biblical sense, to the mother.

Hrdy's "manipulation hypothesis" assumes that primate males respond more benevolently to the offspring of females with whom they have mated, so the females derive obvious benefits from mating with more than one male. In numerous primate species, the mother's multiple sexual partners act like godfathers to the infant, as primatologist Jeanne Altmann calls them. Each of these males will help care for the female's offspring. Baboon males, many of whom could have served as the model for *Three Men and a Baby*, develop special relationships with the infant, carrying it on their backs on times of danger and protecting it from strangers and hazards. These affectionate bonds are possible because of the mother's closeness to the males, says Hrdy, and because the infant comes to trust these males and seek them out.

The manipulation hypothesis may or may not hold up with further research, as Hrdy acknowledges. It certainly does not apply to most human societies, where husbands do not look too kindly on their wives' "special relationships" with other men, let alone their previous lovers, husbands, and wooers. Hrdy's work, nonetheless, shows that theories depend, first and foremost, on what an observer *observes*, and then on how those observations can be blurred by unconscious expectations. Hrdy initially regarded those "wanton" female langurs as aberrations because their behavior did not fit the established theory. Not until researchers began to speculate on the potential benefits of female promiscuity did they come up with different questions and answers about female sexual behavior than had sociobiologists.

In evolutionary biology, if not in the popular press, the myth of the coy female (and, for that matter, the myth of the absent father) is dead. Hrdy is encouraged by the speed with which primatologists, once aware of the male bias that permeated their discipline, have produced "a small stampede by members of both sexes to study female reproductive strategies." This she takes to be a healthy sign, as I do. But Hrdy cautions against "substituting a new set of biases for the old ones":

> That is, among feminist scholars it is now permissible to say that males and females are different, provided one also stipulates that females are more cooperative, more nurturing, more supportive—not to mention equipped with unique moral sensibilities....

Perhaps it is impossible, as biologist Donna Haraway suggests, for any of us to observe the behavior of other species, let alone our own, in a way that does not mirror the assumptions of our own way of life. It is disconcerting, says Hrdy wryly, that primatologists were finding "politically motivated females and nurturing males at roughly the same time that a woman runs for vice president of the United States and [Garry] Trudeau starts to poke fun at 'caring males' in his cartoons." Informally, scientists admit that their prejudices—such as the tendency to identify with the same sex of the species they are studying—affect their research. One woman primatologist told Hrdy, "I sometimes identify with female baboons more than I do with males of my own species."

The recognition of a male-centered bias in primatology and biology proved to be an enormous step forward, allowing scientists of both sexes to revise their theories of animal behavior. Sociobiologists (and their fans like Sam Kash Kachigan) can no longer justify traditional sex roles, particularly male dominance and female nurturance and chastity, by appealing to the universality of such behavior in other species. Other species aren't cooperating.

But that is not the only moral of the Parable of the Primates. The female perspective is invaluable, but, as Hrdy warns, a female-centered bias will provide its own set of distortions. Cultural feminists who look to evolutionary biology to explain women's allegedly sweeter, more cooperative ways are on as shaky ground as the antifeminists they would replace.

If the sociobiological heroine is the coy female who is so different from males, the heroine of modern sexology is the lusty female who is just like them. I like her better, but I'm afraid that she, too, is (as a student of mine once inadvertently said) a fig leaf of the imagination....

Excerpt from *The Mismeasure of Woman* by Carol Tavris, pp. 212–221. © 1992 by Carol Tavris. Reprinted by permission of Simon & Schuster, Inc.

Mothers and Others

From queen bees to elephant matriarchs, many animal mothers are assisted by others in rearing off-spring. Anthropologist Sarah Blaffer Hrdy maintains that our human ancestors, too, were "Cooperative Breeders"—A mode of life that enabled them to thrive in many new environments. Today, argues Hrdy, our continued ability to raise emotionally healthy children may well depend on how well we understand the cooperative aspect of our evolutionary heritage.

By Sarah Blaffer Hrdy

Mother apes—chimpanzees, gorillas, orangutans, humans—dote on their babies. And why not? They give birth to an infant after a long gestation and, in most cases, suckle it for years. With humans, however, the job of providing for a juvenile goes on and on. Unlike all other ape babies, ours mature slowly and reach independence late. A mother in a foraging society may give birth every four years or so, and her first few children remain dependent long after each new baby arrives; among nomadic foragers, grown-ups may provide food to children for eighteen or more years. To come up with the 10–13 million calories that anthropologists such as Hillard Kaplan calculate are needed to rear a young human to independence, a mother needs help.

So how did our prehuman and early human ancestresses living in the Pleistocene Epoch (from 1.6 million until roughly 10,000 years ago) manage to get those calories? And under what conditions would natural selection allow a female ape to produce babies so large and slow to develop that they are beyond her means to rear on her own?

The old answer was that fathers helped out by hunting. And so they do. But hunting is a risky occupation, and fathers may die or defect or take up with other females. And when they do, what then? New evidence from surviving traditional cultures suggests that mothers in the Pleistocene may have had a significant degree of help—from men who thought they just might have been the fathers, from grandmothers and great-aunts, from older children.

These helpers other than the mother, called allomothers by sociobiologists, do not just protect and provision youngsters. In groups such as the Efe and Aka Pygmies of central Africa, allomothers actually hold children and carry them about. In these tight-knit communities of communal foragers—within which men, women, and children still hunt with nets, much as humans are thought to have done tens of thousands of years ago—siblings, aunts, uncles, fathers, and grandmothers hold newborns on the first day of life. When University of New Mexico anthropologist Paula Ivey asked an Efe woman, "Who cares for babies?" the immediate answer was, "We all do!" By three weeks of age, the babies are in contact with allomothers 40 percent of the time. By eighteen weeks, infants actually spend more time with allomothers than with their gestational mothers. On average, Efe babies have fourteen different caretakers, most of whom are close kin. According to Washington State University anthropologist Barry Hewlett, Aka babies are within arm's reach of their fathers for more than half of every day.

Accustomed to celebrating the antiquity and naturalness of mother-centered models of child care, as well as the nuclear family in which the mother nurtures while the father provides, we Westerners tend to regard the practices of the Efe and the Aka as exotic. But to sociobiologists, whose stock in trade is comparisons across species, all this helping has a familiar ring. It's called cooperative breeding. During the past quarter century, as anthropologists and sociobiologists started to compare notes, one of the spectacular surprises has been how much allomaternal care goes on, not just within various human societies but among animals generally. Evidently, diverse organisms have converged on cooperative breeding for the best of evolutionary reasons.

A broad look at the most recent evidence has convinced me that cooperative breeding was the strategy that permitted our own ancestors to produce costly, slow-maturing infants at shorter intervals, to take advantage of new kinds of resources in habitats other than the mixed savanna-woodland of tropical Africa, and to spread more widely and swiftly than any primate had before. We already know that animal mothers who delegate some of the costs of infant care to others are thereby freed to produce more or larger young or to breed more frequently. Consider the case of silver-backed jackals. Patricia Moehlman, of the World Conservation Union, has shown that for every extra helper bringing back food, jackal parents rear one extra pup per litter. Cooperative breeding also helps various species expand into habitats in which they would normally not be able to rear any young at all. Florida scrub-jays, for example, breed in an exposed landscape where unrelenting predation from hawks and snakes usually precludes the fledging of young; survival in this habitat is possible only because older siblings help guard and feed the young. Such cooperative arrangements permit animals as different as naked mole rats (the social insects of the mammal world) and wolves to move into new habitats and sometimes to spread over vast areas.

When animal mothers delegate some infant-care costs to others, they can produce more or larger young and raise them in less-than-ideal habitats.

What does it take to become a cooperative breeder? Obviously, this lifestyle is an option only for creatures capable of living in groups. It is facilitated when young but fully mature individuals (such as young Florida scrub-jays) do not or cannot immediately leave their natal group to breed on their own and instead remain among kin in their natal location. As with delayed maturation, delayed dispersal of young means that teenagers, "spinster" aunts, real and honorary uncles will be on hand to help their kin rear young. Flexibility is another criterion for cooperative breeders. Helpers must be ready to shift to breeding mode should the opportunity arise. In marmosets and tamarins—the little South American monkeys that are, besides us, the only full-fledged cooperative breeders among primates—a female has to be ready to be a helper this year and a mother the next. She may have one mate or several. In canids such as wolves or wild dogs, usually only the dominant, or alpha, male and female in a pack reproduce, but younger group members hunt with the mother and return to the den to regurgitate predigested meat into the mouths of her pups. In a fascinat-

ing instance of physiological flexibility, a subordinate female may actually undergo hormonal transformations similar to those of a real pregnancy: her belly swells, and she begins to manufacture milk and may help nurse the pups of the alpha pair. Vestiges of cooperative breeding crop up as well in domestic dogs, the distant descendants of wolves. After undergoing a pseudopregnancy, my neighbors' Jack Russell terrier chased away the family's cat and adopted and suckled her kittens. To suckle the young of another species is hardly what Darwinians call an adaptive trait (because it does not contribute to the surrogate's own survival). But in the environment in which the dog family evolved, a female's tendency to respond when infants signaled their need—combined with her capacity for pseudopregnancy—would have increased the survival chances for large litters born to the dominant female.

According to the late W.D. Hamilton, evolutionary logic predicts that an animal with poor prospects of reproducing on his or her own should be predisposed to assist kin with better prospects so that at least some of their shared genes will be perpetuated. Among wolves, for example, both male and female helpers in the pack are likely to be genetically related to the alpha litter and to have good reasons for not trying to reproduce on their own: in a number of cooperatively breeding species (wild dogs, wolves, hyenas, dingoes, dwarf mongooses, marmosets), the helpers do try, but the dominant female is likely to bite their babies to death. The threat of coercion makes postponing ovulation the better part of valor, the least-bad option for females who must wait to breed until their circumstances improve, either through the death of a higher-ranking female or by finding a mate with an unoccupied territory.

One primate strategy is to line up extra fathers. Among common marmosets and several species of tamarins, females mate with several males, all of which help rear her young. As primatologist Charles T. Snowdon points out, in three of the four genera of Callitrichidae (*Callithrix, Saguinus,* and *Leontopithecus*), the more adult males the group has available to help, the more young survive.

Among many of these species, females ovulate just after giving birth, perhaps encouraging males to stick around until after babies are born. (In cotton-top tamarins, males also undergo hormonal changes that prepare them to care for infants at the time of birth.) Among cooperative breeders of certain other species, such as wolves and jackals, pups born in the same litter can be sired by different fathers.

Human mothers, by contrast, don't ovulate again right after birth, nor do they produce offspring with more than one genetic father at a time. Ever inventive, though, humans solve the problem of enlisting help from several adult males by other means. In some cultures, mothers rely on a peculiar belief that anthropologists call partible paternity—the notion that a fetus is built up by contributions of semen from all the men with whom women have had sex in the ten months or so prior to giving birth. Among the Canela, a matrilineal tribe in Brazil studied for many years by William Crocker of the Smithsonian Institution, publicly sanctioned intercourse between women and men other than their husbands—sometimes many men—takes place during villagewide ceremonies. What might lead to marital disaster elsewhere works among the Canela because the men believe in partible paternity. Across a broad swath of South America—from Paraguay up into Brazil, westward to Peru, and northward to Venezuela—mothers rely on this convenient folk wisdom to line up multiple honorary fathers to help them provision both themselves and their children. Over hundreds of generations, this belief has helped children thrive in a part of the world where food sources are unpredictable and where husbands are as likely as not to return from the hunt empty-handed.

The Bari people of Venezuela are among those who believe in shared paternity, and according to anthropologist Stephen Beckerman, Bari children with more than one father do especially well. In Beckerman's study of 822 children, 80 percent of those who had both a "primary" father (the man married to their mother) and a "secondary" father survived to age fifteen, compared with 64

Higher survival rate

percent survival for those with a primary father alone. Not surprisingly, as soon as a Bari woman suspects she is pregnant, she accepts sexual advances from the more successful fishermen or hunters in her group. Belief that fatherhood can be shared draws more men into the web of possible paternity, which effectively translates into more food and more protection.

One primate strategy is to line up extra "fathers." In some species of marmosets, females mate with several males, all of which help her raise her young.

But for human mothers, extra mates aren't the only source of effective help. Older children, too, play a significant role in family survival. University of Nebraska anthropologists Patricia Draper and Raymond Hames have just shown that among !Kung hunters and gatherers living in the Kalahari Desert, there is a significant correlation between how many children a parent successfully raises and how many older siblings were on hand to help during that person's own childhood.

Older matrilineal kin may be the most valuable helpers of all. University of Utah anthropologists Kristen Hawkes and James O'Connell and their UCLA colleague Nicholas Blurton Jones, who have demonstrated the important food-gathering role of older women among Hazda hunter-gatherers in Tanzania, delight in explaining that since human life spans may extend for a few decades after menopause, older women become available to care for—and to provide vital food for—children born to younger kin. Hawkes, O'Connell, and Blurton Jones further believe that dating from the earliest days of Homo erectus, the survival of weaned children during food shortages may have depended on tubers dug up by older kin.

At various times in human history, people have also relied on a range of customs, as well as on coercion, to line up allomaternal assistance—for example,

by using slaves or hiring poor women as wet nurses. But all the helpers in the world are of no use if they're not motivated to protect, carry, or provision babies. For both humans and nonhumans, this motivation arises in three main ways: through the manipulation of information about kinship; through appealing signals coming from the babies themselves; and, at the heart of it all, from the endocrinological and neural processes that induce individuals to respond to infants' signals. Indeed, all primates and many other mammals eventually respond to infants in a nurturing way if exposed long enough to their signals. Trouble is, "long enough" can mean very different things in males and females, with their very different response thresholds.

For decades, animal behaviorists have been aware of the phenomenon known as priming. A mouse or rat encountering a strange pup is likely to respond by either ignoring the pup or eating it. But presented with pup after pup, rodents of either sex eventually become sensitized to the baby and start caring for it. Even a male may gather pups into a nest and lick or huddle over them. Although nurturing is not a routine part of a male's repertoire, when sufficiently primed he behaves as a mother would. Hormonal change is an obvious candidate for explaining this transformation. Consider the case of the cooperatively breeding Florida scrub-jays studied by Stephan Schoech, of the University of Memphis. Prolactin, a protein hormone that initiates the secretion of milk in female mammals, is also present in male mammals and in birds of both sexes. Schoech showed that levels of prolactin go up in a male and female jay as they build their nest and incubate eggs and that these levels reach a peak when they feed their young. Moreover, prolactin levels rise in the jays' nonbreeding helpers and are also at their highest when they assist in feeding nestlings.

As it happens, male, as well as immature and nonbreeding female, primates can respond to infants' signals, although quite different levels of exposure and stimulation are required to get them going. Twenty years ago, when elevated prolactin levels were first reported in

common marmoset males (by Alan Dixson, for *Callithrix jacchus*), many scientists refused to believe it. Later, when the finding was confirmed, scientists assumed this effect would be found only in fathers. But based on work by Scott Nunes, Jeffrey Fite, Jeffrey French, Charles Snowdon, Lucille Roberts, and many others—work that deals with a variety of species of marmosets and tamarins—we now know that all sorts of hormonal changes are associated with increased nurturing in males. For example, in the tufted-eared marmosets studied by French and colleagues, testosterone levels in males went down as they engaged in caretaking after the birth of an infant. Testosterone levels tended to be lowest in those with the most paternal experience.

Genetic relatedness alone, in fact, is a surprisingly unreliable predictor of love. What matters are cues from infants and how we process these cues emotionally.

The biggest surprise, however, has been that something similar goes on in males of our own species. Anne Storey and colleagues in Canada have reported that prolactin levels in men who were living with pregnant women went up toward the end of the pregnancy. But the most significant finding was a 30 percent drop in testosterone in men right after the birth. (Some endocrinologically literate wags have proposed that this drop in testosterone levels is due to sleep deprivation, but this would probably not explain the parallel testosterone drop in marmoset males housed with parturient females.) Hormonal changes during pregnancy and lactation are, of course, indisputably more pronounced in mothers than in the men consorting with them, and no one is suggesting that male consorts are equivalent to mothers. But both sexes are surprisingly susceptible to infant signals—explaining why fathers, adoptive parents, wet nurses, and day-care workers can become deeply involved with the infants they care for.

Genetic relatedness alone, in fact, is a surprisingly unreliable predictor of love. What matters are cues from infants and how these cues are processed emotionally. The capacity for becoming emotionally hooked—or primed—also explains how a fully engaged father who is in frequent contact with his infant can become more committed to the infant's well-being than a detached mother will.

But we can't forget the real protagonist of this story: the baby. From birth, newborns are powerfully motivated to stay close, to root—even to creep—in quest of nipples, which they instinctively suck on. These are the first innate behaviors that any of us engage in. But maintaining contact is harder for little humans to do than it is for other primates. One problem is that human mothers are not very hairy, so a human mother not only has to position the baby on her breast but also has to keep him there. She must be motivated to pick up her baby even *before* her milk comes in, bringing with it a host of hormonal transformations.

Within minutes of birth, human babies can cry and vocalize just as other primates do, but human newborns can also read facial expressions and make a few of their own. Even with blurry vision, they engage in eye-to-eye contact with the people around them. Newborn babies, when alert, can see about eighteen inches away. When people put their faces within range, babies may reward this attention by looking back or even imitating facial expressions. Orang and chimp babies, too, are strongly attached to and interested in their mothers' faces. But unlike humans, other ape mothers and infants do not get absorbed in gazing deeply into each other's eyes.

To the extent that psychiatrists and pediatricians have thought about this difference between us and the other apes, they tend to attribute it to human mental agility and our ability to use language. Interactions between mother and baby, including vocal play and babbling, have been interpreted as protoconversations: revving up the baby to learn to talk. Yet even babies who lack face-to-face stimulation—babies born blind, say—learn to talk. Furthermore, humans are not the

only primates to engage in the continuous rhythmic streams of vocalization known as babbling. Interestingly, marmoset and tamarin babies also babble. It may be that the infants of cooperative breeders are specially equipped to communicate with caretakers. This is not to say that babbling is not an important part of learning to talk, only to question which came first—babbling so as to develop into a talker, or a predisposition to evolve into a talker because among cooperative breeders, babies that babble are better tended and more likely to survive.

If humans evolved as cooperative breeders, the degree of a human mother's commitment to her infant should be linked to how much social support she herself can expect. Mothers in cooperatively breeding primate species can afford to bear and rear such costly offspring as they do only if they have help on hand. Maternal abandonment and abuse are very rarely observed among primates in the wild. In fact, the only primate species in which mothers are anywhere near as likely to abandon infants at birth as mothers in our own species are the other cooperative breeders. A study of cotton-top tamarins at the New England Regional Primate Research Center showed a 12 percent chance of abandonment if mothers had older siblings on hand to help them rear twins, but a 57 percent chance when no help was available. Overburdened mothers abandoned infants within seventy-two hours of birth.

This new way of thinking about our species' history, with its implications for children, has made me concerned about the future. So far, most Western researchers studying infant development have presumed that living in a nuclear family with a fixed division of labor (mom nurturing, dad providing) is the normal human adaptation. Most contemporary research on children's psychosocial development is derived from John Bowlby's theories of attachment and has focused on such variables as how available and responsive the mother is, whether the father is present or absent, and whether the child is in the mother's care or in day care. Sure enough, studies done with this model in mind always

show that children with less responsive mothers are at greater risk.

In cooperative breeders, the degree of a mother's commitment to her infant should correlate with how much social support she herself can expect.

It is the baby, first and foremost, who senses how available and how committed its mother is. But I know of no studies that take into account the possibility that humans evolved as cooperative breeders and that a mother's responsiveness also happens to be a good indicator of her social supports. In terms of developmental outcomes, the most relevant factor might not be how securely or insecurely attached to the mother the baby is—the variable that developmental psychologists are trained to measure—but rather how secure the baby is in relation to all the people caring for him or her. Measuring attachment this way might help explain why even children whose relations with their mother suggest they are at extreme risk manage to do fine because of the interventions of a committed father, an older sibling, or a there-when-you-need-her grandmother.

The most comprehensive study ever done on how nonmaternal care affects kids is compatible with both the hypothesis that humans evolved as cooperative breeders and the conventional hypothesis that human babies are adapted to be reared exclusively by mothers. Undertaken by the National Institute of Child Health and Human Development (NICHD) in 1991, the seven-year study included 1,364 children and their families (from diverse ethnic and economic backgrounds) and was conducted in ten different U.S. locations. This extraordinarily ambitious study was launched because statistics showed that 62 percent of U.S. mothers with children under age six were working outside the home and that the majority of them (willingly or unwillingly) were back at work within three to five months of giving birth. Because this was an entirely new social phenomenon, no one really knew what the NICHD's research would reveal.

The study's main finding was that both maternal and hired caretakers' sensitivity to infant needs was a better predictor of a child's subsequent development and behavior (such traits as social "compliance," respect for others, and self-control were measured) than was actual time spent apart from the mother. In other words, the critical variable was not the continuous presence of the mother herself but rather how secure infants felt when cared for by someone else. People who had been convinced that babies need full-time care from mothers to develop normally were stunned by these results, while advocates of day care felt vindicated. But do these and other, similar findings mean that day care is not something we need to worry about anymore?

Not at all. We should keep worrying. The NICHD study showed only that day care was better than mother care if the mother was neglectful or abusive. But excluding such worst-case scenarios, the study showed no detectable ill effects from day care only when infants had a secure relationship with parents to begin with (which I take to mean that babies felt wanted) and only when the day care was of high quality. And in this study's context, "high quality" meant that the facility had a high ratio of caretakers to babies, that it had the same caretakers all the time, and that the caretakers were sensitive to infants' needs—in other words, that the day care staff acted like committed kin.

Bluntly put, this kind of day care is almost impossible to find. Where it exists at all, it's expensive. Waiting lists are long, even for cheap or inadequate care. The average rate of staff turnover in day care centers is 30 percent per year, primarily because these workers are paid barely the minimum wage (usually less, in fact, than parking-lot attendants). Furthermore, day care tends to be age-graded, so even at centers where staff members stay put, kids move annually to new teachers. This kind of day care is unlikely to foster trusting relationships.

What conclusion can we draw from all this? Instead of arguing over "mother care" versus "other care," we need to make day care better. And this is where I think today's evolution-minded researchers have something to say. Impressed by just how variable child-rearing conditions can be in human societies, several anthropologists and psychologists (including Michael Lamb, Patricia Draper, Henry Harpending, and James Chisholm) have suggested that babies are up to more than just maintaining the relationship with their mothers. These researchers propose that babies actually monitor mothers to gain information about the world they have been born into. Babies ask, in effect, Is this world filled with people who are going to provide for me and help me survive? Can I count on them to care about me? If the answer to those questions is yes, they begin to sense that developing a conscience and a capacity for compassion would be a great idea. If the answer is no, they may then be asking, Can I not afford to count on others? Would I be better off just grabbing what I need, however I can? In this case, empathy, or thinking about others' needs, would be more of a hindrance than a help.

For a developing baby and child, the most practical way to behave might vary drastically, depending on whether the mother has kin who help, whether the father is around, whether foster parents are well-meaning or exploitative. These factors, however unconsciously perceived by the child, affect important developmental decisions. Being extremely self-centered or selfish, being oblivious to others or lacking in conscience—traits that psychologists and child-development theorists may view as pathological—are probably quite adaptive traits for an individual who is short on support from other group members.

If I am right that humans evolved as cooperative breeders, Pleistocene babies whose mothers lacked social support and were less than fully committed to infant care would have been unlikely to survive. But once people started to settle down—10,000 or 20,000 or perhaps 30,000 years ago—the picture changed. Ironically, survival chances for neglected children increased. As people lingered longer in one place, eliminated predators, built walled houses, stored food—not to mention inventing things such as rubber nipples and pasteurized milk—infant survival became decoupled from continuous contact with a caregiver.

Since the end of the Pleistocene, whether in preindustrial or industrialized environments, some children have been surviving levels of social neglect that previously would have meant certain death. Some children get very little attention, even in the most benign of contemporary homes. In the industrialized world, children routinely survive caretaking practices that an Efe or a !Kung mother would find appallingly negligent. In traditional societies, no decent mother leaves her baby alone at any time, and traditional mothers are shocked to learn that Western mothers leave infants unattended in a crib all night.

In effect, babies ask: Is this world filled with people who are going to provide for me and help me survive? Can I count on them to care about me?

Without passing judgment, one may point out that only in the recent history of humankind could infants deprived of supportive human contact survive to reproduce themselves. Certainly there are a lot of humanitarian reasons to worry about this situation: one wants each baby, each child, to be lovingly cared for. From my evolutionary perspective, though, even more is at stake.

Even if we manage to survive what most people are worrying about—global warming, emergent diseases, rogue viruses, meteorites crashing into earth—will we still be human thousands of years down the line? By that I mean human in the way we currently define ourselves. The reason our species has managed to survive and proliferate to the extent that 6 billion people currently occupy the planet has to do with how readily we can learn to cooperate when we want to. And our capacity for empathy is one of the things that made us good at doing that.

At a rudimentary level, of course, all sorts of creatures are good at reading intentions and movements and anticipating what other animals are going to do. Predators from gopher snakes to lions have to be able to anticipate where their quarry will dart. Chimps and gorillas can figure out what another individual is likely to know or not know. But compared with that of humans, this capacity to entertain the psychological perspective of other individuals is crude.

During early childhood, through relationships with mothers and other caretakers, individuals learn to look at the world from someone else's perspective.

The capacity for empathy is uniquely well developed in our species, so much so that many people (including me) believe that along with language and symbolic thought, it is what makes us human. We are capable of compassion, of understanding other people's "fears and motives, their longings and griefs and vanities," as novelist Edmund White puts it. We spend time and energy worrying about people we have never even met, about babies left in dumpsters, about the existence of more than 12 million AIDS orphans in Africa.

Psychologists know that there is a heritable component to emotional capacity and that this affects the development of compassion among individuals. By fourteen months of age, identical twins (who share all genes) are more alike in how they react to an experimenter who pretends to painfully pinch her finger on a clipboard than are fraternal twins (who share only half their genes). But empathy also has a learned component, which has more to do with analytical skills. During the first years of life, within the context of early relationships with mothers and other committed caretakers, each individual learns to look at the world from someone else's perspective.

And this is why I get so worried. Just because humans have evolved to be smart enough to chronicle our species' histories, to speculate about its origins, and to figure out that we have about 30,000 genes in our genome is no reason to assume that evolution has come to a standstill. As gene frequencies change, natural selection acts on the outcome, the expression of those genes. No one doubts, for instance, that fish benefit from being able to see. Yet species reared in total darkness—as are the small, cave-dwelling characin of Mexico—fail to develop their visual capacity. Through evolutionary time, traits that are unexpressed are eventually lost. If populations of these fish are isolated in caves long enough, youngsters descended from those original populations will no longer be able to develop eyesight at all, even if reared in sunlight.

If human compassion develops only under particular rearing conditions, and if an increasing proportion of the species survives to breeding age without developing compassion, it won't make any difference how useful this trait was among our ancestors. It will become like sight in cave-dwelling fish.

No doubt our descendants thousands of years from now (should our species survive) will still be bipedal, symbol-generating apes. Most likely they will be adept at using sophisticated technologies. But will they still be human in the way we, shaped by a long heritage of cooperative breeding, currently define ourselves?

This article was adapted from "Cooperation, Empathy, and the Needs of Human Infants," a Tanner Lecture delivered at the University of Utah. It is used with the permission of the Tanner Lectures on Human Values, a Corporation, University of Utah, Salt Lake City.

Big Brains and Parenting

Large-brained, slowly developing, dependent offspring require long-surviving parents
to reach maturity. A measure of this parental dependency effect is the
differential survival of caretakers versus noncaretakers.

By John M. Allman

Having a large brain is linked to enhanced survival. This being the case, why don't more animals have large brains? The answer to this puzzle is that the cost of growing and maintaining a big brain are very high both for the individual and for its parents. In a newborn human the brain absorbs nearly two thirds of all the metabolic energy used by the entire body. This enormous burden results from the very large relative size of the brain in human infants and from the additional energy required for dendritic growth, synapse formation, and myelination, which is far greater even than the considerable energy required to maintain the adult brain. Because the brain requires nearly two thirds of the infant's energy supply, this constraint probably sets an upper limit in the evolution of brain size because the muscles and other vital organs, the heart, the liver, the kidneys, the stomach, and intestines, must use energy as well.

Nurturing a large-brained baby imposes enormous energy costs on the mother because of the burden of lactation, which is far more costly than gestation. In small mammals lactation can triple the mother's food requirements. The nutritional constituents of breast milk are probably optimized for brain growth in particular species. In a carefully controlled study of children tested at age eight, those who had been bottle-fed human milk as babies had an average IQ 10 points higher than did the children who had been fed formula.

Not only are the energetic costs high, but development is slow in big-brained babies. George Sacher proposed that the brain serves as a pacemaker for the growth of embryos. In primate species,

relative brain mass scales with the time after birth required to reach maturity, implying that the development of larger brains requires more time.

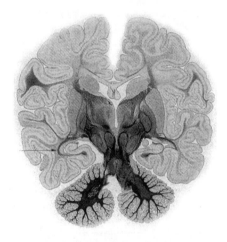

The myelinating pathways in a 7-week-old human infant, from the work of Paul Flechsig. This is a horizontal section through the forebrain and cerebellum; myelin is stained blue. Note that the myelinated pathways are already well developed in the cerebellum and the central parts of the brain at this stage, but there is relatively little myelin in the white matter associated with the neocortex. However, there is a U-shaped pathway (arrow) of myelinating fibers leading from the lateral geniculated nucleus of the thalamus to the primary visual cortex. Bands of fibers also lead to the primary somatosensory and motor cortical areas. The fiber connections of the higher cortical areas myelinate much later in development.

The additional time is needed for the postnatal growth of the brain, which in humans reaches its full adult size only by about the time of puberty. This postnatal growth includes the formation of myelin insulation around axons, which proceeds at different rates in different parts of the brain. Paul Flechsig showed that the axons of subcortical structures

acquire their myelin insulation before the cortex, and within the cortex the primary sensory areas are myelinated long before the higher cortical areas in the temporal, parietal, and frontal lobes.

The rate of synapse formation also varies among cortical areas. Peter Huttenlocher found that synapto-genesis is much slower in the frontal cortex than in primary visual cortex. Time is also required for the formation of experience-dependent connections essential for adult functioning. For example, the capacity to judge the size and distance of objects develops very slowly and is still quite immature in eight-year-old children. The gradual refinement of this capacity probably depends on countless interactions between the child and his or her spatial environment, which in turn influences synaptic changes in the visual cortex that continue quite late in childhood. Because the brain is unique among the organs of the body in requiring a great deal of feedback from experience to develop to its full capacities, brain maturation may serve as a rate-limiting factor that governs the maturation of the entire body. As Steven Quartz and Terrence Sejnowski have suggested, the animal's experience in interacting with its environment directs the growth of dendrites and the formation of synaptic connections. They propose that learning is a process that occurs in successive stages, each building on the earlier ones. Larger brains require a longer time to develop because more stages are involved.

Thus the rearing of large-brained babies requires parental support for commensurately long periods. Moreover, large-brained offspring are mostly single

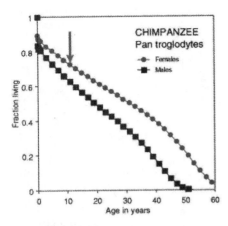
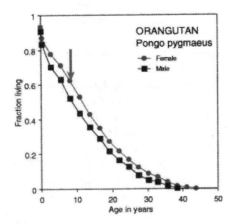
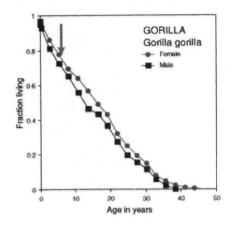

Differential survival between male and female apes. The chimpanzee data are from the work of Bennett Dyke and his colleagues; the orangutan and gorilla data were compiled from zoo records by Roshan Kumar, Aaron Rosin, Andrea Hasenstaub, and the author. (All the data in this chapter were published in the *Proceedings of the National Academy of Science*, Vol. 95, pages 6866-69, June 1998.) The arrow indicates the average age at which females give birth to their first offspring. The graphs show that at every age there are fewer surviving males than females.

births and the interbirth intervals are long, which probably reflect the large costs of rearing these offspring. The parents must live long enough past their sexual maturity to sustain the serial production and maintenance of a sufficient number of offspring to replace themselves while allowing for the early death or infertility of their children. Therefore, I hypothesized that in large-brained species that have single births, the sex that bears the greater burden in the nurturing of offspring will tend to survive longer. If the caretaking parent dies, the offspring will probably die as well, but if the noncaretaking parent dies, this event will have little impact on the offspring's chances of survival. The death of a noncaretaking parent might even enhance the survival of its offspring by removing a competitor for scarce food and resources. Thus genes enhancing the survival of the caretaking parent will be favored by natural selection, since they will be more likely to be transmitted to the next generation than genes that might enhance the survival of the noncaretaking parent. Male primates are incapable of gestating infants and lactating; but in several species, fathers carry their offspring for long periods, and the young may stay close to the father even after they move independently. According to the caretaking theory, females should live longer than males in the species where the mother does most or all of the care of offspring; there should be no difference in survival between the sexes in species in

which both parents participate about equally in infant care, and in those few species where the father does a greater amount of care than the mother, males should live longer. Roshan Kumar, Aaron Rosin, Andrea Hasenstaub, and I tested this hypothesis by constructing mortality tables similar to those used by the life insurance industry for male and female anthropoids (monkeys, apes, and humans) and comparing these data with the sexual division of care for offspring.

The great apes are our closest relatives. Chimpanzees, orangutans, and gorillas nearly always give birth to a single offspring, and the interval between births ranges from four to eight years. Female chimpanzees, orangutans, and gorillas have a large survival advantage in data obtained from captive populations.

For example, in captivity the average female chimpanzee lives 42 percent longer than the average male. In the case of chimpanzees there also are data available from populations living in nature. In a 22-year study of a population of 228 chimpanzees living in the Mahale Mountains near the shores of Lake Tanganyika, Toshisada Nishida and his colleagues found an equivalent number of male and female births but three times as many females as males in the adult population. This difference was not due to differential patterns of strong female survival advantage for chimpanzees living in the wild. Chimpanzee mothers generally provide nearly all the care for their offspring, and

females possess a very strong survival advantage. Although male care of infants is rare in chimpanzees, Pascal Gagneux and his colleagues have observed instances in which males have adopted orphaned infants and cared for them. Their observations indicate that the potential for male care is present in chimpanzees though rarely expressed. Orangutan mothers provide all the care for their offspring, which have very little contact with the solitary adult males. Gorilla mothers provide most of the care for their offspring, but the fathers protect and play with them. The female survival advantage in gorillas, while significant, is not so large as in chimpanzees or orangutans.

The lesser apes are our next closest relatives. Gibbons and siamangs live in pairs and have a single baby about once every three years. They maintain their pair bonds and defend their territories through spectacular vocalizations similar to the pair-bonding songs of birds. Gibbon mothers provide nearly all the care for their offspring, but David Chivers found that siamang males play a much larger parental role than do gibbon males. Siamang mothers carry their infants for the first year, but during the second year the male carries the growing infant. Siamang males are unique among apes in carrying their infants and in the closeness of their bonding with their offspring. Gibbon females have a survival advantage over males, but the situation is reversed in siamangs, where the males have a small advantage.

Gibbon females on average live about 20 percent longer than males, but siamang males live 9 percent *longer* than females. Siamang fathers are the only male apes that carry their infants and the only apes in which males outlive females.

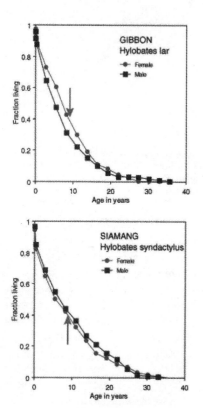

Differential survival patterns in gibbons and siamangs, closely related species living in the same habitat. Note that the female gibbons outlive males, but that male siamangs slightly outlive females. Siamang fathers are the only apes that carry their offspring on a regular basis. The data were compiled from zoo records by Roshan Kumar, Aaron Rosin, Andrea Hasenstaub, and the author.

In Old World monkeys, females do most of the infant care, and several studies from natural populations show a female survival advantage. In New World monkeys, we found a significant survival advantage in captive spider monkeys, and John Robinson found a female survival advantage in the natural population of capuchin monkeys observed in Venezuela. In both spider and capuchin monkey, mothers do virtually all the infant care. However the situation is dramatically reversed in two other New World primates, the owl monkeys and titi monkeys. These monkeys live in pairs like gibbons and siamangs, and also maintain their pair bonds and defend their territory through

vocalizations. The fathers carry their infants from shortly after birth except for brief nursing periods on the mother and occasional rides on older siblings. I have observed in my colony of owl monkeys that if the father dies, the mother will not carry the infant, and thus the survival of the infant depends on the father. In both owl and titi monkeys, males and females die at the same rate until maturity, but after maturity the males have a survival advantage over females. Thus the timing of the male survival advantage corresponds to the period in their lives when they carry their offspring.

It is well known that women tend to live longer than men. It is often assumed that this is a modern phenomenon resulting from the greatly reduced risk of death in childbirth and other improvements in women's health practices. However, the female survival advantage is present in the oldest systematic records from a human population, which were collected in Sweden beginning in 1780, long before modern health practices were instituted. The female advantage is present at every age and for every Swedish census since 1780. In the Swedish population women live 5 to 8 percent longer than men. Similar female advantages were recorded in the earliest data from England and France in the 19th century and a female advantage has been present in most nations throughout the 20th century. A female survival advantage has also been found for adults in the Aché, a well-studied hunter-gatherer population living in the forests of eastern Paraguay. These data strongly suggest that the survival advantage in human females has deep biological roots. However, it is smaller in relative terms than in gorillas, gibbons, orangutans, spider monkeys, and chimpanzees.

In most species there is a female advantage throughout life, but in all the anthropoids in which there are single births and the males carry their offspring, there is either no difference in survival between the sexes or there is a definite male survival advantage. These results run counter to the reasonable expectation that lugging a heavy squirming infant through the trees would increase the risk of falling or being eaten by predators. The magnitude of the difference in survival corresponds to the difference in the amount of care given to

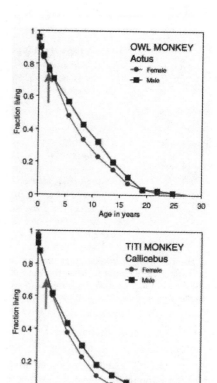

The adult male survival advantage in owl monkeys and titi monkeys, species in which the father carry their infants from shortly after their birth. The data were compiled from zoo records by Roshan Kumar, Aaron Rosin, Andrea Hasenstaub, and the author.

the offspring by each sex. Thus in the great apes where the mothers do virtually all the care, there is a large female advantage. Human males contribute significantly, but human females are the primary caregivers, and in humans there is a proportionally smaller, but still sizable, female advantage. In Goeldi's monkeys both sexes provide about the same amount of care and there is no difference in survival. In siamangs, both parents participate with the father taking over in the later stages of infant development, and siamang males have a small advantage. In owl monkeys and titi monkeys, males carry the babies most of the time from shortly after birth, and thus infant survival depends substantially on the male; in these monkeys there is a large male advantage.

Similar data have come from a non-primate, big-brained species. Killer whales have very large brains. Their calves are born singly with an inter-birth interval of 5 years, and they remain in close association with the mother

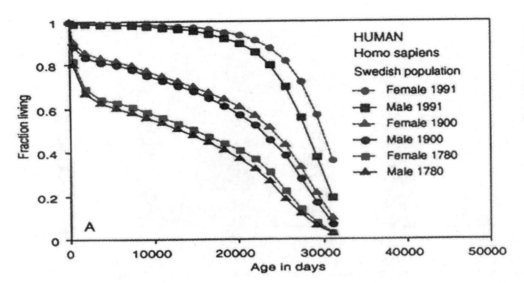

The human female survival advantage in the Swedish population in 1780, 1900, and 1991, plotted from data in the demographic study by Nathan Keyfitz and Wilhelm Fleiger and from the United Nations demographic database. (30,000 days is about 80 years.)

throughout their lives. Males appear to have little direct role in parenting. A long-term demographic study of a natural population of killer whales in Puget Sound found that female life expectancy is more than 20 years longer than in males. The average female lives about 75 percent longer than the average male.

The differential mortality between caretakers and noncaretakers may be in part because the former are risk-averse and the latter tend to be risk-seeking. Caretakers tend to avoid risk because they risk not only themselves but also their offspring. This may be a conscious decision or the result of genetically determined instincts that would be favored by natural selection because they would lead to more surviving offspring. A sec-

ond major factor may be a differential vulnerability to the damaging effects of stress. Natural selection would also favor the evolution of genes in caretakers that protect them against the damage induced by stress. The ratio between the rates at which males and females die varies during the course of life. In humans, the female survival advantage begins shortly after conception and continues throughout life with the largest advantage, in terms of the size of the ratio between male and female age-specific death rates, occurring at around age 25. In many countries, including the United States, Japan, and Sweden, there is evidence for a second smaller peak in the male to female death ratios later in life. Although smaller, these two peaks were present in

the Swedish population in 1780. They also are present at about the same stages in the life cycle in some nonhuman primates such as gorillas and gibbons. The peak in early adulthood corresponds approximately to the period of greatest responsibility for childcare in women. The second peak appears to be related to a higher risk of heart disease and other afflictions in men. I believe that these two peaks represent two underlying mechanisms, one of which is mainly acting on the young and the other on the old. The first peak is largely due to differences between males and females in risk-taking behavior which results in higher rates resulting from accidents and violence in younger males. The second peak may result from increased male vulnerability to

PRIMATE	FEMALE/MALE SURVIVAL RATIO	MALE CARE
chimpanzee	1.418	rare
spider monkey	1.272	rare
orangutan	1.203	none
gibbon	1.199	pair-living, but little direct role
gorilla	1.125	protects, plays with offspring
human (Sweden, 1780–1991)	1.052–1.082	supports economically, some care
Goeldi's monkey	0.974	both parents carry infant
siamang	0.915	carries infant in second year
owl monkey	0.869	carries infant from birth
titi monkey	0.828	carries infant from birth

increasing male survival

increasing male care

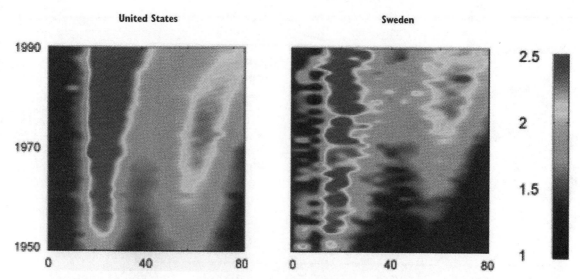

United States   **Sweden**

Excess male deaths as a function of age from 1950 to 1990 in the United States (left) and Sweden (right). Similar patterns are present in the data for Japan, Canada, and many other countries with well-developed health-care systems. The medium grey pattern in the young-adult years indicates that more than twice as many men as women die at this stage of life. The pattern is smoother for the United States because of the much larger population size. The earlier Swedish data, going back to 1780, consistently show similar peaks in early and late adulthood, although the peaks are not as large as for modern data. This consistency suggests that biological factors are partially responsible. The second peak occurs after child rearing but reflects differential responses to stress earlier in life. The analysis was done by Andrea Hasenstaub and the author.

pathological conditions that develop without overt symptoms over a long period of time, such as high blood pressure and clogged arteries, which may be related to the cumulative effects of stress. By contrast, in owl monkeys and titi monkeys, the male survival advantage emerges shortly after maturity at the time when fathers begin to care for their offspring. This hypothesis would predict that their enhanced survival may be due to reduced risk-taking and vulnerability to stress.

In the contemporary United States population, women have lower risks than men of dying from the 13 most prevalent causes of death, indicating that the female survival advantage has an extremely broad base. A hormonal basis for this effect is evidenced by the observation by Francine Grodstein and her collaborators that post-menopausal women who currently receive estrogen replacement have a lower risk of death as compared to post-menopausal women who have never received supplemental estrogen. Estrogen enhances the actions of serotonin and thus may be responsible for reducing risk-taking behavior. Melanie Pecins-Thompson and her colleagues found in macaque monkeys that estrogen inhibits the expression of the gene that makes the transporter protein responsible for serotonin re-

uptake. Thus estrogen acts like drugs such as Prozac that inhibit the removal of serotonin at synapses and consequently increase the synaptic concentration of serotonin. Because of estrogen's effects of the serotonergic system it has been called nature's psychoprotectant.

Another possible basis for differential survival may be related to the stress hormones, the corticosteroids. The clearest evidence for this comes from a study by Robert Sapolsky who encountered and studied a group of vervets that had previously been subjected to chronic stress by overcrowded living conditions. Vervets are a type of monkey in which females do most of the care for offspring. Sapolsky found a substantial loss of neurons in a part of the cerebral cortex, the hippocampus, in males but not in females. The hippocampal neurons are richly supplied with receptors for the corticosteroid hormones, which are produced by the adrenal cortex to mobilize the body's defenses when subjected to stress. One role of the hippocampus is to regulate the pituitary's secretion of adrenocorticotropic hormone, which in turns signals the adrenal cortex to secrete the corticosteroid hormones into the bloodstream. The secretion of the corticosteroid hormones is the body's way of responding to severe, life-threatening emergencies, but the

chronic secretion of these hormones can be very damaging. The hippocampal neurons are particularly vulnerable because they have many receptors for these hormones. Corticosteroids also suppress serotonin receptors in hippocampal neurons, which may diminish their stability and further increase their vulnerability. Because the serotonin reuptake mechanism is inhibited by estrogen, males may be more vulnerable than females in some species. The loss of the hippocampal neurons due to hyperexcitation means that the brakes on the secretion of the stress hormones are burned out, leading to escalating levels of damage and ultimately to death. Sapolsky's results indicate that male vervets are much more vulnerable to the destruction of the brain's system for regulating the stress response than are females. This may be the mechanism for male vulnerability in other species where females are the primary caregivers, and this theory predicts that the opposite would be true for those species where males are the primary caregivers.

What is the biological role for the higher level of risk-taking in males in some species? In *The Descent of Man* in a section entitled the "Law of Battle," Darwin linked male aggression to competition among males for females. This has led to the widely accepted idea that

normal　　　　　**stressed**

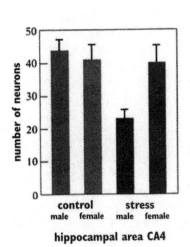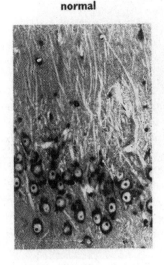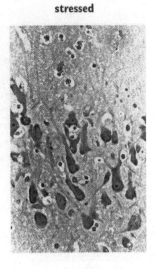

The graph above shows the number of neurons in samples of hippocampal area CA4 in unstressed male and female controls and in stressed males and females. Robert Sapolsky and his colleagues also found similar neuronal losses in the other CA fields of the hippocampus of stressed males. In these monkeys, the stress resulted when they were captured by the Kenyan government at the request of farmers and housed under crowded conditions. The photomicrographs at right illustrate neuron loss in the hippocampus of stressed male monkeys. The left one is from the hippocampus of a control monkey; the right photo-micrograph, from the same place in the hippocampus of a stressed male, shows a loss of neurons and dendritic atrophy in the remaining neurons.

aggressive males become socially dominant and because of their dominance enjoy greater sexual access to females and therefore greater reproductive success. However, there is evidence to suggest that other factors may be involved in male risk-taking.

Let us begin by examining the first part of this relationship: does aggression lead to social dominance? In Chapter 2 [*Evolving Brains*, by author], I discussed the changes in social status in male vervet monkeys induced by experimentally manipulating serotonin levels. In this study, male status was invariably preceded by

Cooperative Male Care in Marmoset and Tamarins

Marmosets and tamarins, which are small New World monkeys, have many more offspring than other monkeys and have an unusual solution to providing care for their infants. Unlike other monkeys which have single births, marmosets and tamarins usually give birth to twins or sometimes triplets. Shortly after birth, females become sexually receptive and can conceive again. Thus marmosets and tamarin females can produce up to six babies per year. These primates have developed a different way to nurture their multiple, slowly developing, large-brained infants. Marmosets and tamarin live in extended families in which everyone and especially the males participate in infant care. Marc Van Roosmalen has even observed a male assisting in the birth process by cutting the umbilical cords and eating the afterbirth. Paul Garber found that the presence of up to 4 males in the family enhances the survival of the infants.

The males cooperate in caring for the infants in their group, and there is little aggression among males within the family. The males are very strongly attracted to infants; they carry them whether or not they are actually their biological offspring, and they share food with them. I have even observed a male kidnapping the offspring of another family so as to carry it. Because of the cooperative care, offspring are less dependent on the survival of a particular caretaker. In our studies thus far we have found little difference in the survival of male and female marmosets and tamarins.

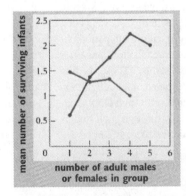

The graph shows that infant survival in tamarins increases as a function of the number of caretaking males in the extended family groups; having more females results in a slight reduction in the number of surviving infants. (Black represents surviving infants based on the number of adult males; grey is surviving infants based on the number of adult females.) This graph, from the work of Paul Garber, is based on observations of 47 extended tamarin families living in nature.

changes in affiliative behaviors with females in the social group such as grooming interactions. Increased affiliative behavior led to increased female support in dominance interactions with other males, which in turn led to rising status. Decreased affiliative behavior led to decreased female support, which in turn led to declining status. This investigation and many observational studies indicate that high status in primate groups is much more dependent on social skills and coalition building than on aggression.

Now let us turn to the second part of the aggression-dominance-reproductive success theory: does the possession of high rank lead to reproductive success? Pascal Gagneux and his colleagues have conducted a long term study of the social structure of chimpanzees living in the Tai forest in the Ivory Coast. In order to measure male lineages, they extracted DNA from cells attached to hair samples for all the members of this group, and thus they were able to determine which chimpanzees had fathered which offspring. They found two surprising results. First, on the basis of the DNA patterns, they were able to rule out all the males in the group as possible fathers of half of the youngsters. Thus the females were covertly mating with males outside their social group; the status of those males within their own groups is unknown. Second, for the youngsters that were fathered by males within the social group, there was only a weak relationship between dominance and reproductive success. Brutus, the top ranking male for 10 years, and Macho, who was the alpha male for 1.5 years, sired no offspring during their periods of dominance, although each sired one after they declined in status. These results highlight the importance of actually determining male parentage through DNA studies, because it is only through such studies that male reproductive success can be determined, which is crucial for measuring the influences of different behaviors on the evolutionary process. Until there is a substantial body of genetically established data for a number of carefully observed primate species, the role of male domi-

nance in reproductive success will remain undetermined. However, observations by Sapolsky in baboons does suggest that high male status does confer a different advantage. He found that the levels of cortisol, a corticosteroid hormone, are inversely related to social status. Therefore, high status males are less at risk to adverse consequences of this hormone. Important advantages of high status in males are reduced vulnerability to the deleterious effects of stress and better access to food resources.

There is strong evidence that high status does confer reproductive success in female chimpanzees, and it is clear that social competence plays an important role in determining the female dominance hierarchy. Goodall and her collaborators found that the offspring of high-status females are more likely to survive and that they mature at an earlier age. They also found evidence that the high-status females live longer than the low-status females. These effects may be the consequence of less stress and better access to food and other resources in the high-status females.

Social competence probably counts for more than aggression in achieving either high status or reproductive success in primates. Why then are the noncaretaking males aggressive and prone to risk-taking? Why would natural selection favor the evolution of behaviors that increase the risk of dying? I think the answer is that risk-takers constantly probe their world, seeking out new opportunities and detecting hazards in a constantly changing environment. Through their probing they generate new information that they communicate to close kin, thus enhancing their kin's survival and the propagation of their shared genes. Specific vocalization for types of food and predators serve this communicative function. The risk-takers may also be crucial to colonizing new habitats during changing environmental conditions.

Both the evolution of large brains and the evolution of temperature homeostasis, as discussed in Chapter 5, [*Evolving Brains*] require new developments in parenting behavior. Warm-blooded infants are dependent and cannot grow without parents to provide warmth and

nutrition. Increasing brain size slows down postnatal development as measured by the ages at which different teeth erupt and by the age of sexual maturation. Large-brained, slowly developing, dependent offspring require long-surviving parents to reach maturity. A measure of this parental dependency effect is the differential survival of caretakers versus noncaretakers. In primates, the caretaker effect has a large influence on the patterns of survival with as much as a 42 percent female advantage when males have little role in nurturing offspring versus as much as a 20 percent male advantage when males carry offspring from soon after birth. The male caretaking effect is not as large because only females provide nutrition for their slowing developing offspring through lactation. The mechanisms responsible for the survival differences between caretakers and noncaretakers may ultimately be related to neuro-chemical differences that favor risk-aversive behavior in caretakers and risk-seeking behavior in noncaretakers, as well as greater vulnerability to the damaging effects of stress in noncaretakers.

John Allman has been working with owl monkeys since his graduate student days spent mapping the owl monkey's visual cortex. Much of his work since then has concerned how the brain is organized and how it processes and interprets visual information. In 1990 he received the Golden Brain Award from the Minerva Foundation for this body of work. Although known as a neurobiologist, all of Allman's degrees are in anthropology: BA, University of Virginia, 1965; and MA (1968) and PhD (1970), University of Chicago. He has been a member of the Caltech faculty since 1974 and professor of biology since 1984; he was named the Hixon Professor of Psychobiology in 1989. In the book from which this chapter is excerpted, he combines his neurobiological research with a life-long interest in evolution—and in behavior. And the owl monkey, whose relatively simple neocortex made it a good neurophysiological model, turns out to have interesting parenting behavior as well, as the father and child pictured on the cover illustrate.

John Allman's Evolving Brains *(A Scientific American Library volume) is available in bookstores, or it can be ordered directly from the publisher, W. H. Freeman and Company.*

A Woman's Curse?

Why do cultures the world over treat menstruating women as taboo?
An anthropologist offers a new answer—and a challenge to Western
ideas about contraception

By Meredith F. Small

THE PASSAGE FROM GIRLHOOD TO womanhood is marked by a flow of blood from the uterus. Without elaborate ceremony, often without discussion, girls know that when they begin to menstruate, their world is changed forever. For the next thirty years or so, they will spend much energy having babies, or trying not to, reminded at each menstruation that either way, the biology of reproduction has a major impact on their lives.

Anthropologists have underscored the universal importance of menstruation by documenting how the event is interwoven into the ideology as well as the daily activities of cultures around the world. The customs attached to menstruation take peculiarly negative forms: the so-called menstrual taboos. Those taboos may prohibit a woman from having sex with her husband or from cooking for him. They may bar her from visiting sacred places or taking part in sacred activities. They may forbid her to touch certain items used by men, such as hunting gear or weapons, or to eat certain foods or to wash at certain times. They may also require that a woman paint her face red or wear a red hip cord, or that she segregate herself in a special hut while she is menstruating. In short, the taboos set menstruating women apart from the rest of their society, marking them as impure and polluting.

Anthropologists have studied menstrual taboos for decades, focusing on the negative symbolism of the rituals as a cultural phenomenon. Perhaps, suggested one investigator, taking a Freudian perspective, such taboos reflect the anxiety that men feel about castration, an anxiety that would be prompted by women's genital bleeding. Others have suggested that the taboos serve to prevent menstrual odor from interfering with hunting, or that they protect men from microorganisms that might otherwise be transferred during sexual intercourse with a menstruating woman. Until recently, few investigators had considered the possibility that the taboos—and the very fact of menstruation—might instead exist because they conferred an evolutionary advantage.

In the mid-1980s the anthropologist Beverly I. Strassmann of the University of Michigan in Ann Arbor began to study the ways men and women have evolved to accomplish (and regulate) reproduction. Unlike traditional anthropologists, who focus on how culture affects human behavior, Strassmann was convinced that the important role played by biology was being neglected. Menstruation, she suspected, would be a key for observing and understanding the interplay of biology and culture in human reproductive behavior.

To address the issue, Strassmann decided to seek a culture in which making babies was an ongoing part of adult life. For that she had to get away from industrialized countries, with their bias toward contraception and low birthrates. In a "natural-fertility population," she reasoned, she could more clearly see the connection between the physiology of women and the strategies men and women use to exploit that physiology for their own reproductive ends.

Strassmann ended up in a remote corner of West Africa, living in close quarters with the Dogon, a traditional society whose indigenous religion of ancestor worship requires that menstruating women spend their nights at a small hut. For more than two years Strassmann kept track of the women staying at the hut, and she confirmed the menstruations by testing urine samples for the appropriate hormonal changes. In so doing, she amassed the first long-term data describing how a traditional society appropriates a physiological event—menstruation—and refracts that event through a prism of behaviors and beliefs.

What she found explicitly challenges the conclusions of earlier investigators about the cultural function of menstrual taboos. For the Dogon men, she discovered, enforcing visits to the menstrual hut serves to channel parental resources into the upbringing of their own children. But more, Strassmann, who also had training as a reproductive physiologist, proposed a new theory of why menstruation itself evolved as it did—and again, the answer is essentially a story of conserving resources. Finally, her observations pose provocative questions about women's health in industrialized societies, raising serious doubts about the tactics favored by Western medicine for developing contraceptive technology.

MENSTRUATION IS THE VISIBLE stage of the ovarian cycle, orchestrated primarily by hormones secreted by the ovaries: progesterone and a family of hormones called estrogens. At the beginning of each cycle (by convention, the first day of a woman's period) the levels of the estrogens begin to rise. After about five days, as their concentrations increase, they cause the blood- and nutrient-rich inner lining of the uterus, called the endometrium, to thicken and acquire a densely branching network of blood vessels. At about the middle of the cycle, ovulation takes place, and an egg makes its way from one of the two ovaries down one of the paired fallopian tubes to the uterus. The follicle from which the egg was released in the ovary now begins to secrete progesterone as well as estrogens, and the progesterone causes the endometrium to swell and become even richer with blood vessels—in short, fully ready for a pregnancy, should conception take place and the fertilized egg become implanted.

If conception does take place, the levels of estrogens and progesterone continue to rise throughout the pregnancy. That keeps the endometrium thick enough to support the quickening life inside the uterus. When the baby is born and the new mother begins nursing, the estrogens and progesterone fall to their initial levels, and lactation hormones keep them suppressed. The uterus thus lies quiescent until frequent lactation ends, which triggers the return to ovulation.

If conception does not take place after ovulation, all the ovarian hormones also drop to their initial levels, and menstruation—the shedding of part of the uterine lining—begins. The lining is divided into three layers: a basal layer that is constantly maintained, and two superficial layers, which shed and regrow with each menstrual cycle. All mammals undergo cyclical changes in the state of the endometrium. In most mammals the sloughed-off layers are resorbed into the body if fertilization does not take place. But in some higher primates, including

humans, some of the shed endometrium is not resorbed. The shed lining, along with some blood, flows from the body through the vaginal opening, a process that in humans typically lasts from three to five days.

OF COURSE, PHYSIOLOGICAL FACTS alone do not explain why so many human groups have infused a bodily function with symbolic meaning. And so in 1986 Strassmann found herself driving through the Sahel region of West Africa at the peak of the hot season, heading for a sandstone cliff called the Bandiagara Escarpment, in Mali. There, permanent Dogon villages of mud or stone houses dotted the rocky plateau. The menstrual huts were obvious: round, low-roofed buildings set apart from the rectangular dwellings of the rest of the village.

The Dogon are a society of millet and onion farmers who endorse polygyny, and they maintain their traditional culture despite the occasional visits of outsiders. In a few Dogon villages, in fact, tourists are fairly common, and ethnographers had frequently studied the Dogon language, religion and social structure before Strassmann's arrival. But her visit was the first time someone from the outside wanted to delve into an intimate issue in such detail.

It took Strassmann a series of hikes among villages, and long talks with male elders under the thatched-roof shelters where they typically gather, to find the appropriate sites for her research. She gained permission for her study in fourteen villages, eventually choosing two. That exceptional welcome, she thinks, emphasized the universality of her interests. "I'm working on all the things that really matter to [the Dogon]—fertility, economics—so they never questioned my motives or wondered why I would be interested in these things," she says. "It seemed obvious to them." She set up shop for the next two and a half years in a stone house in the village, with no running water or electricity. Eating the daily fare of the Dogon, millet porridge, she and a research assistant began to integrate themselves into village life, learning the language, getting to know people and tracking visits to the menstrual huts.

Following the movements of menstruating women was surprisingly easy. The menstrual huts are situated outside the walled compounds of the village, but in full view of the men's thatched-roof shelters. As the men relax under their shelters, they can readily see who leaves the huts in the morning and returns to them in the evening. And as nonmenstruating women pass the huts on their way to and from the fields or to other compounds, they too can see who is spending the night there. Strassmann found that when she left her house in the evening to take data, any of the villagers could accurately predict whom she would find in the menstrual huts.

THE HUTS THEMSELVES ARE CRAMPED, dark buildings—hardly places where a woman might go to escape the drudgery of work or to avoid an argument with her husband or a co-wife. The huts sometimes become so crowded that some occupants are forced outside—making the women even more conspicuous. Although babies and toddlers can go with their mothers to the huts, the women consigned there are not allowed to spend time with the rest of their families. They must cook with special pots, not their usual household possessions. Yet they are still expected to do their usual jobs, such as working in the fields.

Why, Strassmann wondered, would anyone put up with such conditions?

The answer, for the Dogon, is that a menstruating woman is a threat to the sanctity of religious altars, where men pray and make sacrifices for the protection of their fields, their families and their village. If menstruating women come near the altars, which are situated both indoors and outdoors, the Dogon believe that their aura of pollution will ruin the altars and bring calamities upon the village. The belief is so ingrained that the women themselves have internalized it, feeling its burden of responsibility and potential guilt. Thus violations of the taboo are rare, because a menstruating woman who breaks the rules knows that she is personally responsible if calamities occur.

NEVERTHELESS, STRASSMANN STILL thought a more functional explanation for menstrual taboos might also exist, one closely related to reproduction. As she was well aware, even before her studies among the Dogon, people around the world have a fairly sophisticated view of how reproduction works. In general, people everywhere know full well that menstruation signals the absence of a pregnancy and the possibility of another one. More precisely, Strassmann could frame her hypothesis by reasoning as follows: Across cultures, men and women recognize that a lack of menstrual cycling in a woman implies she is either pregnant, lactating or menopausal. Moreover, at least among natural-fertility cultures that do not practice birth control, continual cycles during peak reproductive years imply to people in those cultures that a woman is sterile. Thus, even though people might not be able to pinpoint ovulation, they can easily identify whether a woman will soon be ready to conceive on the basis of whether she is menstruating. And that leads straight to Strassmann's insightful hypothesis about the role of menstrual taboos: information about menstruation can be a means of tracking paternity.

"There are two important pieces of information for assessing paternity," Strassmann notes: timing of intercourse and timing of menstruation. "By forcing women to signal menstruation, men are trying to gain equal access to one part of that critical information." Such information, she explains, is crucial to Dogon men, because they invest so many resources in their own offspring. Descent is marked through the male line; land and the food that comes from the land is passed down from fathers to sons. Information about paternity is thus crucial to a man's entire lineage. And because each man has as many as four wives, he cannot possibly track them all. So forcing women to signal their menstrual periods, or lack thereof, helps men avoid cuckoldry.

TO TEST HER HYPOTHESIS, STRASS-mann tracked residence in the menstrual huts for 736 consecutive days, collecting data on 477 complete cycles. She noted who was at each hut and how long each woman stayed. She also collected urine from ninety-three women over a ten-week period, to check the correlation between residence in the menstrual hut and the fact of menstruation.

The combination of ethnographic records and urinalyses showed that the Dogon women mostly play by the rules. In 86 percent of the hormonally detected menstruations, women went to the hut. Moreover, none of the tested women went to the hut when they were not menstruating. In the remaining 14 percent of the tested menstruations, women stayed home from the hut, in violation of the taboo, but some were near menopause and so not at high risk for pregnancy. More important, none of the women who violated the taboo did it twice in a row. Even they were largely willing to comply.

Thus, Strassmann concluded, the huts do indeed convey a fairly reliable signal, to men and to everyone else, about the status of a woman's fertility. When she leaves the hut, she is considered ready to conceive. When she stops going to the hut, she is evidently pregnant or menopausal. And women of prime reproductive age who visit the hut on a regular basis are clearly infertile.

It also became clear to Strassmann that the Dogon do indeed use that information to make paternity decisions. In several cases a man was forced to marry a pregnant woman, simply because everyone knew that the man had been the woman's first sexual partner after her last visit to the menstrual hut. Strassmann followed one case in which a child was being brought up by a man because he was the mother's first sexual partner after a hut visit, even though the woman soon married a different man. (The woman already knew she was pregnant by the first man at the time of her marriage, and she did not visit the menstrual hut before she married. Thus the truth was obvious to everyone, and the real father took the child.)

In general, women are cooperative players in the game because without a man, a woman has no way to support herself or her children. But women follow the taboo reluctantly. They complain about going to the hut. And if their husbands convert from the traditional religion of the Dogon to a religion that does not impose menstrual taboos, such as Is-

lam or Christianity, the women quickly cease visiting the hut. Not that such a religious conversion quells a man's interest in his wife's fidelity: far from it. But the rules change. Perhaps the sanctions of the new religion against infidelity help keep women faithful, so the men can relax their guard. Or perhaps the men are willing to trade the reproductive advantages of the menstrual taboo for the economic benefits gained by converting to the new religion. Whatever the case, Strassmann found an almost perfect correlation between a husband's religion and his wives' attendance at the hut. In sum, the taboo is established by men, backed by supernatural forces, and internalized and accepted by women until the men release them from the belief.

BUT BEYOND THE CULTURAL MACHI-nations of men and women that Strassmann expected to find, her data show something even more fundamental—and surprising—about female biology. On average, she calculates, a woman in a natural-fertility population such as the Dogon has only about 110 menstrual periods in her lifetime. The rest of the time she will be prepubescent, pregnant, lactating or menopausal. Women in industrialized cultures, by contrast, have more than three times as many cycles: 350 to 400, on average, in a lifetime. They reach menarche (their first menstruation) earlier—at age twelve and a half, compared with the onset age of sixteen in natural-fertility cultures. They have fewer babies, and they lactate hardly at all. All those factors lead women in the industrialized world to a lifetime of nearly continuous menstrual cycling.

The big contrast in cycling profiles during the reproductive years can be traced specifically to lactation. Women in more traditional societies spend most of their reproductive years in lactation amenorrhea, the state in which the hormonal changes required for nursing suppress ovulation and inhibit menstruation. And it is not just that the Dogon bear more children (eight to nine on average); they also nurse each child on demand rather than in scheduled bouts, all through the night as well as the day, and intensely enough that ovulation simply stops for about twenty months per child. Women in industrialized societies typically do not breast-feed as intensely (or at all), and rarely breast-feed each child for as long as the Dogon women do. (The average for American women is four months.)

The Dogon experience with menstruation may be far more typical of the human condition over most of evolutionary history than is the standard menstrual experience in industrialized nations. If so, Strassmann's findings alter some of the most closely held beliefs about female biology. Contrary to what the Western medical establishment might think, it is not particularly "normal" to menstruate each month. The female body, according to Strassmann, is biologically designed to spend much more time in lactation amenorrhea than in menstrual cycling. That in itself suggests that oral contraceptives, which alter hormone levels to suppress ovulation and produce a bleeding, could be forcing a continual state of cycling for which the body is ill-prepared. Women might be better protected against reproductive cancers if their contraceptives mimicked lactation amenorrhea and depressed the female reproductive hormones, rather than forcing the continual ebb and flow of menstrual cycles.

Strassmann's data also call into question a recently popularized idea about menstruation: that regular menstrual cycles might be immunologically beneficial for women. In 1993 the controversial writer Margie Profet, whose ideas about evolutionary and reproductive biology have received vast media attention, proposed in The Quarterly Review of Biology that menstruation could have such an adaptive value. She noted that viruses and bacteria regularly enter the female body on the backs of sperm, and she hypothesized that the best way to get them out is to flush them out. Here, then, was a positive, adaptive role for something unpleasant, an evolutionary reason for suffering cramps each month. Menstruation, according to Profet, had evolved to rid the body of pathogens. The "anti-pathogen" theory was an exciting hypothesis, and it

helped win Profet a MacArthur Foundation award. But Strassmann's work soon showed that Profet's ideas could not be supported because of one simple fact: under less-industrialized conditions, women menstruate relatively rarely.

Instead, Strassmann notes, if there is an adaptive value to menstruation, it is ultimately a strategy to conserve the body's resources. She estimates that maintaining the endometrial lining during the second half of the ovarian cycle takes substantial metabolic energy. Once the endometrium is built up and ready to receive a fertilized egg, the tissue requires a sevenfold metabolic increase to remain rich in blood and ready to support a pregnancy. Hence, if no pregnancy is forthcoming, it makes a lot of sense for the body to let part of the endometrium slough off and then regenerate itself, instead of maintaining that rather costly but unneeded tissue. Such energy conservation is common among vertebrates: male rhesus monkeys have shrunken testes during their nonbreeding season, Burmese pythons shrink their guts when they are not digesting, and hibernating animals put their metabolisms on hold.

Strassmann also suggests that periodically ridding oneself of the endometrium could make a difference to a woman's long-term survival. Because female reproductive hormones affect the brain and other tissues, the metabolism of the entire body is involved during cycling. Strassmann estimates that by keeping hormonal low through half the cycle, a woman can save about six days' worth of energy for every four nonconceptive cycles. Such caloric conservation might have proved useful to early hominids who lived by hunting and gathering, and even today it might be helpful for women living in less affluent circumstances than the ones common in the industrialized West.

BUT PERHAPS THE MOST PROVOCATIVE implications of Strassmann's work have to do with women's health. In 1994 a group of physicians and anthropologists pub-

lished a paper, also in The Quarterly Review of Biology, suggesting that the reproductive histories and lifestyles of women in industrialized cultures are at odds with women's naturally evolved biology, and that the differences lead to greater risks of reproductive cancers. For example, the investigators estimated that women in affluent cultures may have a hundredfold greater risk of breast cancer than do women who subsist by hunting and gathering. The increased risk is probably caused not only by low levels of exercise and a high-fat diet, but also by a relatively high number of menstrual cycles over a lifetime. Repeated exposure to the hormones of the ovarian cycle—because of early menarche, late menopause, lack of pregnancy and little or no breast-feeding—is implicated in other reproductive cancers as well.

Those of us in industrialized cultures have been running an experiment on ourselves. The body evolved over millions of years to move across the landscape looking for food, to live in small kin-based groups, to make babies at intervals of four years or so and to invest heavily in each child by nursing intensely for years. How many women now follow those traditional patterns? We move little, we rely on others to get our food, and we rarely reproduce or lactate. Those culturally initiated shifts in lifestyles may pose biological risks.

Our task is not to overcome that biology, but to work with it. Now that we have a better idea of how the female body was designed, it may be time to rework our lifestyles and change some of our expectations. It may be time to borrow from our distant past or from our contemporaries in distant cultures, and treat our bodies more as nature intended.

MEREDITH F. SMALL is a professor of anthropology at Cornell University in Ithaca, New York. Her latest book, OUR BABIES, OURSELVES: HOW BIOLOGY AND CULTURE SHAPE THE WAY WE PARENT, *was published in May 1998 [see Laurence A. Marschall's review in Books in Brief, November/December 1998].*

WHY WOMEN CHANGE

The winners of evolution's race are those who can leave behind the most offspring to carry on their progenitors' genes. So doesn't it seem odd that human females should be hobbled in their prime by menopause?

JARED DIAMOND

Most wild animals remain fertile until they die. So do human males: although some may eventually become less fertile, men in general experience no shutdown of fertility, and indeed there are innumerable well-attested cases of old men, including a 94-year-old, fathering children.

But for women the situation is different. Human females undergo a steep decline in fertility from around the age of 40 and within a decade or so can no longer produce children. While some women continue to have regular menstrual cycles up to the age of 54 or 55, conception after the age of 50 was almost unknown until the recent advent of hormone therapy and artificial fertilization.

Human female menopause thus appears to be an inevitable fact of life, albeit sometimes a painful one. But to an evolutionary biologist, it is a paradoxical aberration in the animal world. The essence of natural selection is that it promotes genes for traits that increase one's number of descendants bearing those genes. How could natural selection possibly result in every female member of a species carrying genes that throttle her ability to leave more descendants? Of course, evolutionary biologists (including me) are not implying that a woman's only proper role is to stay home and care for babies and to forget about other fulfilling experiences. Instead I am using standard evolutionary

reasoning to try to understand how men's and women's bodies came to be the way they are. That reasoning tends to regard menopause as among the most bizarre features of human sexuality. But it is also among the most important. Along with the big brains and upright posture that every text of human evolution emphasizes, I consider menopause to be among the biological traits essential for making us distinctively human—something qualitatively different from, and more than, an ape.

Not everyone agrees with me about the evolutionary importance of human female menopause. Many biologists see no need to discuss it farther, since they don't think it poses an unsolved problem. Their objections are of three types. First, some dismiss it as a result of a recent increase in human expected life span. That increase stems not just from public health measures developed within the last century but possibly also from the rise of agriculture 10,000 years ago, and even more likely from evolutionary changes leading to increased human survival skills within the last 40,000 years.

According to proponents of this view, menopause could not have been a frequent occurrence for most of the several million years of human evolution, because (supposedly) almost no women or men used to survive past the age of 45 or 50. Of course the female reproductive

tract was programmed to shut down by age 50, since it would not have had the opportunity to operate thereafter anyway. The increase in human life span, these critics believe, has occurred much too recently in our evolutionary history for the female reproductive tract to have had time to adjust.

What this view overlooks, however, is that the human male reproductive tract and every other biological function of both women and men continue to function in most people for decades after age 50. If all other biological functions adjusted quickly to our new long life span, why was female reproduction uniquely incapable of doing so?

Furthermore, the claim that in the past few women survived until the age of menopause is based solely on paleodemography, which attempts to estimate age at time of death in ancient skeletons. Those estimates rest on unproven, implausible assumptions, such as that the recovered skeletons represent an unbiased sample of an entire ancient population, or that ancient adult skeletons' age of death can accurately be determined. While there's no question that paleodemographers can distinguish an ancient skeleton of a 10-year-old from that of a 25-year-old, they have never demonstrated that they can distinguish an ancient 40-year-old from a 55-year-old. One can hardly reason by comparison with skeletons of modern people, whose bones surely age at different rates from bones of ancients with different life-styles, diets, and diseases.

A second objection acknowledges that human female menopause may be an ancient phenomenon but denies that it is unique to humans. Many wild animals undergo a decline in fertility with age. Some elderly individuals of many wild mammal and bird species are found to be infertile. Among animals in laboratory cages or zoos, with their lives considerably extended over expected spans in the wild by a gourmet diet, superb medical care, and protection from enemies, many elderly female rhesus monkeys and individuals of several strains of laboratory mice do become infertile. Hence some biologists object that human female menopause is merely part of a widespread phenomenon of animal menopause, not something peculiar to humans.

However, one swallow does not make a summer, nor does one sterile female constitute menopause. Establishing the existence of menopause as a biologically significant phenomenon in the wild requires far more than just coming upon the occasional sterile elderly individual in the wild or observing regular sterility in caged animals with artificially extended life spans. It requires finding a wild animal population in which a substantial proportion of females become sterile and spend a significant fraction of their life spans after the end of their fertility.

The human species does fulfill that definition, but only one wild animal species is known to do so: the short-finned pilot whale. One-quarter of all adult females killed by whalers prove to be post-menopausal, as judged by the condition of their ovaries. Female pilot whales enter menopause at the age of 30 or 40 years, have a mean survival of at least 14 years after menopause, and may live for over 60 years. Menopause as a biologically significant phenomenon is thus not strictly unique to humans, being shared at least with that one species of whale.

But human female menopause remains sufficiently unusual in the animal world that its evolution requires explanation. We certainly did not inherit it from pilot whales, from whose ancestors our own ancestors parted company over 50 million years ago. In fact, we must have evolved it after we separated from the apes just 7 million to 5 million years ago, because we undergo menopause whereas chimps and gorillas appear not to (or at least not regularly).

There is no obvious reason we had to evolve eggs that degenerate by the end of half a century. Eggs of elephants, baleen whales, and tortoises remain viable for at least 60 years.

The third and last objection acknowledges human menopause as an ancient phenomenon that is indeed unusual among animals. But these critics say that we need not seek an explanation for menopause, because the puzzle has already been solved. The solution, they say is the physiological mechanism of menopause: the senescence and exhaustion of a woman's egg supply, fixed at birth and not added to after birth. An egg is lost at each menstrual cycle. By the time a woman is 50 years old, most of that original egg supply has been depleted. The remaining eggs are half a century old and increasingly unresponsive to hormones.

But there is a fatal counterobjection to this objection. While the objection is not wrong, it is incomplete. Yes, exhaustion and aging of the egg supply are the immediate cause of human menopause, but why did natural selection program women so that their eggs become exhausted or aged in their forties? There is no obvious reason we had to evolve eggs that degenerate by the end of half a century. Eggs of elephants, baleen whales, and tortoises remain viable for at least 60 years. A mutation only slightly altering how eggs degenerate might have sufficed for women to remain fertile until age 60 or 75.

The easy part of the menopause puzzle is identifying the physiological mechanism by which a woman's egg supply becomes depleted or impaired by the time she is around 50 years old. The challenging problem is understanding why we evolved that seemingly self-defeating detail of reproductive physiology. Apparently there was nothing physiologically inevitable about human female menopause, and there was nothing evolutionarily inevitable about it from the perspective of mammals in general. Instead the human female, but not the human male, was programmed by natural selection, at some time within the last few million years, to shut down reproduction prematurely. That premature senescence is all the more surprising because it goes against an overwhelming trend: in other respects, we humans have evolved to age more slowly, not more rapidly, than most other animals.

As a woman ages, she can do more to increase the number of people bearing her genes by devoting herself to her existing children and grandchildren than by producing yet another child.

Any theory of menopause evolution must explain how a woman's apparently counterproductive evolutionary strategy of making fewer babies could actually result in her making more. Evidently, as a woman ages, she can do more to increase the number of people bearing her genes by devoting herself to her existing children, her potential grandchildren, and her other relatives than by producing yet another child.

The evolutionary chain of reasoning rests on several cruel facts. One is that the human child depends on its parents for an extraordinarily long time, longer than in any other animal species. A baby chimpanzee, as soon as it starts to be weaned, begins gathering its own food, mostly with its own hands. (Chimpanzee use of tools, such as fishing for termites with blades of grass or cracking nuts with stones, is of great interest to human scientists but of only limited dietary significance to chimpanzees.) The baby chimpanzee also prepares its food with its own hands. But human hunter-gatherers acquire most food with tools (digging sticks, nets, spears), prepare it with other tools (knives, pounders, huskers), and then cook it in a fire made by still other tools. Furthermore, they use tools to protect themselves against dangerous predators, unlike other prey animals, which use teeth and strong muscles. Making and wielding all those tools are completely beyond the manual dexterity and mental ability of young children. Tool use and toolmaking are transmitted not just by imitation but also by language, which takes over a decade for a child to master.

As a result, human children in most societies do not become capable of economic independence until their teens or twenties. Before that, they remain dependent on their parents, especially on the mother, because mothers tend to provide more child care than do fathers. Parents not only bring food and teach toolmaking but also provide protection and status within the tribe. In traditional societies, early death of either parent endangers a child's life even if the surviving parent remarries, because of possible conflicts with the stepparent's genetic interests. A young orphan who is not adopted has even worse chances of surviving.

Hence a hunter-gatherer mother who already has several children risks losing her genetic investment in them if she does not survive until the youngest is at least a teenager. That's one cruel fact underlying human female menopause. Another is that the birth of each successive child immediately jeopardizes a mother's previous children because the mother risks dying in childbirth. In most other animal species that risk is very low. For example, in one study of 401 rhesus monkey pregnancies, only three mothers died in childbirth. For humans in traditional societies, the risk is much higher and increases with age. Even in affluent twentieth-century Western societies, the risk of dying in childbirth is seven times higher for a mother over the age of 40 than for a 20-year-old. But each new child puts the mother's life at risk not only because of the immediate risk of death in childbirth but also because of

the delayed risk of death related to exhaustion by lactation, carrying a young child, and working harder to feed more mouths.

Infants of older mothers are themselves increasingly unlikely to survive or be healthy, because the risks of abortion, stillbirth, low birth weight, and genetic defects rise as the mother grows older. For instance, the risk of a fetus's carrying the genetic condition known as Down syndrome increases from one in 2,000 births for a mother under 30, one in 300 for a mother between the ages of 35 and 39, and one in 50 for a 43-year-old mother to the grim odds of one in 10 for a mother in her late forties.

Thus, as a woman gets older, she is likely to have accumulated more children, and she has been caring for them longer, so she is putting a bigger investment at risk with each successive pregnancy. But her chances of dying in or after childbirth, and the chances that the infant will die, also increase. In effect, the older mother is risking more for less potential gain. That's one set of factors that would tend to favor human female menopause and that would paradoxically result in a woman's having more surviving children by giving birth to fewer children.

But a hypothetical nonmenopausal older woman who died in childbirth, or while caring for an infant, would thereby be throwing away even more than her investment in her previous children. That is because a woman's children eventually begin producing children of their own, and those children count as part of the woman's prior investment. Especially in traditional societies, a woman's survival is important not only to her children but also to her grandchildren.

That extended role of postmenopausal women has been explored by anthropologists Kristen Hawks, James O'Connell, and Nicholas Blurton Jones, who studied foraging by women of different ages among the Hadza hunter-gatherers of Tanzania. The women who devoted the most time to gathering food (especially roots, honey, and fruit) were postmenopausal women. Those hardworking Hadza grandmothers put in an impressive seven hours per day, compared with a mere three hours for girls

not yet pregnant and four and a half hours for women of childbearing age. As one might expect, foraging returns (measured in pounds of food gathered per hour) increased with age and experience, so that mature women achieved higher returns than teenagers. Interestingly, the grandmothers' returns were still as high as women in their prime. The combination of putting in more foraging hours and maintaining an unchanged foraging efficiency meant that the postmenopausal grandmothers brought in more food per day than women of any of the young groups, even though their large harvests were greatly in excess of their own personal needs and they no longer had dependent young children of their own to feed.

Observations indicated that the Hadza grandmothers were sharing their excess food harvest with close relatives, such as their grandchildren and grown children. As a strategy for transforming food calories into pounds of baby, it's more efficient for an older woman to donate the calories to grandchildren and grown children than to infants of her own, because her fertility decreases with age anyway, while her children are young adults at peak fertility. Naturally, menopausal grandmothers in traditional societies contribute more to their offspring than just food. They also act as baby-sitters for grandchildren, thereby helping their adult children churn out more babies bearing Grandma's genes. And though they work hard for their grandchildren, they're less likely to die as a result of exhaustion than if they were nursing infants as well as caring for them.

But menopause has another virtue, one that has received little attention. That is the importance of old people to their entire tribe in preliterate societies, which means every human society in the world from the time of human origins until the rise of writing in Mesopotamia around 3300 B.C.

A common genetics argument is that natural selection cannot weed out mutations that do not damage people until they are old, because old people are supposedly "postreproductive." I believe that such statements overlook an essential fact distinguishing humans from most animal species. No humans, except hermits, are ever truly postreproductive, in the sense of being unable to aid in the survival and reproduction of other people bearing their genes. Yes, I grant that if any orangutans lived long enough in the wild to become sterile, they would count as postreproductive, since orangutans (other than mothers with one young offspring) tend to be solitary. I also grant that the contributions of very old people to modern literate societies tend to decrease with age. That new phenomenon of modern societies is at the root of the enormous problems that old age now poses, both for the elderly themselves and for the rest of society. But we moderns get most of our information through writing, television, or radio. We find it impossible to conceive of the overwhelming importance of elderly people in preliterate societies as repositories of information and experience.

Here is an example of that role. During my field studies of bird ecology on New Guinea and adjacent southwestern Pacific islands, I live among people who traditionally were without writing, depended on stone tools, and subsisted by farming and fishing supplemented by hunting and gathering. I am constantly asking villagers to tell me the names of local birds, animals, and plants in their language, and to tell me what they know about each species. New Guineans and Pacific islanders possess an enormous fund of biological knowledge, including names for a thousand or more species, plus information about where each species occurs, its behavior, its ecology, and its usefulness to humans. All that information is important because wild plants and animals furnish much of the people's food and all their building materials, medicines, and decorations.

Again and again, when I ask about some rare bird, only the older hunters know the answer, and eventually I ask a question that stumps even them. The hunters reply, "We have to ask the old man [or the old woman]." They take me to a hut where we find an old man or woman, blind with cataracts and toothless, able to eat food only after someone else has chewed it. But that old person is

the tribe's library. Because the society traditionally lacked writing, that old person knows more about the local environment than anyone else and is the sole person with accurate knowledge of events that happened long ago. Out comes the rare bird's name, and a description of it.

Supposedly, natural selection can't weed out mutations that affect only old people, because old people are postreproductive. But no humans, except hermits, are ever truly postreproductive.

The accumulated experience that the elderly remember is important for the whole tribe's survival. In 1976, for instance, I visited Rennell Island, one of the Solomon Islands, lying in the southwestern Pacific's cyclone belt. When I asked about wild fruits and seeds that birds ate, my Rennellese informants named dozens of plant species by Rennell language names, named for each plant species all the bird and bat species that eat its fruit, and said whether the fruit is edible for people. They ranked fruits in three categories: those that people never eat, those that people regularly eat, and those that people eat only in famine times, such as after—and here I kept hearing a Rennell term initially unfamiliar to me—the hungi kengi.

Those words proved to be the Rennell name for the most destructive cyclone to have hit the island in living memory— apparently around 1910, based on people's references to datable events of the European colonial administration. The hungi kengi blew down most of Rennell's forest, destroyed gardens, and drove people to the brink of starvation. Islanders survived by eating fruits of wild plant species that were normally not eaten. But doing so required detailed knowledge about which plants are poisonous, which are not poisonous, and whether and how the poison can be re-

moved by some technique of food preparation.

When I began pestering my middle-aged Rennellese informants with questions about fruit edibility, I was brought into a hut. There, once my eyes had become accustomed to the dim light, I saw the inevitable frail old woman. She was the last living person with direct experience of which plants were found safe and nutritious to eat after the *hungi kengi*, until people's gardens began producing again. The old woman explained that she had been a child not quite of marriageable age at the time of the *hungi kengi*. Since my visit to Rennell was in 1976, and since the cyclone had struck 66 years before, the woman was probably in her early eighties. Her survival after the 1910 cyclone had depended on information remembered by aged survivors of the last big cyclone before the *hungi kengi*. Now her people's ability to survive another cyclone would depend on her own memories, which were fortunately very detailed.

Such anecdotes could be multiplied indefinitely. Traditional human societies face frequent minor risks that threaten a few individuals, and also face rare natural catastrophes or intertribal wars that threaten the lives of everybody in the society. But virtually everyone in a small traditional society is related to one another. Hence old people in a traditional society are essential to the survival not only of their children and grandchildren but also of hundreds of other people who share their genes. In preliterate societies, no one is ever postreproductive.

Any preliterate human societies that included individuals old enough to remember the last *hungi kengi* had a much better chance of surviving the next one than did societies without such old people. The old men were not at risk from childbirth or from exhausting responsibilities of lactation and child care, so they did not evolve protection by menopause. But old women who did not undergo menopause tended to be eliminated from the human gene pool because they remained exposed to the risk of childbirth and the burden of child care. At times of crisis, such as a *hungi kengi*, the prior death of such an older woman also tended to eliminate all the woman's relatives from the gene pool—a huge genetic price to pay just for the dubious privilege of continuing to produce another baby or two against lengthening odds. That's what I see as a major driving force behind the evolution of human female menopause. Similar considerations may have led to the evolution of menopause in female pilot whales. Like us, whales are long-lived, involved in complex social relationships and life-long family ties, and capable of sophisticated communication and learning.

If one were playing God and deciding whether to make older women undergo menopause, one would do a balance sheet, adding up the benefits of menopause in one column for comparison with its costs in another column. The costs of menopause are the potential children of a woman's old age that she forgoes. The potential benefits include avoiding the increased risk of death due to childbirth and parenting at an advanced age, and thereby gaining the benefit of improved survival for one's grandchildren, prior children, and more distant relatives. The sizes of those benefits depend on many details: for example, how large the risk of death is in and after childbirth, how much that risk increases with age, how rapidly fertility decreases with age before menopause, and how rapidly it would continue to decrease in an aging woman who did not undergo menopause. All those factors are bound to differ between societies and are not easy for anthropologists to estimate. But natural selection is a more skilled mathematician because it has had millions of years in which to do the calculation. It concluded that menopause's benefits outweigh its costs, and that women can make more by making less.

Jared Diamond is a contributing editor of DISCOVER, a professor of physiology at the UCLA School of Medicine, a recipient of a MacArthur genius award, and a research associate in ornithology at the American Museum of Natural History. Expanded versions of many of his DISCOVER articles appear in his book The Third Chimpanzee: The Evolution and Future of the Human Animal, *which won Britain's 1992 COPUS prize for best science book and the Los Angeles Times science book prize.*

What's Love Got to Do With It?

Sex Among Our Closest Relatives Is a Rather Open Affair

Meredith F. Small

Maiko and Lana are having sex. Maiko is on top, and Lana's arms and legs are wrapped tightly around his waist. Lina, a friend of Lana's, approaches from the right and taps Maiko on the back, nudging him to finish. As he moves away, Lina enfolds Lana in her arms, and they roll over so that Lana is now on top. The two females rub their genitals together, grinning and screaming in pleasure.

This is no orgy staged for an X-rated movie. It doesn't even involve people— or rather, it involves them only as observers. Lana, Maiko, and Lina are bonobos, a rare species of chimplike ape in which frequent couplings and casual sex play characterize every social relationship—between males and females, members of the same sex, closely related animals, and total strangers. Primatologists are beginning to study the bonobos' unrestrained sexual behavior for tantalizing clues to the origins of our own sexuality.

In reconstructing how early man and woman behaved, researchers have generally looked not to bonobos but to common chimpanzees. Only about 5 million years ago human beings and chimps shared a common ancestor, and we still have much behavior in common: namely, a long period of infant dependency, a reliance on learning what to eat and how to obtain food, social bonds that persist over generations, and the need to deal as a group with many everyday conflicts. The assumption has been that chimp behavior today may be similar to the behavior of human ancestors.

Bonobo behavior, however, offers another window on the past because they, too, shared our 5-million-year-old ancestor, diverging from chimps just 2 million years ago. Bonobos have been less studied than chimps for the simple reason that they are difficult to find. They live only on a small patch of land in Zaire, in central Africa. They were first identified, on the basis of skeletal material, in the 1920s, but it wasn't until the 1970s that their behavior in the wild was studied, and then only sporadically.

Bonobos, also known as pygmy chimpanzees, are not really pygmies but welterweights. The largest males are as big as chimps, and the females of the two species are the same size. But bonobos are more delicate in build, and their arms and legs are long and slender.

On the ground, moving from fruit tree to fruit tree, bonobos often stand and walk on two legs—behavior that makes them seem more like humans than chimps. In some ways their sexual behavior seems more human as well, suggesting that in the sexual arena, at least,

bonobos are the more appropriate ancestral model. Males and females frequently copulate face-to-face, which is an uncommon position in animals other than humans. Males usually mount females from behind, but females seem to prefer sex face-to-face. "Sometimes the female will let a male start to mount from behind," says Amy Parish, a graduate student at the University of California at Davis who's been watching female bonobo sexual behavior in several zoo colonies around the world. "And then she'll stop, and of course he's really excited, and then she continues face-to-face." Primatologists assume the female preference is dictated by her anatomy: her enlarged clitoris and sexual swellings are oriented far forward. Females presumably prefer face-to-face contact because it feels better.

"Sex is fun. Sex makes them feel good and keeps the group together."

Like humans but unlike chimps and most other animals, bonobos separate sex from reproduction. They seem to treat sex as a pleasurable activity, and they rely on it as a sort of social glue, to make or break all sorts of relationships. "Ancestral humans behaved like this," proposes Frans de Waal, an ethologist at the Yerkes Regional Primate Research Center at Emory University. "Later, when we developed the family system, the use of sex for this sort of purpose became more limited, mainly occurring within families. A lot of the things we see, like pedophilia and homosexuality, may be leftovers that some now consider unacceptable in our particular society."

Depending on your morals, watching bonobo sex play may be like watching humans at their most extreme and perverse. Bonobos seem to have sex more often and in more combinations than the average person in any culture, and most of the time bonobo sex has nothing to do with making babies. Males mount females and females sometimes mount them back; females rub against other females just for fun; males stand rump to rump and press their scrotal areas together. Even juveniles participate by rubbing their genital areas against adults, although ethologists don't think that males actually insert their penises into juvenile females. Very young animals also have sex with each other: little males suck on each other's penises or French-kiss. When two animals initiate sex, others freely join in by poking their fingers and toes into the moving parts.

One thing sex does for bonobos is decrease tensions caused by potential competition, often competition for food. Japanese primatologists observing bonobos in Zaire were the first to notice that when bonobos come across a large fruiting tree or encounter piles of provisioned sugarcane, the sight of food triggers a binge of sex. The atmosphere of this sexual free-for-all is decidedly friendly, and it eventually calms the group down. "What's striking is how rapidly the sex drops off," says Nancy Thompson-Handler of the State University of New York at Stony Brook, who has observed bonobos at a site in Zaire called Lomako. "After ten minutes, sexual behavior decreases by fifty percent." Soon the group turns from sex to feeding.

But it's tension rather than food that causes the sexual excitement. "I'm sure the more food you give them, the more

sex you'll get," says De Waal. "But it's not really the food, it's competition that triggers this. You can throw in a cardboard box and you'll get sexual behavior." Sex is just the way bonobos deal with competition over limited resources and with the normal tensions caused by living in a group. Anthropologist Frances White of Duke University, a bonobo observer at Lomako since 1983, puts it simply: "Sex is fun. Sex makes them feel good and therefore keeps the group together."

"Females rule the business. It's a good species for feminists, I think."

Sexual behavior also occurs after aggressive encounters, especially among males. After two males fight, one may reconcile with his opponent by presenting his rump and backing up against the other's testicles. He might grab the penis of the other male and stroke it. It's the male bonobo's way of shaking hands and letting everyone know that the conflict has ended amicably.

Researchers also note that female bonobo sexuality, like the sexuality of female humans, isn't locked into a monthly cycle. In most other animals, including chimps, the female's interest in sex is tied to her ovulation cycle. Chimp females sport pink swellings on their hind ends for about two weeks, signaling their fertility, and they're only approachable for sex during that time. That's not the case with humans, who show no outward signs that they are ovulating, and can mate at all phases of the cycle. Female bonobos take the reverse tack, but with similar results. Their large swellings are visible for weeks before and after their fertile periods, and there is never any discernibly wrong time to mate. Like humans, they have sex whether or not they are ovulating.

What's fascinating is that female bonobos use this boundless sexuality in all their relationships. "Females rule the business—sex and food," says De Waal. "It's a good species for feminists, I think." For instance, females regularly

use sex to cement relationships with other females. A genital-genital rub, better known as GG-rubbing by observers, is the most frequent behavior used by bonobo females to reinforce social ties or relieve tension. GG-rubbing takes a variety of forms. Often one female rolls on her back and extends her arms and legs. The other female mounts her and they rub their swellings right and left for several seconds, massaging their clitorises against each other. GG-rubbing occurs in the presence of food because food causes tension and excitement, but the intimate contact has the effect of making close friends.

Sometimes females would rather GG-rub with each other than copulate with a male. Parish filmed a 15-minute scene at a bonobo colony at the San Diego Wild Animal Park in which a male, Vernon, repeatedly solicited two females, Lisa and Loretta. Again and again he arched his back and displayed his erect penis—the bonobo request for sex. The females moved away from him, tactfully turning him down until they crept behind a tree and GG-rubbed with each other.

Unlike most primate species, in which males usually take on the dangerous task of leaving home, among bonobos females are the ones who leave the group when they reach sexual maturity, around the age of eight, and work their way into unfamiliar groups. To aid in their assimilation into a new community, the female bonobos make good use of their endless sexual favors. While watching a bonobo group at a feeding tree, White saw a young female systematically have sex with each member before feeding. "An adolescent female, presumably a recent transfer female, came up to the tree, mated with all five males, went into the tree, and solicited GG-rubbing from all the females present," says White.

Once inside the new group, a female bonobo must build a sisterhood from scratch. In groups of humans or chimps, unrelated females construct friendships through the rituals of shopping together or grooming. Bonobos do it sexually. Although pleasure may be the motivation

HIDDEN HEAT

Standing upright is not a position usually—or easily—associated with sex. Among people, at least, anatomy and gravity prove to be forbidding obstacles. Yet our two-legged stance may be the key to a distinctive aspect of human sexuality: the independence of women's sexual desires from a monthly calendar.

Males in the two species most closely related to us, chimpanzees and bonobos, don't spend a lot of time worrying, "Is she interested or not?" The answer is obvious. When ovulatory hormones reach a monthly peak in female chimps and bonobos, and their eggs are primed for fertilization, their genital area swells up, and both sexes appear to have just one thing on their mind. "These animals really turn on when this happens. Everything else is dropped," says primatologist Frederick Szalay of Hunter College in New York.

Women, however, don't go into heat. And this departure from our relatives' sexual behavior has long puzzled researchers. Clear signals of fertility and the willingness to do something about it bring major evolutionary advantages: ripe eggs lead to healthier pregnancies, which leads to more of your genes in succeeding generations, which is what evolution is all about. In addition, male chimps give females that are waving these red flags of fertility first chance at high-protein food such as meat.

So why would our ancestors give this up? Szalay and graduate student Robert Costello have a simple explanation. Women gave heat up, they say, because our ancestors stood up. Fossil footprints indicate that somewhere around 3.5 million years ago hominids—non-ape primates—began walking on two legs. "In hominids, something dictated getting up. We don't know what it was," Szalay says. "But once it did, there was a problem with the signaling system." The problem was that it didn't work. Swollen genital areas that were visible when their owners were down on all fours became hidden between the legs. The mating signal was lost.

"Uprightness meant very tough times for females working with the old ovarian cycle," Szalay says. Males wouldn't notice them, and the swellings themselves, which get quite large, must have made it hard for two-legged creatures to walk around.

Those who found a way out of this quandary, Szalay suggests, were females with small swellings but with a little less hair on their rears and a little extra fat. It would have looked a bit like the time-honored mating signal. They got more attention, and produced more offspring. "You don't start a completely new trend in signaling," Szalay says. "You have a little extra fat, a little nakedness to mimic the ancestors. If there was an ever-so-little advantage because, quite simply, you look good, it would be selected for."

And if a little nakedness and a little fat worked well, Szalay speculates, then a lot of both would work even better. "Once you start a trend in sexual signaling, crazy things happen," he notes. "It's almost like: let's escalate, let's add more. That's what happens in horns with sheep. It's a particular part of the body that brings an advantage." In a few million years human ancestors were more naked than ever, with fleshy rears not found in any other primate. Since these features were permanent, unlike the monthly ups and downs of swellings, sex was free to become a part of daily life.

It's a provocative notion, say Szalay's colleagues, but like any attempt to conjure up the past from the present, there's no real proof of cause and effect. Anthropologist Helen Fisher of the American Museum of Natural History notes that Szalay is merely assuming that fleshy buttocks evolved because they were sex signals. Yet their mass really comes from muscles, which chimps don't have, that are associated with walking. And anthropologist Sarah Blaffer Hrdy of the University of California at Davis points to a more fundamental problem: our ancestors may not have had chimplike swellings that they needed to dispense with. Chimps and bonobos are only two of about 200 primate species, and the vast majority of those species don't have big swellings. Though they are our closest relatives, chimps and bonobos have been evolving during the last 5 million years just as we have, and swollen genitals may be a recent development. The current unswollen human pattern may be the ancestral one.

"Nobody really knows what happened," says Fisher. "Everybody has an idea. You pays your money and you takes your choice."

—Joshua Fischman

behind a female-female assignation, the function is to form an alliance.

These alliances are serious business, because they determine the pecking order at food sites. Females with powerful friends eat first, and subordinate females may not get any food at all if the resource is small. When times are rough, then, it pays to have close female friends. White describes a scene at Lomako in which an adolescent female, Blanche, benefited from her established friendship with Freda. "I was following Freda and her boyfriend, and they found a tree that they didn't expect to be there. It was a small tree, heavily in fruit with one of their favorites. Freda went straight up the tree and made a food call to Blanche. Blanche came tearing over—she was quite far away—and went tearing up the tree to join Freda, and they GG-rubbed like crazy."

Alliances also give females leverage over larger, stronger males who otherwise would push them around. Females have discovered there is strength in numbers. Unlike other species of primates, such as chimpanzees or baboons (or, all too often, humans), where tensions run high between males and females, bonobo females are not afraid of males, and the sexes mingle peacefully. "What is consistently different from chimps," says Thompson-Handler, "is the composition of parties. The vast majority are mixed, so there are males and females of all different ages."

Female bonobos cannot be coerced into anything, including sex. Parish recounts an interaction between Lana and a male called Akili at the San Diego Wild Animal Park. "Lana had just been introduced into the group. For a long time she lay on the grass with a huge swelling. Akili would approach her with a big erection and hover over her. It would have been easy for him to do a mount. But he wouldn't. He just kept trying to catch her eye, hovering around her, and she would scoot around the ground, avoiding him. And then he'd try again. She went around full circle." Akili was big enough to force himself on her. Yet he refrained.

In another encounter, a male bonobo was carrying a large clump of branches. He moved up to a female and presented his erect penis by spreading his legs and arching his back. She rolled onto her back and they copulated. In the midst of

their joint ecstasy, she reached out and grabbed a branch from the male. When he pulled back, finished and satisfied, she moved away, clutching the branch to her chest. There was no tension between them, and she essentially traded copulation for food. But the key here is that the male allowed her to move away with the branch—it didn't occur to him to threaten her, because their status was virtually equal.

Although the results of sexual liberation are clear among bonobos, no one is sure why sex has been elevated to such a high position in this species and why it is restricted merely to reproduction among chimpanzees. "The puzzle for me," says De Waal, "is that chimps do all this bonding with kissing and embracing, with body contact. Why do bonobos do it in a sexual manner?" He speculates that the use of sex as a standard way to underscore relationships began between adult males and adult females as an extension of the mating process and later spread to all members of the group. But no one is sure exactly how this happened.

It is also unclear whether bonobo sexually became exaggerated only after their split from the human lineage or whether the behavior they exhibit today is the modern version of our common an-

cestor's sex play. Anthropologist Adrienne Zihlman of the University of California at Santa Cruz, who has used the evidence of fossil bones to argue that our earliest known non-ape ancestors, the australopithecines, had body proportions similar to those of bonobos, says, "The path of evolution is not a straight line from either species, but what I think is important is that the bonobo information gives us more possibilities for looking at human origins."

Some anthropologists, however, are reluctant to include the details of bonobo life, such as wide-ranging sexuality and a strong sisterhood, into scenarios of human evolution. "The researchers have all these commitments to male dominance [as in chimpanzees], and yet bonobos have egalitarian relationships," says De Waal. "They also want to see humans as unique, yet bonobos fit very nicely into many of the scenarios, making humans appear less unique."

Our divergent, non-ape path has led us away from sex and toward a culture that denies the connection between sex and social cohesion. But bonobos, with their versatile sexuality, are here to remind us that our heritage may very well include a primordial urge to make love, not war.

Apes of Wrath

Barbara Smuts

Sexual assault

Nearly 20 years ago I spent a morning dashing up and down the hills of Gombe National Park in Tanzania, trying to keep up with an energetic young female chimpanzee, the focus of my observations for the day. On her rear end she sported the small, bright pink swelling characteristic of the early stages of estrus, the period when female mammals are fertile and sexually receptive. For some hours our run through the park was conducted in quiet, but then, suddenly, a chorus of male chimpanzee pant hoots shattered the tranquility of the forest. My female rushed forward to join the males. She greeted each of them, bowing and then turning to present her swelling for inspection. The males examined her perfunctorily and resumed grooming one another, showing no further interest.

Some female primates use social bonds to escape male aggression. Can women?

At first I was surprised by their indifference to a potential mate. Then I realized that it would be many days before the female's swelling blossomed into the large, shiny sphere that signals ovulation. In a week or two, I thought, these same males will be vying intensely for a chance to mate with her.

The attack came without warning. One of the males charged toward us, hair on end, looking twice as large as my small female and enraged. As he rushed by he picked her up, hurled her to the ground, and pummeled her. She cringed and screamed. He ran off, rejoining the other males seconds later as if nothing had happened. It was not so easy for the female to return to normal. She whimpered and darted nervous glances at her attacker, as if worried that he might renew his assault.

In the years that followed I witnessed many similar attacks by males against females, among a variety of Old World primates, and eventually I found this sort of aggression against females so puzzling that I began to study it systematically— something that has rarely been done. My long-term research on olive baboons in Kenya showed that, on average, each pregnant or lactating female was attacked by an adult male about once a week and seriously injured about once a year. Estrous females were the target of even more aggression. The obvious question was, Why?

In the late 1970s, while I was in Africa among the baboons, feminists back in the United States were turning their attention to male violence against women. Their concern stimulated a wave of research documenting disturbingly high levels of battering, rape, sexual harassment, and murder. But although scientists investigated this kind of behavior from many perspectives, they mostly ignored the existence of similar behavior in other animals. My observations over the years have convinced me that a deeper understanding of male aggression against females in other species can help us understand its counterpart in our own.

Researchers have observed various male animals—including insects, birds, and mammals—chasing, threatening, and attacking females. Unfortunately, because scientists have rarely studied such aggression in detail, we do not know exactly how common it is. But the males of many of these species are most aggressive toward potential mates, which suggests that they sometimes use violence to gain sexual access.

Jane Goodall provides us with a compelling example of how males use violence to get sex. In her 1986 book, *The Chimpanzees of Gombe*, Goodall describes the chimpanzee dating game. In one of several scenarios, males gather around attractive estrous females and try to lure them away from other males for a one-on-one sexual expedition that may last for days or weeks. But females find some suitors more appealing than others and often resist the advances of less desirable males. Males often rely on aggression to counter female resistance. For example, Goodall describes how Evered, in "persuading" a reluctant Winkle to accompany him into the forest, attacked her six times over the course of five hours, twice severely.

Sometimes, as I saw in Gombe, a male chimpanzee even attacks an estrous female days before he tries to mate with her. Goodall thinks that a male uses such aggression to train a female to fear him so that she will be more likely to surrender to his subsequent sexual advances. Similarly, male hamadryas baboons, who form small harems by kidnapping child brides, maintain a tight rein over their females through threats and intimidation. If, when another male is nearby, a hamadryas female strays even a few feet from her mate, he shoots her a threatening stare and raises his brows. She usually responds by rushing to his side; if not, he bites the back of her neck. The neck bite is ritualized—the male does not actually sink his razor-sharp canines into her flesh—but the threat of injury is clear. By repeating this behavior hundreds of times, the male lays claim to particular females months or even years before mating with them. When a female comes into estrus, she solicits sex only from her harem master, and other males rarely challenge his sexual rights to her.

In some species, females remain in their birth communities their whole lives, joining forces with related females to defend vital food resources against other females

---

These chimpanzee and hamadryas males are practicing sexual coercion: male use of force to increase the chances that a female victim will mate with him, or to decrease the chances that she will mate with someone else. But sexual coercion is much more common in some primate species than in others. Orangutans and chimpanzees are the only nonhuman primates whose males in the wild force females to copulate, while males of several other species, such as vervet monkeys and bonobos (pygmy chimpanzees), rarely if ever try to coerce females sexually. Between the two extremes lie many species, like hamadryas baboons, in which males do not force copulation but nonetheless use threats and intimidation to get sex.

These dramatic differences between species provide an opportunity to investigate which factors promote or inhibit sexual coercion. For example, we might expect to find more of it in species in which males are much larger than females—and we do. However, size differences between the sexes are far from the whole story. Chimpanzee and bonobo males both have only a slight size advantage, yet while male chimps frequently resort to force, male bonobos treat the fair sex with more respect. Clearly, then, although size matters, so do other factors. In particular, the social relationships females form with other females and with males appear to be as important.

In some species, females remain in their birth communities their whole lives, joining forces with related females

to defend vital food resources against other females. In such "female bonded" species, females also form alliances against aggressive males. Vervet monkeys are one such species, and among these small and exceptionally feisty African monkeys, related females gang up against males. High-ranking females use their dense network of female alliances to rule the troop; although smaller than males, they slap persistent suitors away like annoying flies. Researchers have observed similar alliances in many other female-bonded species, including other Old World monkeys such as macaques, olive baboons, patas and rhesus monkeys, and gray langurs; New World monkeys such as the capuchin; and prosimians such as the ring-tailed lemur.

Females in other species leave their birth communities at adolescence and spend the rest of their lives cut off from their female kin. In most such species, females do not form strong bonds with other females and rarely support one another against males. Both chimpanzees and hamadryas baboons exhibit this pattern, and, as we saw earlier, in both species females submit to sexual control by males.

Some of the factors that influence female vulnerability to male sexual coercion in different species may also help explain such variation among different groups in the same species.

This contrast between female-bonded species, in which related females gang together to thwart males, and non-female-bonded species, in which they don't, breaks down when we come to the bonobo. Female bonobos, like their close relatives the chimpanzees, leave their kin and live as adults with unrelated females. Recent field studies show that these unrelated females hang out together and engage in frequent homoerotic behavior, in which they embrace face-to-face and rapidly rub their genitals together; sex

seems to cement their bonds. Examining these studies in the context of my own research has convinced me that one way females use these bonds is to form alliances against males, and that, as a consequence, male bonobos do not dominate females or attempt to coerce them sexually. How and why female bonobos, but not chimpanzees, came up with this solution to male violence remains a mystery.

Female primates also use relationships with males to help protect themselves against sexual coercion. Among olive baboons, each adult female typically forms long-lasting "friendships" with a few of the many males in her troop. When a male baboon assaults a female, another male often comes to her rescue; in my troop, nine times out of ten the protector was a friend of the female's. In return for his protection, the defender may enjoy her sexual favors the next time she comes into estrus. There is a dark side to this picture, however. Male baboons frequently threaten or attack their female friends—when, for example, one tries to form a friendship with a new male. Other males apparently recognize friendships and rarely intervene. The female, then, becomes less vulnerable to aggression from males in general, but more vulnerable to aggression from her male friends.

As a final example, consider orangutans. Because their food grows so sparsely adult females rarely travel with anyone but their dependent offspring. But orangutan females routinely fall victim to forced copulation. Female orangutans, it seems, pay a high price for their solitude.

Some of the factors that influence female vulnerability to male sexual coercion in different species may also help explain such variation among different groups in the same species. For example, in a group of chimpanzees in the Taï Forest in the Ivory Coast, females form closer bonds with one another than do females at Gombe. Taï females may consequently have more egalitarian relationships with males than their Gombe counterparts do.

Such differences between groups especially characterize humans. Among the South American Yanomamö, for instance, men frequently abduct and rape women from neighboring villages and severely beat their wives for suspected adultery. However, among the Aka people of the Central African Republic, male aggression against women has never been observed. Most human societies, of course, fall between these two extremes.

How are we to account for such variation? The same social factors that help explain how sexual coercion differs among nonhuman primates may deepen our understanding of how it varies across different groups of people. In most traditional human societies, a woman leaves her birth community when she marries and goes to live with her husband and his relatives. Without strong bonds to close female kin, she will probably be in danger of sexual coercion. The presence of close female kin, though, may protect her. For example, in a community in Belize, women live near their female relatives. A man will sometimes beat his wife if he becomes jealous or suspects her of infidelity, but when this happens, onlookers run to tell her female kin. Their arrival on the scene, combined with the presence of other glaring women, usually shames the man enough to stop his aggression.

Even in societies in which women live away from their families, kin may provide protection against abusive husbands, though how much protection varies dramatically from one society to the next. In some societies a woman's kin, including her father and brothers, consistently support her against an abusive husband, while in others they rarely help her. Why?

The key may lie in patterns of male-male relationships. Alliances between males are much more highly developed in humans than in other primates, and men frequently rely on such alliances to compete successfully against other men. They often gain more by supporting their male allies than they do by supporting female kin. In addition, men often use their alliances to defeat rivals and abduct or rape their women, as painfully illustrated by recent events in Bosnia. When women live far from close kin, among men who value their alliances with other men more than their bonds with women, they may be even more vulnerable to sexual coercion than many nonhuman primate females.

Even in societies in which women live away from their families, kin may provide protection against abusive husbands.

Like nonhuman primate females, many women form bonds with unrelated males who may protect them from other males. However, reliance on men exacts a cost—women and other primate females often must submit to control by their protectors. Such control is more elaborate in humans because allied men agree to honor one another's proprietary rights over women. In most of the world's cultures, marriage involves not only the exclusion of other men from sexual access to a man's wife—which protects the woman against rape by other men—but also entails the husband's right to complete control over his wife's sexual life, including the right to punish her for real or suspected adultery, to have sex with her whenever he wants, and even to restrict her contact with other people, especially men.

In modern industrial society, many men—perhaps most—maintain such traditional notions of marriage. At the same time, many of the traditional sources of support for women, including censure of abusive husbands by the woman's kinfolk or other community members, are eroding as more and more people end up without nearby kin or long-term neighbors. The increased vulnerability of women isolated from their birth communities, however, is not just a by-product of modern living. Historically, in highly patriarchal societies like those found in China and northern India, married women lived in households ruled by their husband's mother and male kin, and their ties with their own kin were virtually severed. In these societies, today as in the past, the husband's female kin often view the wife as a competitor for resources. Not only do they fail to support her against male coercive control, but they sometimes actively encourage it. This scenario illustrates an important point: women do not invariably support other women against men, in part because women may perceive their interests as best served through alliances with men, not with other women. When men have most of the power and control most of the resources, this looks like a realistic assessment.

Decreasing women's vulnerability to sexual coercion, then, may require fundamental changes in social alliances. Women gave voice to this essential truth with the slogan SISTERHOOD IS POWERFUL—a reference to the importance of women's ability to cooperate with unrelated women as if they were indeed sisters. However, among humans, the male-dominant social system derives support from political, economic, legal, and ideological institutions that other primates can't even dream of. Freedom from male control—including male sexual coercion—therefore requires women to form alliances with one another (and with like-minded men) on a scale beyond that shown by nonhuman primates and humans in the past. Although knowledge of other primates can provide inspiration for this task, its achievement depends on the uniquely human ability to envision a future different from anything that has gone before.

Barbara Smuts is a professor of psychology and anthropology at the University of Michigan. She has been doing fieldwork in animal behavior since the early 1970s, studying baboons, chimps, and dolphins. "In my work I combine research in animal behavior with an abiding interest in feminist perspectives on science," says Smuts. She is the author of Sex and Friendship in Baboons.

UNIT 4
The Fossil Evidence

Unit Selections

Key Points to Consider

- Under what circumstances did bipedalism evolve?

- What is the "man the hunter" hypothesis, and how might the "scavenging theory" better suit the early hominid data?

- How would you draw the early hominid family tree?

 **Links: www.dushkin.com/online/**
These sites are annotated in the World Wide Web pages.

The African Emergence and Early Asian Dispersals of the Genus *Homo*
http://www.sigmaxi.org/amsci/subject/EvoBio.html

Anthropology, Archaeology, and American Indian Sites on the Internet
http://dizzy.library.arizona.edu/users/jlcox/first.html

Long Foreground: Human Prehistory
http://www.wsu.edu:8001/vwsu/gened/learn-modules/top_longfor/lfopen-index.html

A primary focal point of this book, as well as of the whole of biological anthropology, is the search for and interpretation of fossil evidence for hominid (meaning human or humanlike) evolution. Paleoanthropologists are those who carry out this task by conducting the painstaking excavations and detailed analyses that serve as a basis for understanding our past. Every fragment found is cherished like a ray of light that may help to illuminate the path taken by our ancestors in the process of becoming "us." At least, that is what we would like to believe.

In reality, each discovery leads to further mystery, and for every fossil-hunting paleoanthropologist who thinks his or her find supports a particular theory, there are many others anxious to express their disagreement. (See "Early Hominid Fossils From Africa" by Meave Leakey and Alan Walker and "A New Human Ancestor?" by Elizabeth Culotta.)

How wonderful it would be, we sometimes think in moments of frustration over inconclusive data, if the fossils would just speak for themselves, and every primordial piece of humanity were to carry with it a self-evident explanation for its place in the evolutionary story. Paleoanthropology would then be more a quantitative problem of amassing enough material to reconstruct our ancestral development than a qualitative problem of interpreting what it all means. It would certainly be a simpler process, but would it be as interesting?

Most scientists tolerate, welcome, or even (dare it be said?) thrive on controversy, recognizing that diversity of opinion refreshes the mind, rouses students, and captures the imagination of the general public. After all, where would paleoanthropology be without the gadflies, the near-mythic heroes, and, lest we forget, the research funds they generate? Consider, for example, the issue of the differing roles played by males and females in the transition to humanity and all that it implies with regard to bipedalism, tool making, and the origin of the family. Did bipedalism really evolve in the grasslands? (See "One Giant Step for Mankind" by Michael Lemonick and Andrea Dorfman.) Should the primary theme of human evolution be summed up as "man the hunter" or "woman the gatherer?"

Not all the research and theoretical speculation taking place in the field of paleoanthropology is so controversial. Most scientists, in fact, go about their work quietly and methodically, gener-

ating hypotheses that are much less explosive and yet have the cumulative effect of enriching our understanding of the details of human evolution. In "Scavenger Hunt," for instance, Pat Shipman tells how modern technology, in the form of the scanning electron microscope, combined with meticulous detailed analysis of cut marks on fossil animal bones, can help us better understand the locomotor and food-getting adaptations of our early hominid ancestors. In one stroke, she is able to challenge the traditional "man the hunter" theme that has pervaded most early hominid research and writing and to set forth simultaneously an alternative hypothesis that will, in turn, inspire further research.

As we mull over the controversies outlined in this unit, we should not take them as reflecting an inherent weakness of the field of paleoanthropology, but rather as symbolic of its strength: the ability and willingness to scrutinize, question, and reflect (seemingly endlessly) on every bit of evidence.

Contrary to the way that the creationists would have it, an admission of doubt is not an expression of ignorance but simply a frank recognition of the imperfect state of our knowledge. If we are to increase our understanding of ourselves, we must maintain an atmosphere of free inquiry without preconceived notions and an unquestioning commitment to a particular point of view.

To paraphrase anthropologist Ashley Montagu, whereas creationism seeks certainty without proof, science seeks proof without certainty.

Early Hominid Fossils from Africa

A new species of Australopithecus, *the ancestor of* Homo,
pushes back the origins of bipedalism to some four million years ago

**by Meave Leakey
and Alan Walker**

The year was 1965. Bryan Patterson, a paleoanthropologist from Harvard University, unearthed a fragment of a fossil arm bone at a site called Kanapoi in northern Kenya. He and his colleagues knew it would be hard to make a great deal of anatomic or evolutionary sense out of a small piece of elbow joint. Nevertheless, they did recognize some features reminiscent of a species of early hominid (a hominid is any upright-walking primate) known as *Australopithecus*, first discovered 40 years earlier in South Africa by Raymond Dart of the University of the Witwatersrand. In most details, however, Patterson and his team considered the fragment of arm bone to be more like those of modern humans than the one other *Australopithecus* humerus known at the time.

The age of the Kanapoi fossil proved somewhat surprising. Although the techniques for dating the rocks where the fossil was uncovered were still fairly rudimentary, the group working in Kenya was able to show that the bone was probably older than the various *Australopithecus* specimens previously found. Despite this unusual result, however, the significance of Patterson's discovery was not to be confirmed for another 30

years. In the interim, researchers identified the remains of so many important early hominids that the humerus from Kanapoi was rather forgotten.

Yet Patterson's fossil would eventually help establish the existence of a new species of *Australopithecus*—the oldest yet to be identified—and push back the origins of upright walking to more than four million years (Myr) ago. But to see how this happened, we need to trace the steps that paleoanthropologists have taken in constructing an outline for the story of hominid evolution.

EVOLVING STORY OF EARLY HOMINIDS

Scientists classify the immediate ancestors of the genus *Homo* (which includes our own species, *Homo sapiens*) in the genus *Australopithecus*. For several decades, it was believed that these ancient hominids first inhabited the earth at least three and a half million years ago. The specimens found in South Africa by Dart and others indicated that there were at least two types of *Australopithecus—A. africanus* and *A. robustus*. The leg bones of both species suggested that they had the striding, bipedal locomotion that is a hallmark of humans among living mam-

mals. (The upright posture of these creatures was vividly confirmed in 1978 at the Laetoli site in Tanzania, where a team led by archaeologist Mary Leakey discovered a spectacular series of footprints made 3.6 Myr ago by three *Australopithecus* individuals as they walked across wet volcanic ash.) Both *A. africanus* and *A. robustus* were relatively small-brained and had canine teeth that differed from those of modern apes in that they hardly projected past the rest of the tooth row. The younger of the two species, *A. robustus*, had bizarre adaptations for chewing—huge molar and premolar teeth combined with bony crests on the skull where powerful chewing muscles would have been attached.

Paleoanthropologists identified more species of *Australopithecus* over the next several decades. In 1959 Mary Leakey unearthed a skull from yet another East African species closely related to *robustus* Skulls of these species uncovered during the past 40 years in the northeastern part of Africa, in Ethiopia and Kenya, differed considerably from those found in South Africa; as a result, researchers think that two separate *robustus*-like species—a northern one and a southern one—existed.

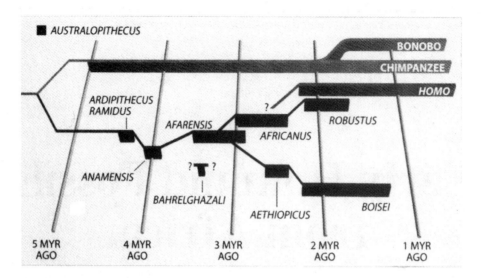

ANDREW CHRISTIE

FAMILY TREE of the hominid species known as *Australopithecus* includes a number of species that lived between roughly 4 and 1.25 Myr ago. Just over 2 Myr ago a new genus, *Homo* (which includes our own species, *Homo sapiens*), evolved from one of the species of Australopithecus.

In 1978 Donald C. Johanson, now at the Institute of Human Origins in Berkeley, Calif., along with his colleagues, identified still another species of *Australopithecus*. Johanson and his team had been studying a small number of hominid bones and teeth discovered at Laetoli, as well as a large and very important collection of specimens from the Hadar region of Ethiopia (including the famous "Lucy" skeleton). The group named the new species *afarensis*. Radiometric dating revealed that the species had lived between 3.6 and 2.9 Myr ago, making it the oldest *Australopithecus* known at the time.

This early species is probably the best studied of all the *Australopithecus* recognized so far, and it is certainly the one that has generated the most controversy over the past 20 years. The debates have ranged over many issues: whether the afarensis fossils were truly distinct from the africanus fossils from South Africa; whether there was one or several species at Hadar; whether the Tanzanian and Ethiopian fossils were of the same species; whether the fossils had been dated correctly.

But the most divisive debate concerns the issue of how extensively the bipedal *afarensis* climbed in trees. Fossils of *afarensis* include various bone and joint structures typical of tree climbers. Some

scientists argue that such characteristics indicate that these hominids must have spent at least some time in the trees. But others view these features as simply evolutionary baggage, left over from arboreal ancestors. Underlying this discussion is the question of where *Australopithecus* lived—in forests or on the open savanna.

By the beginning of the 1990s, researchers knew a fair amount about the various species of *Australopithecus* and how each had adapted to its environmental niche. A description of any one of the species would mention that the creatures were bipedal and that they had ape-size brains and large, thickly enameled teeth in strong jaws, with nonprojecting canines. Males were typically larger than females, and individuals grew and matured rapidly. But the origins of *Australopithecus* were only hinted at, because the gap between the earliest well-known species in the group (*afarensis*, from about 3.6 Myr ago) and the postulated time of the last common ancestor of chimpanzees and humans (between 5 and 6 Myr ago) was still very great. Fossil hunters had unearthed only a few older fragments of bone, tooth and jaw from the intervening 1.5 million years to indicate the anatomy and course of evolution of the very earliest hominids.

FILLING THE GAP

Discoveries in Kenya over the past several years have filled in some of the missing interval between 3.5 and 5 Myr ago. Beginning in 1982, expeditions run by the National Museums of Kenya to the Lake Turkana basin in northern Kenya began finding hominid fossils nearly 4 Myr old. But because these fossils were mainly isolated teeth—no jawbones or skulls were preserved— very little could be said about them except that they resembled the remains of *afarensis* from Laetoli. But our recent excavations at an unusual site, just inland from Allia Bay on the east side of Lake Turkana yielded more complete fossils.

The site at Allia Bay is a bone bed, where millions of fragments of weathered tooth and bone from a wide variety of animals, including hominids, spill out of the hillside. Exposed at the top of the hill lies a layer of hardened volcanic ash called the Moiti Tuff, which has been dated radiometrically to just over 3.9 Myr old. The fossil fragments lie several meters below the tuff, indicating that the remains are older than the tuff. We do not yet understand fully why so many fossils are concentrated in this spot, but we can be certain that they were deposited by the precursor of the present-day Omo River.

Today the Omo drains the Ethiopian highlands located to the north, emptying into Lake Turkana, which has no outlet. But this has not always been so. Our colleagues Frank Brown of the University of Utah and Craig Feibel of Rutgers University have shown that the ancient Omo River dominated the Turkana area for much of the Pliocene (roughly 5.3 to 1.6 Myr ago) and the early Pleistocene (1.6 to 0.7 Myr ago). Only infrequently was a lake present in the area at all. Instead, for most of the past four million years, an extensive river system flowed across the broad floodplain, proceeding to the Indian Ocean without dumping its sediments into a lake.

The Allia Bay fossils are located in one of the channels of this ancient river system. Most of the fossils collected from Allia Bay are rolled and weathered bones and teeth of aquatic animals—fish, crocodiles, hippopotamuses and the like—that were damaged during transport down the river from some distance away. But some of the fossils are much better preserved; these come from the animals that lived on or near the riverbanks. Among these creatures are several different species of leaf-eating monkeys, related to modern colobus monkeys, as well as antelopes whose living relatives favor closely wooded areas. Reasonably well preserved hominid fossils can also be found here, suggesting that, at least occasionally, early hominids inhabited a riparian habitat.

Where do these *Australopithecus* fossils fit in the evolutionary history of hominids? The jaws and teeth from Allia Bay, as well as a nearly complete radius (the outside bone of the forearm) from the nearby sediments of Sibilot just to the north, show an interesting mixture of characteristics. Some of the traits are primitive ones—that is, they are ancestral features thought to be present before the split occurred between the chimpanzee and human lineages. Yet these bones also share characteristics seen in later hominids and are therefore said to have more advanced features. As our team continues to unearth more bones and teeth at Allia Bay, these new fossils add to our knowledge of the wide range of traits present in early hominids.

RETURN TO KANAPOI

Across Lake Turkana, some 145 kilometers (about 90 miles) south of Allia Bay, lies the site of Kanapoi, where our story began. One of us (Leakey) has mounted expeditions from the National Museums of Kenya to explore the sediments located southwest of Lake Turkana and to document the faunas present during the earliest stages of the basin's history. Kanapoi, virtually unexplored since Patterson's day, has proved to be one of the most rewarding sites in the Turkana region.

A series of deep erosion gullies, known as badlands, has exposed the sediments at Kanapoi. Fossil hunting is difficult here, though, because of a carapace of lava pebbles and gravel that makes it hard to spot small bones and teeth. Studies of the layers of sediment, also carried out by Feibel, reveal that the fossils here have been preserved by deposits from a river ancestral to the present-day Kerio River, which once flowed into the Turkana basin and emptied into an ancient lake we call Lonyumun. This lake reached its maximum size about 4.1 Myr ago and thereafter shrank as it filled with sediments.

Excavations at Kanapoi have primarily yielded the remains of carnivore meals, so the fossils are rather fragmentary. But workers at the site have also recovered two nearly complete lower jaws, one complete upper jaw and lower face, the upper and lower thirds of a tibia (the larger bone of the lower leg), bits of skull and several sets of isolated teeth. After careful study of the fossils from both Allia Bay and Kanapoi—including Patterson's fragment of an arm bone—we felt that in details of anatomy, these specimens were different enough from previously known hominids to warrant designating a new species. So in 1995, in collaboration with both Feibel and Ian McDougall of the Australian National University, we named this new species *Australopithecus anamensis*, drawing on the Turkana word for lake (*anam*) to refer to both the present and ancient lakes.

To establish the age of these fossils, we relied on the extensive efforts of Brown, Feibel and McDougall, who have been investigating the paleogeographic history of the entire lake basin. If there study of the basin's development is correct, the *ana-*

mensis fossils should be between 4.2 and 3.9 Myr old. Currently McDougall is working to determine the age of the so-called Kanapoi Tuff—the layer of volcanic ash that covers most of the fossils at this site. We expect that once McDougall successfully ascertains the age of the tuff, we will be confident in both the age of the fossils and Brown's and Feibel's understanding of the history of the lake basin.

A major question in paleoanthropology today is how the anatomic mosaic of the early hominids evolved. By comparing the nearly contemporaneous Allia Bay and Kanapoi collections of *anamensis*, we can piece together a fairly accurate picture of certain aspects of the species, even though we have not yet uncovered a complete skull.

The jaws of *anamensis* are primitive—the sides sit close together and parallel to each other (as in modern apes), rather than widening at the back of the mouth (as in later hominids, including humans). In its lower jaw, *anamensis* is also chimp-like in terms of the shape of the region where the left and right sides of the jaw meet (technically known as the mandibular symphysis).

Teeth from *anamensis*, however, appear more advanced. The enamel is relatively thick, as it is in all other species of *Australopithecus*; in contrast, the tooth enamel of African great apes is much thinner. The thickened enamel suggests *anamensis* had already adapted to a changed diet—possibly much harder food—even though its jaws and some skull features were still very apelike. We also know that *anamensis* had only a tiny external ear canal. In this regard, it is more like chimpanzees and unlike all later hominids, including humans, which have large external ear canals. (The size of the external canal is unrelated to the size of the fleshy ear.)

The most informative bone of all the ones we have uncovered from this new hominid is the nearly complete tibia—the larger of the two bones in the lower leg. The tibia is revealing because of its important role in weight bearing: the tibia of a biped is distinctly different from the tibia of an animal that walks on all four legs. In size and practically all details of the knee and ankle joints, the tibia found at Kanapoi closely resembles the one from the fully bi-

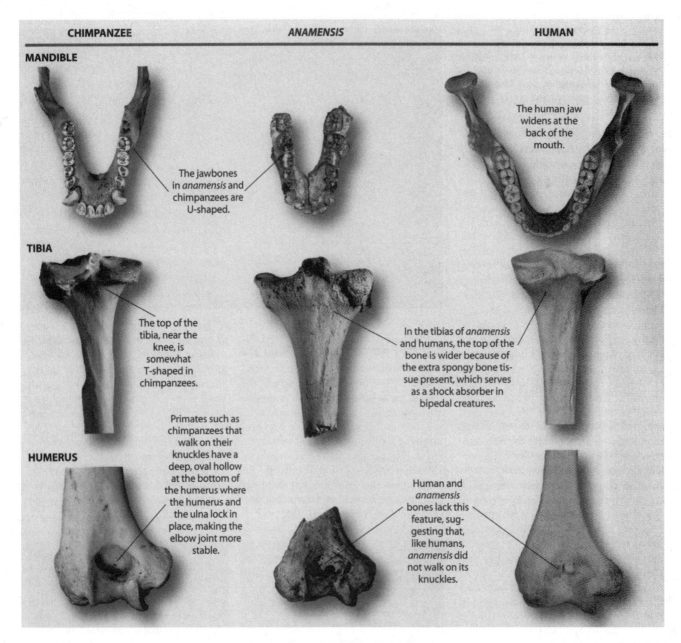

| CHIMPANZEE | ANAMENSIS | HUMAN |

MANDIBLE

The jawbones in *anamensis* and chimpanzees are U-shaped.

The human jaw widens at the back of the mouth.

TIBIA

The top of the tibia, near the knee, is somewhat T-shaped in chimpanzees.

In the tibias of *anamensis* and humans, the top of the bone is wider because of the extra spongy bone tissue present, which serves as a shock absorber in bipedal creatures.

HUMERUS

Primates such as chimpanzees that walk on their knuckles have a deep, oval hollow at the bottom of the humerus where the humerus and the ulna lock in place, making the elbow joint more stable.

Human and *anamensis* bones lack this feature, suggesting that, like humans, *anamensis* did not walk on its knuckles.

ALAN WALKER; © NATIONAL MUSEUMS OF KENYA (*chimpanzee and* anamensis); VIDEO SURGERY *Photo Researchers, Inc.* (*human*)

FOSSILS from *anamensis* (*center*) share features in common with both humans (*right*) and modern chimpanzees (*left*). Scientists use the similarities and differences among these species to determine their interrelationships and thereby piece together the course of hominid evolution since the lineages of chimpanzees and humans split some five or six million years ago.

pedal *afarensis* found at Hadar, even though the latter specimen is nearly a million years younger.

Fossils of other animals collected at Kanapoi point to a somewhat different paleoecological scenario from the setting across the lake at Allia Bay. The channels of the river that laid down the sediments at Kanapoi were probably lined with narrow stretches of forest that grew close to the riverbanks in otherwise open country. Researchers have recovered the remains of

the same spiral-horned antelope found at Allia Bay that very likely lived in dense thickets. But open-country antelopes and hartebeest appear to have lived at Kanapoi as well, suggesting that more open savanna prevailed away from the rivers. These results offer equivocal evidence regarding the preferred habitat of *anamensis:* we know that bushland was present at both sites that have yielded fossils of the species, but there are clear signs of more diverse habitats at Kanapoi.

AN EVEN OLDER HOMINID?

At about the same time that we were finding new hominids at Allia Bay and Kanapoi, a team led by our colleague Tim D. White of the University of California at Berkeley discovered fossil hominids in Ethiopia that are even older than *anamensis*. In 1992 and 1993 White led an expedition to the Middle Awash area of Ethiopia, where his team uncovered hominid fossils at a site known as

Aramis. The group's finds include isolated teeth, a piece of baby's mandible (the lower jaw), fragments from an adult's skull and some arm bones, all of which have been dated to around 4.4 Myr ago. In 1994, together with his colleagues Berhane Asfaw of the Paleoanthropology Laboratory in Addis Ababa and Gen Suwa of the University of Tokyo, White gave these fossils a new name: *Australopithecus ramidus*. In 1995 the group renamed the fossils, moving them to a new genus, *Ardipithecus*. Other fossils buried near the hominids, such as seeds and the bones of forest monkeys and antelopes, strongly imply that these hominids, too, lived in a closed-canopy woodland.

This new species represents the most primitive hominid known—a link between the African apes and *Australopithecus*. Many of the *Ardipithecus ramidus* fossils display similarities to the anatomy of the modern African great apes, such as thin dental enamel and strongly built arm bones. In other features, though—such as the opening at the base of the skull, technically known as the foramen magnum, through which the spinal cord connects to the brain—the fossils resemble later hominids.

Describing early hominids as either primitive or more advanced is a complex issue. Scientists now have almost decisive molecular evidence that humans and chimpanzees once had a common ancestor and that this lineage had previously split from gorillas. This is why we often use the two living species of chimpanzee (*Pan troglodytes* and *P. paniscus*) to illustrate ancestral traits. But we must remember that since their last common ancestor with humans, chimpanzees have had exactly the same amount of time to evolve as humans have. Determining which features were present in the last common ancestor of humans and chimpanzees is not easy.

But *Ardipithecus*, with its numerous chimplike features, appears to have taken the human fossil record back close to the time of the chimp-human split. More recently, White and his group have found parts of a single *Ardipithecus* skeleton in the Middle Awash region. As White and his team extract these exciting new fossils from the enclosing stone, reconstruct them and prepare them for study, the paleoanthropological community eagerly anticipates the publication of the group's analysis of these astonishing finds.

But even pending White's results, new *Australopithecus* fossil discoveries are offering other surprises, particularly about where these creatures lived. In 1995 a team led by Michel Brunet of the University of Poitiers announced the identification in Chad of *Australopithecus* fossils believed to be about 3.5 Myr old. The new fossils are very fragmentary—only the front part of a lower jaw and isolated tooth. In 1996, however, Brunet and his colleagues designated a new species for their specimen: *A. bahrelghazali*. Surprisingly, these fossils were recovered far from either eastern or southern Africa, the only areas where *Australopithecus* had been found until now. The site, in the Bahr el Ghazal region of Chad, lies 2,500 kilometers west of the western part of the Rift Valley, thus extending the range of *Australopithecus* well into the center of Africa.

The *bahrelghazali* fossils debunk a hypothesis about human evolution postulated in the pages of *Scientific American* by Yves Coppens of the College of France [see "East Side Story: The Origin of Humankind," May 1994]; ironically, Coppens is now a member of Brunet's team. Coppens's article proposed that the formation of Africa's Rift Valley subdivided a single ancient species, isolating the ancestors of hominids on the east side from the ancestors of modern apes on the west side. In general, scientists believe such geographical isolation can foster the development of new species by prohibiting continued interbreeding among the original populations. But the new Chad fossils show that early hominids did live west of the Rift Valley. The geographical separation of apes and hominids previously apparent in the fossil record may be more the result of accidental circumstances of geology and discovery than the species' actual ranges.

The fossils of *anamensis* that we have identified should also provide some answers in the long-standing debate over whether early *Australopithecus* species lived in wooded areas or on the open savanna. The outcome of this discussion has important implications: for many years, paleoanthropologists have accepted that upright-walking behavior originated on the savanna, where it most likely provided benefits such as keeping the hot sun off the back or freeing hands for carrying food. Yet our evidence suggests that the earliest bipedal hominid known to date lived at least part of the time in wooded areas. The discoveries of the past several years represent a remarkable spurt in the sometimes painfully slow process of uncovering human evolutionary past. But clearly there is still much more to learn.

FURTHER READING

Australopithecus Ramidus, a New Species of Early Hominid from Aramis, Ethiopia. Tim D. White, Gen Suwa and Berhane Asfaw in *Nature*, Vol. 371, pages 306–312; September 22, 1994.

New Four-Million-Year-Old Hominid Species from Kanapoi and Allia Bay, Kenya. Meave G. Leakey, Craig S. Feibel, Ian McDougall and Alan Walker in *Nature*, Vol. 376, pages 565–571; August 17, 1995.

From Lucy to Language. Donald C. Johanson and Blake Edgar. Peter Nevraumont, Simon & Schuster, 1996.

Reconstructing Human Origins: A Modern Synthesis. Glenn C. Conroy. W. W. Norton, 1997.

THE AUTHORS

MEAVE LEAKEY and ALAN WALKER, together with Leakey's husband, Richard, have collaborated for many years on the discovery and analysis of early hominid fossils from Kenya. Leakey is head of the division of paleontology at the National Museums of Kenya in Nairobi. Walker is Distinguished Professor of anthropology and biology at Pennsylvania State University. He is a MacArthur Fellow and a member of the American Academy of Arts and Sciences.

One Giant Step for Mankind

**Meet your newfound ancestor, a chimplike forest creature
that stood up and walked 5.8 million years ago**

By Michael D. Lemonick and Andrea Dorfman

Though this all was possible

The region of Ethiopia called the Middle Awash, some 140 miles northeast of the capital of Addis Ababa, is a hot, harsh and inhospitable place—a rocky desert punctuated by tree-lined rivers, the occasional lake and patches of lava that are slowly being buried by sediments flushed out of the hills by the torrential rains that come along twice a year.

But between 5 million and 6 million years ago, the landscape here was very different. The same tectonic forces that racked the region with earthquakes and volcanic eruptions had also thrust the land up as much as a mile higher than it is today. As a result, the area was cooler and wetter and overgrown with trees, bushes and patches of grass. These fertile woodlands were rich in wildlife. Primitive elephants, giant bears, horses, rhinos, pigs, rats and monkeys lived here, along with dozens of other mammal species long since extinct.

And it was here too that nature indulged in what was perhaps her greatest evolutionary experiment. For it was in eastern Africa at about this time that a new type of primate arose—an animal not so different from its apelike ancestors except in one crucial respect: this creature stood on two legs instead of scurrying along chimplike on all fours. Its knuckle-walking cousins would stay low to the ground and never get much smarter. But while it wouldn't happen until millions of years in the future, this

new primate's evolutionary descendants would eventually develop a large, complex brain. And from that would spring all of civilization, from Mesopotamia to Mozart to *Who Wants to Be a Millionaire*.

That's the broad outline, anyway. While this view of human evolution has generally been accepted by scientists for decades, no one has yet been able to say precisely when that first evolutionary step on the road to humanity happened, nor what might have triggered it.

But a discovery reported last week in the journal *Nature* has brought paleontologists tantalizingly close to answering both these questions. Working as part of an international team led by U.S. and Ethiopian scientists, a graduate student named Yohannes Haile-Selassie (no relation to the Emperor), enrolled at the University of California, Berkeley, has found the remains of what appears to be the most ancient human ancestor ever discovered. It's a chimp-size creature that lived in the Ethiopian forests between 5.8 million and 5.2 million years ago—nearly a million and a half years earlier than the previous record holder and very close to the time when humans and chimps first went their separate evolutionary ways.

"Having a fossil in this region of time, very near the divergence point, is really exciting," says anthropologist C. Owen Lovejoy of Ohio's Kent State University. "Going all the way back to Darwin, people have speculated how, when and

why humans stood up on two legs. For paleontologists, this find is a dream come true."

As is often the case with discoveries like this, Haile-Selassie was not specifically looking for the things he found. He had set out to better understand how the ancient ecosystems worked and evolved. "I didn't even think about finding hominids," he says. "All I wanted to do was collect enough vertebrate bones so that I could write my dissertation." In December 1997, though, at a place called Alayla, he spotted a piece of jawbone lying on the rock-strewn ground. "I picked up the mandible less than five minutes after we got there," he recalls, "but didn't realize I had something really special until a year later, when we found some more bones and I started the serious analysis."

In all, the team eventually found 11 specimens—from at least five different individuals—in a cluster of sites, including Haile-Selassie's partial lower jaw with associated teeth, several hand and foot bones, and pieces of three arm bones and a collarbone. Luckily, the fossils were trapped in sediments that were sandwiched between layers of volcanic ash, whose age can be accurately gauged by a technique known as argon-argon dating. (This layering is still visible in places that have not been so heavily eroded, enabling the scientists to trace the area's geologic history.) The verdict, confirmed by a second dating method and by the other primitive animals found with the hominid remains: most of the fossils are between 5.6 million and 5.8 million years old, although one toe bone is a few hundred thousand years younger.

It was the detailed anatomy of these fragmentary fossils, especially the teeth, that convinced Haile-Selassie that he had discovered a new human ancestor. Although apelike, the lower canines and upper premolars, in particular, display certain traits found only in the teeth of later hominids—the term scientists use to describe ourselves and our non-ape ancestors. They also differ in shape from the teeth of all known fossil and modern apes. Even the way in which the teeth had been worn down was telling. Explains Haile-Selassie's thesis adviser, Berkeley paleontologist Tim White: "Apes all sharpen their upper canines as they chew. Hominids don't." The new creature's back teeth are larger than a chimp's too, while the front teeth are narrower, suggesting that its diet included a variety of fibrous foods, rather than the fruits and soft leaves that chimps prefer.

When Haile-Selassie compared the newly discovered bones and teeth with those of *Ardipithecus ramidus*, a 4.4 million-year-old hominid found in the Middle Awash in the early 1990s that was the previous record holder, he realized that the two creatures were very similar. But the older one's teeth, while different from an ape's, do have a number of characteristics that are decidedly more apelike than those of the younger hominid.

On the basis of these minor but distinctive differences, Haile-Selassie decided to classify the new human ancestor as a subspecies, or variant, of *ramidus* and has given it the name *Ardipithecus ramidus kadabba*. (The name is derived from the local Afar language. *Ardi* means ground or floor; *ramid* means root; and *kadabba* means basal family ancestor. In accordance with the sometimes bizarre nomenclature of science, the younger creature now gets renamed *Ardipithecus ramidus*.)

Haile-Selassie and his colleagues haven't collected enough bones yet to reconstruct with great precision what

kadabba looked like. But they do know it was about the size of modern common chimpanzees, which when standing average about 4 ft. tall. That makes it roughly the same size as its close relative *A. ramidus ramidus* and about 20% taller than Lucy, the famous 3.2 million-year-old human ancestor discovered about 50 miles away in 1974 that is even further along the evolutionary track. The size of *kadabba's* brain and the relative proportions of its arms and legs were probably chimplike as well.

But unlike a chimp or any of the other modern apes that amble along on four limbs, *kadabba* almost certainly walked upright much of the time. The inch-long toe bone makes that clear. Two-legged primates (modern humans included) propel themselves forward by leaving the front part of their foot on the ground and lifting the heel. This movement, referred to as toeing off, causes the bones in the middle of the foot to take on a distinctive shape—a shape that is readily apparent in the ancient toe bone. "If you compare a chimp's foot bones with its hand bones, they look the same because they're used for the same thing"—that is, for grasping—Haile-Selassie explains. "Hominid fingers and toes don't look alike at all."

Exactly how this hominid walked is still something of a mystery, though with a different skeletal structure, its gait would have been unlike ours. Details of *kadabba's* lifestyle remain speculative too, but many of its behaviors undoubtedly resembled those of chimpanzees today. It probably still spent some time in trees. It probably lived in large social groups that would include both sexes. And rather than competing with one another for mates, the males may well have banded together to defend the troop against predators, forage for food and even hunt for game.

But that *kadabba* walked upright at all is hugely significant. Paleontologists have suspected for nearly 200 years that bipedalism was probably the key evolutionary transition that split the human line off from the apes, and fossil discoveries as far back as Java Man in the 1890s supported that notion. The astonishingly complete skeleton of Lucy, with its clearly apelike skull but upright pos-

ture, cemented the idea a quarter-century ago. *we adopted to new conditions we adapted for safety.*

What's been much tougher to pin down is just why two-leggedness arose. The conventional wisdom has long focused on the fact that eastern Africa became significantly dryer about the time that humans first evolved. The change would have tended to favor grasslands over forests, and, so went the theory, our ancestors changed to take advantage of the new conditions. We learned to walk upright so that we could see over the tall grasses to spot predators coming; an upright posture, moreover, would offer a much smaller target for the oppressive heat of the grassland sun, and a larger target for cooling breezes.

The only trouble with this theory is that it's wrong. The earliest humans, it turns out, didn't live in grasslands. Dry climate or not, a companion paper published last week in *Nature* shows on the basis of the other fossilized flora and fauna, as well as the chemistry of the ancient soil, that *Ardipithecus ramidus kadabba* lived in a well-forested environment. That's also the case with other extremely ancient hominids found during the past several years, including *Ardipithecus ramidus* and a species called *Orrorin tugenensis,* announced last December by French and Kenyan researchers. And while the ability to walk on two legs probably started out as an increasingly frequent behavior, evolution demands an explanation for why it persisted. On first blush, bipedalism just doesn't make much sense. For our earliest ancestors, it would have been slower than walking on all fours, while requiring the same amount of energy. Says Lovejoy bluntly: "It's unnatural. It's bizarre." *Inefficiency if it never mind boggling*

Yet the advantages of walking upright *to* were somehow so great that the behavior *under* endured through thousands of genera- *stand* tions. Indeed, the anatomy of our ances- *and* tors underwent all sorts of basic changes *explain* to accommodate this new way of moving. Many of the changes help the body stay balanced by stabilizing the weight-bearing leg and keeping the upper torso centered over the feet. Lovejoy, who studies the anatomy and biomechanics of

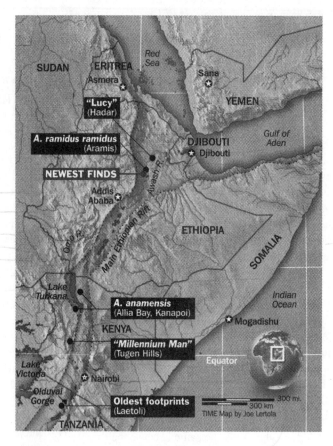

DISCOVERY ZONE Africa's Rift Valley has yielded most of our earliest ancestors

locomotion, thinks the changes may have improved coordination as well. "To walk upright in a habitual way, you have to do so in synchrony," he says. "If the ligaments and muscles are out of synch, that leads to injuries. And then you'd be cheetah meat."

By far the most crucial changes, according to Lovejoy, were those in the spine. The distance between chest and pelvis is longer in humans than in apes, allowing the lower spine to curve, which locates the upper body over the pelvis for balance. The pelvis grew broader, meanwhile, and humans developed a hip joint and associated muscles that stabilize the pelvis. Explains Lovejoy: "That's why a chimp sways from side to side as it walks upright and humans don't."

Changes also had to take place in the femur, or thighbone. For example, the femoral neck—the bent portion at the top of the bone—is broader in humans than it is in apes, which improves balance. The human knee is specialized for walking upright too: to compensate for the thigh-

bone's being at an angle, there's a lump, or groove, at the end of the femur that prevents the patella from sliding off the joint. "A chimp doesn't have this groove because there is no angulation between the hip and the knee," Lovejoy says. "This change says you're a biped."

Finally, there's the foot. "What's important here is the arch," Lovejoy says. "It's a really important shock absorber. It's like wearing a good pair of running shoes." In order to create that arch, the chimp's opposable great toe became aligned with the others, and the toe's muscles and ligaments, which had been used for grasping and climbing, were repositioned under the foot. "The shape of the big toe is indicative of this. You can see it in Lucy's species," Lovejoy says, but not in the bone Haile-Selassie found, because it's from a different toe. "What we can see [in the new discovery's foot] is that the base of the bone adjacent to the knuckle has a distinct angle, showing that the creature walked step after step

after step with its heel off the ground, using the front of its foot as a platform."

That's how it walked. *Why* it walked is tougher to understand, since motivation leaves behind no physical remains. But armed with knowledge about our ancestors' physical attributes and the environment that surrounded them, scientists have come up with several theories. Anthropologist Henry McHenry, of the University of California, Davis, for example, champions the idea that climate variation was part of the picture after all. When Africa dried out, say McHenry and his colleague Peter Rodman, the change left patches of forest widely spaced between open savannah. The first hominids lived mostly in these forest refuges but couldn't find enough food in any one place. Learning to walk on two legs helped them travel long distances over ground to the next woodsy patch, and thus to more food.

Meave Leakey, head of paleontology at the National Museums of Kenya and a

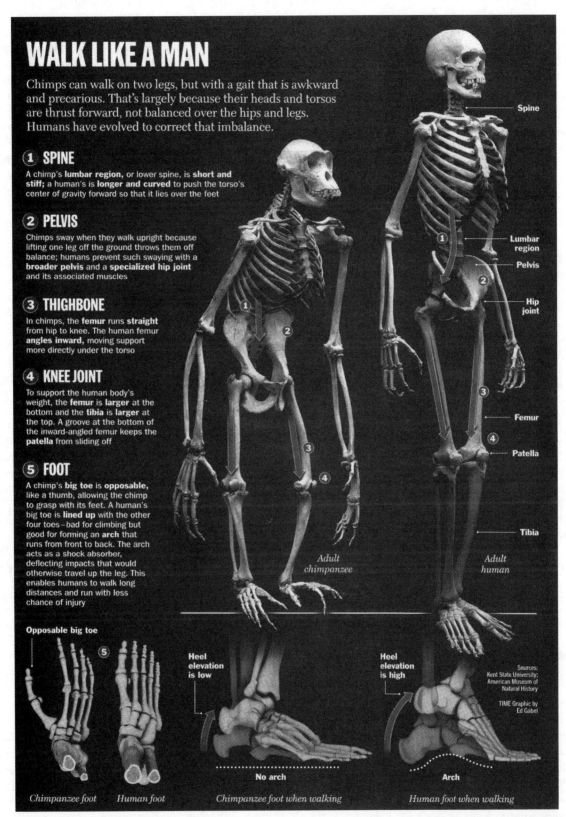

WALK LIKE A MAN

Chimps can walk on two legs, but with a gait that is awkward and precarious. That's largely because their heads and torsos are thrust forward, not balanced over the hips and legs. Humans have evolved to correct that imbalance.

① SPINE

A chimp's **lumbar region,** or lower spine, is **short and stiff;** a human's is **longer and curved** to push the torso's center of gravity forward so that it lies over the feet

② PELVIS

Chimps sway when they walk upright because lifting one leg off the ground throws them off balance; humans prevent such swaying with a **broader pelvis** and a **specialized hip joint** and its associated muscles

③ THIGHBONE

In chimps, the **femur** runs **straight** from hip to knee. The human femur **angles inward,** moving support more directly under the torso

④ KNEE JOINT

To support the human body's weight, the **femur** is **larger** at the bottom and the **tibia** is **larger** at the top. A groove at the bottom of the inward-angled femur keeps the **patella** from sliding off

⑤ FOOT

A chimp's **big toe** is **opposable,** like a thumb, allowing the chimp to grasp with its feet. A human's big toe is **lined up** with the other four toes—bad for climbing but good for forming an **arch** that runs from front to back. The arch acts as a shock absorber, deflecting impacts that would otherwise travel up the leg. This enables humans to walk long distances and run with less chance of injury

Spine

Lumbar region

Pelvis

Hip joint

Femur

Patella

Tibia

Adult chimpanzee

Adult human

Opposable big toe

Heel elevation is low

Heel elevation is high

Sources:
Kent State University;
American Museum of
Natural History

TIME Graphic by
Ed Gabel

No arch

Arch

Chimpanzee foot *Human foot*   *Chimpanzee foot when walking*   *Human foot when walking*

TIM WHITE

member of the world's most famous fossil-hunting family, suspects the change in climate rewarded bipedalism for a different reason. Yes, the dryer climate made for more grassland, but our early ancestors, she argues, spent much of their time not in dense forest or on the savannah but in an environment with some trees, dense shrubbery and a bit of grass. "And if you're moving into more open country with grasslands and bushes and things like this, and eating a lot of fruits and berries coming off low bushes, there is a hell of an advantage to be able to reach higher. That's why the gerenuk [a type of antelope] evolved its long neck and stands on its hind legs, and why the giraffe evolved its long neck. There's strong pressure to be able to reach a wider range of levels."

But for Kent State's Lovejoy, the real answer is sex. Males who were best at walking upright would get more of it, leading to more offspring who were good on two legs, who in turn got more sex. His reasoning, first proposed nearly two decades ago, goes like this: like many modern Americans, monkeys and apes of both genders work outside the home—in the latter case, searching for food. Early humans, though, discovered the *Leave It to Beaver* strategy: if males handled the breadwinning, females could stay closer to home and devote more time to rearing the children, thus giving them a better shot at growing up strong and healthy.

And if you're going to bring home the bacon, or the Miocene equivalent, it helps to have your hands free to carry it. Over time, female apes would choose to mate only with those males who brought them food—presumably the ones who were best adapted for upright walking. Is that the way it actually happened? Maybe, but we may never know for sure. Leakey, for one, is unconvinced. "There are all sorts of hypotheses," she says, "and they are all fairy tales really because you can't prove anything."

If paleontologists argue about why bipedalism evolved, they're even more contentious over the organization of the human family tree. According to Haile-Selassie and his colleagues, the picture looks pretty straightforward from about 5.8 million years ago to the present. First comes *Ardipithecus ramidus kadabba,* the newest find. Then, more than a million years later, its descendant, the newly renamed *Ardipithecus ramidus*, appears. After that comes a new genus, called *Australopithecus* (where Lucy belongs), and finally, about 2 million years ago, the first members of the human genus Homo.

But not everyone buys the story. Indeed, the French and Kenyan team that presented a 6 million-year-old fossil last December insists that theirs, known as *Orrorin tugenensis* (or, more familiarly, Millennium Man because it was announced in 2000), is the true human ancestor and that *Ardipithecus* is nothing more than a monkey's uncle—or a chimp's great-great-grandfather, anyway. They even dismiss Lucy and her close kin, about as firmly entrenched in the human lineage as you can get, as evolutionary dead ends that left no living descendants.

No one disputes that this competing ancestor is 6 million years old and thus more ancient than *Ardipithecus*. What's still to be proved is that it's a hominid. Says Leakey: "If you read their paper, almost everything they say about the teeth suggests it's more apelike." And when they get to the femur, she says, they present no evidence disproving that it walked on all fours. Haile-Selassie makes precisely the same point. But Brigitte Senut of the National Museum of Natural History in Paris and Martin Pickford, chairman of paleoanthropology and prehistory at the Collège de France, co-leaders of the team that found *Orrorin,* dismiss the criticisms. Additional fossils found just last March, they say, along with the more detailed analysis they now have in hand of the earlier bones, will prove their case. "We are absolutely delighted about it," says Senut. "We had the possibility to show the evidence to some colleagues in South Africa recently, and just looking at the cast they said, '"Fantastic, it's a biped! And a better biped than Lucy.'"

Even if they're right, though, establishing the precise path of human descent might be very hard. For most of the past 6 million years, multiple hominid species roamed the earth at the same time—including a mere 30,000 years ago, when modern humans and Neanderthals still coexisted. We still can't figure out exactly how Neanderthals relate to the human family; it's all the more difficult to know where these newly discovered species, with far fewer fossil remains to study, belong.

In the case of *Ardipithecus,* says Donald Johanson, professor of anthro-pology and director of the Institute of Human Origins at Arizona State University (and the man who discovered Lucy back in 1974), "when you put 5.5 million-year-old fossils together with 4.4 million-year-old ones as members of the same species, you're not taking into consideration that these could be twigs on a tree. Everything's been forced into a straight line." Beyond that, he's dubious about categorizing the 5.2 million-year-old toe bone with the rest of the fossils: not only is it separated in time by several hundred thousand years, but it was also found some 10 miles away from the rest.

If *Orrorin* turns out to be a hominid, the same skepticism will apply to any claims about its pivotal position on the family tree. According to University of Tokyo paleontologist Gen Suwa, a co-discoverer of the 4.4. million-year-old *Ardipithecus ramidus ramidus, Orrorin* could well be ancestral to the new *Ardipithecus* remains, rather than the other way around. "There is nothing in the fossils," he says, "that would preclude such a position. But which side of the chimp-hominid split *Orrorin* occupies can be determined only by further analyses and new finds." Indeed, suggests Haile-Selassie, while *Orrorin* may be one of the earliest chimps or an ape that became extinct, it could also turn out to be the last common ancestor of humans and chimps—a creature paleontologists have been dreaming of finding for decades.

One of the most intriguing questions the new discoveries raise, says Bernard Wood, a professor of human origins at George Washington University, is whether bipedalism should still be considered the defining characteristic of being human. After all, all birds have wings, but not all creatures with wings are birds. It's already clear that eastern Africa was bubbling with evolutionary experiments 6 million years ago. Maybe two-legged walking evolved independently in several branches of the primate family. Says Wood: "This might be the first example of a creature it's not possible to label as hominid ancestor or chimp ancestor. But that doesn't make it the last common ancestor of both. I think it's going to be very hard to pin the tail on that donkey."

A WALK THROUGH HUMAN EVOLUTION

The newest fossils have brought scientists tantalizingly close to the time when humans first walked upright—splitting off from chimpanzees. Their best guess is that it happened at least 6 million years ago

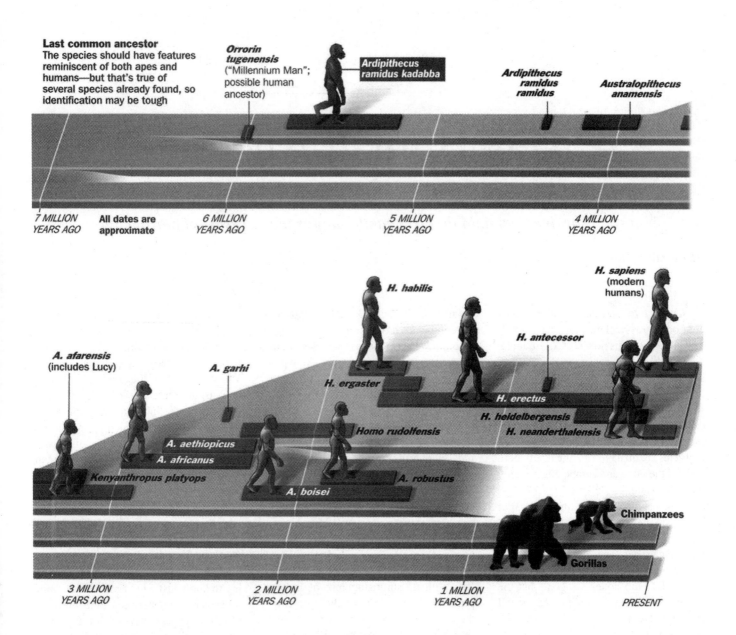

In the end, that may be the most exciting thing about these latest discoveries from the human race's birthing ground. Not that long ago, paleontologists were pretty certain we started on the road to becoming human by standing upright on the grassy savannah. Now that science is actually bringing in hard evidence, the story is getting more complicated—and more interesting. Clearly, there are still plenty of questions to ask, and plenty of surprises left to uncover, in the ancient sediments of eastern Africa.

—With reporting by Simon Robinson/ Nairobi

From *Time*, July 23, 2001, pp. 54-61. © 2001 by Time Inc. Reprinted by permission.

A New Human Ancestor?

Ethiopian fossils reveal a new branch on the hominid family tree:
a small-brained hominid that is a candidate for the ancestor of our lineage

Elizabeth Culotta

Because of this, This

Is A. garhi Part of Homo or not

About two and half million years ago, on a grassy plain bordering a shallow lake in what is now eastern Ethiopia, a humanlike creature began dismembering an antelope carcass. Nothing remains of the hominid, but the antelope bones show that it wrenched a leg off the carcass, then used a stone tool to slice off the meat and smash the bone. After several tries, it managed to break off both ends of the bone and scrape out the juicy marrow inside.

At just about the same time, two other hominids died near the lake. One, perhaps 1.4 meters tall, had long legs and a human gait but long, apelike forearms. The other, a male, lay some distance away. His limb bones are gone, but the remains of his skull show he had a small brain, big teeth, and an apelike face.

These new fossils give different glimpses of each hominid, and no one can be sure all three belonged to the same species. But even if not, their details are starting to fill in a mysterious chapter of human prehistory. According to the international team that made all three discoveries, the big-toothed skull represents an unusual new species that is the best candidate for the ancestor of our own genus, *Homo*. Not everyone in the contentious field of paleoanthropology agrees, but the new species, which Ethi-

opian anthropologist Berhane Asfaw and his colleagues have named *Australopithecus garhi* (*garhi* means "surprise" in the language spoken by the local Afar people), is certain to shake up views of the transition from the apelike australopithecines to humankind. And the scored bones from the first hominid's feast are the earliest recorded evidence of hominids butchering animals, bolstering the notion that meat eating was important in human evolution.

"They've put together a whole package here, so that you can say a fair amount about a time we don't know much about," says anthropologist F. Clark Howell of the University of California (UC), Berkeley. With its surprising mix of traits—primitive face and unusually big teeth—the new australopithecine doesn't match the profile many researchers expected for a human ancestor at this stage. "It's very exciting," says paleoanthropologist Alan Walker of Pennsylvania State University in University Park. "Until now it's all been just scraps of teeth and bits of mandible from this time. And this [morphology] is a surprise."

But this rare glimpse of a murky period in human evolution raises as many questions as it answers. *A. garhi* has few traits that definitively link it to *Homo*, and like other hominids from the same

period, it may simply be an evolutionary dead end that brings us only slightly closer to understanding our own ancestors, says paleoanthropologist Bernard Wood of George Washington University in Washington, D.C. The debate is complicated by the fact that paleoanthropologists are deeply divided over who the first humans, or members of *Homo*, were, and indeed what makes a human. "These are magnificent fossils," says Wood, but he's not ready to admit *A. garhi* into the gallery of our ancestors. "At this point it's impossible to tell what's ancestral to what," he says. "This won't be the last 'surprise.'"

Anthropologists have long been itching to know just what East African hominids were doing between 2 million and 3 million years ago, says one of the team's leaders, paleoanthropologist Tim White of UC Berkeley. Decades of fieldwork and analysis have allowed researchers to identify many characters in the human evolutionary story (see diagram), starting with apelike species such as the 4.2-million-year-old *A. anamensis*. Next in line, known from 3.7 million to 3.0 million years ago, is *A. afarensis*, best known for the famed "Lucy" skeleton: a meter-tall, small-brained, upright hominid that retained apelike limb proportions and a protruding lower face.

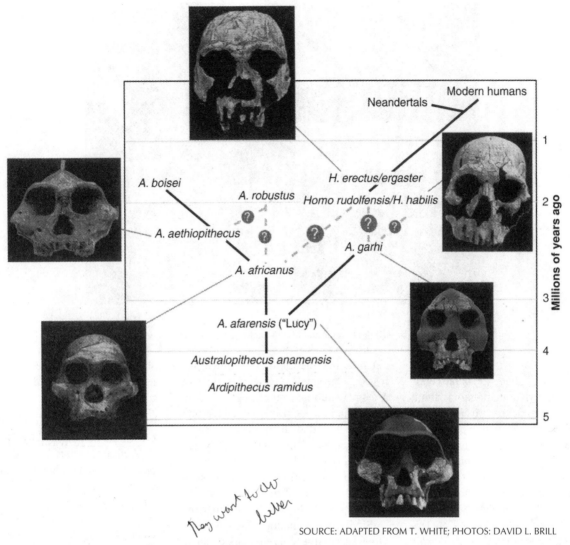

Neandertals   Modern humans

H. erectus/ergaster

A. boisei

A. robustus   Homo rudolfensis/H. habilis

A. aethiopithecus

A. garhi

A. africanus

Millions of years ago

A. afarensis ("Lucy")

Australopithecus anamensis

Ardipithecus ramidus

SOURCE: ADAPTED FROM T. WHITE; PHOTOS: DAVID L. BRILL

Untangling the family tree. Fossil finds suggest an outline of our evolutionary history, but the ancestor of our genus remains in question.

More than a million years separate Lucy from the first specimens usually considered to be part of our own genus, which appear in East Africa around 2 million years ago and tend to have larger brains and a more human face, although they are highly variable. In the interim, the South African fossil record is diverse and confusing, and the East African record has been sparse. The period includes three species that fall into the "robust" australopithecine group—heavy-jawed hominids with skull crests and large back teeth, perhaps for eating hard roots and tubers—that are not part of our own lineage. More promising for those seeking a human ancestor is *A. africanus*, known from South Africa starting at around 2.8 million years ago, which has a more humanlike face than the Lucy species.

But the *A. africanus* fossils were found half a continent away from the East African cradle of *Homo*, and some anthropologists have been hoping for a stronger candidate for the root of our lineage. "After the split with the robust lineage, we have very little evidence," says Walker. That's why White and his team zeroed in on sediments in the desert of Ethiopia's Afar depression. They struck gold with three separate discoveries, all dated securely to 2.5 million years ago by radiometric techniques on an underlying volcanic rock layer.

One dramatic find came in 1997, when El Niño-driven rains washed away stones and dirt on steep slopes near the village of Bouri. Berkeley graduate student Yohannes Haile-Selassie spotted fragments of the skull—the color and

thickness of a coconut shell—on the surface. A closer look revealed teeth poking out of the ground. Much of the rest of the skull had washed down the hill, so the team, which includes 40 members from 13 countries, took the slope apart. They dug tons of material from the hill, then sieved it and picked through it for bone—twice. "It was probably the most difficult fossil recovery we've ever done," says White. "We spent 7 weeks on that slope." Although the delicate bones of the middle face were gone for good, the team found many more skull fragments.

After reconstructing the skull, the researchers were confronted with a face that is apelike in the lower part, with a protruding jaw resembling that of *A. afarensis*. The large size of the palate and

CREDIT: DAVID L. BRILL

Tools were used

Treasure site. *A garhi's* skull was found on this Ethiopian desert slope.

Butchery

teeth suggests that it is a male, with a small braincase of about 450 cubic centimeters. (A modern human brain is about 1400 cubic centimeters.) It is like no other hominid species and is clearly not a robust form. And in a few dental traits, such as the shape of the premolar and the size ratio of the canine teeth to the molars, *A. garhi* resembles specimens of early *Homo*. But its molars are huge—the second molar is 17.7 millimeters across, even larger than the *A. robustus* average. "Selection was driving bigger teeth in both lineages—that's a big surprise," says Walker.

The other dramatic skeletal find had come a year earlier: leg and arm bones of a single ancient hominid individual, found together. The new hominid femur or upper leg bone is relatively long, like that of modern humans. But the forearm is long too, a condition found in apes and other australopithecines but not in humans. The fossils show that human proportions evolved in steps, with the legs lengthening before the forearms shortened, says co-author Owen Lovejoy of Kent State University in Ohio.

The third major find, at the same stratigraphic level and only a meter away from the skeletal bones, preserves dramatic evidence of hominid behavior: bones of antelopes, horses, and other animals bearing cut marks, suggesting that

butchery may be the oldest human profession. One antelope bone, described by a team including archaeologist J. Desmond Clark of UC Berkeley and White, records a failed hammerstone blow, which scratched the bone slightly and caused a bone flake to fly off; a second blow was struck from exactly the same angle. Both ends of the bone were broken off, presumably to get at the marrow.

Similarly, an antelope jawbone bears three successive curved marks, apparently made as a hominid sliced out the tongue. In cross section under the microscope, these marks show a parallel series of ragged V-shaped striations with rough inner walls—the telltale signature of a stone tool rather than a predator's teeth, says White. Marks on the leg bone of a three-toed horse show that hominids dismembered the animal and filleted the meat from the bone.

The Bouri sites yielded few of the stone tools the hominids must have used, perhaps because there is no local source of stone. The hominids "must have brought flakes and cobbles in from some distance, so that obviously shows quite a bit of forethought," says Clark. Tool use by this point is no surprise: At other sites, anthropologists have found tools dated to 2.6 million years ago. But there had been little hard evidence of what the oldest tools were used for. The new find

shows that tools enabled hominids to get at "a whole new world of food"—bone marrow, says White.

Marrow is rich in fat, and few animals other than humans and hyenas can get at it. Anthropologists have theorized that just such a dietary breakthrough allowed the dramatic increase in brain size (*Science*, 29 May 1998, p. 1345), to perhaps 650 cc or larger, that took place in the *Homo* lineage by 2 million years ago. Two researchers recently proposed that cooked tubers were the crucial new food source (*Science*, 26 March, p. 2004), but most others have assumed it was meat. The cut marks present convincing evidence that they were right, says Yale University anthropologist Andrew Hill.

Whether or not the three finds can be connected, *A. garhi*, as based on the new skull, is now a prime candidate as an ancestor of our genus. The species is in the right place—East Africa—and the right time—between the time of *A. afarensis* and that of early *Homo*—says White. But making the link to the human lineage isn't easy, in part because the nature of "early *Homo*" is itself something of a mystery. White notes that some of the early *Homo* specimens have large teeth, and that in the teeth "there's not much change at all from *A. garhi* to those specimens of early *Homo*."

The link between *A. garhi* and *Homo* would be strengthened, of course, if researchers could show that the humanlike long bones come from *A. garhi* rather than from some other humanlike hominid. For now White is willing only to "make up a hypothesis to be tested": *A. garhi*, a small-brained, big-toothed hominid with humanlike leg proportions, began butchering animals by 2.5 million years ago. Thanks in part to the better diet, brain size rapidly increased to that seen in early *Homo*, and the trend toward large back teeth reversed—changes that quickly transformed other parts of the skull as well, such as flattening the protruding jaw.

But some other researchers don't buy that as a likely scenario. There's no reason to expect that every new branch on the hominid tree is our ancestor, says George Washington's Wood. He adds that he is not surprised by *A. garhi's* mix of humanlike and robust features, because, given that climate was changing, "we should expect a variety of creatures with mixtures of adaptations at this time." Other researchers note that the dental data linking the species to *Homo* are weak. "Nothing here aligns *garhi* closely with *Homo*," says paleoanthropologist Fred Grine of the State University of New York, Stony Brook. "It's a possible candidate [for *Homo* ancestry], but no better than *africanus*."

Some anthropologists also say that there may not have been enough time for evolution to have transformed *A. garhi* into *Homo*. The oldest known specimen assigned to *Homo*, a 2.33-million-year-old palate from Hadar, Ethiopia, is more humanlike than *A. garhi*, with smaller teeth. That requires either a burst of evolution or some other explanation, such as sexual dimorphism, if *A. garhi* is to be considered part of our lineage, notes paleoanthropologist Juan Luis Arsuaga of the Universidad Complutense de Madrid in Spain. White says that only further discoveries and analysis will show just where the hominids of that long-vanished plain stand in relation to our own species: "*A. garhi* isn't the end; it's the first step."

Reprinted with permission from *Science,* April 23, 1999, pp. 572–572. © 1999 by the American Association for the Advancement of Science.

Scavenger Hunt

*As paleoanthropologists close in on their quarry, it may turn out
to be a different beast from what they imaged*

Pat Shipman

In both textbooks and films, ancestral humans (hominids) have been portrayed as hunters. Small-brained, big-browed, upright, and usually mildly furry, early hominid males gaze with keen eyes across the gold savanna, searching for prey. Skillfully wielding a few crude stone tools, they kill and dismember everything from small gazelles to elephants, while females care for young and gather roots, tubers, and berries. The food is shared by group members at temporary camps. This familiar image of Man the Hunter has been bolstered by the finding of stone tools in association with fossil animal bones. But the role of hunting in early hominid life cannot be determined in the absence of more direct evidence.

I discovered one means of testing the hunting hypothesis almost by accident. In 1978, I began documenting the microscopic damage produced on bones by different events. I hoped to develop a diagnostic key for identifying the post-mortem history of specific fossil bones, useful for understanding how fossil assemblages were formed. Using a scanning electron microscope (SEM) because of its excellent resolution and superb depth of field, I inspected high-fidelity replicas of modern bones that had been subjected to known events or conditions. (I had to use replicas, rather than real bones, because specimens must fit into the SEM's small vacuum chamber.) I soon established that such common events as weathering, root etching, sedimentary abrasion, and carnivore

chewing produced microscopically distinctive features.

In 1980, my SEM study took an unexpected turn. Richard Potts (now of Yale University), Henry Bunn (now of the University of Wisconsin at Madison), and I almost simultaneously found what appeared to be stone-tool cut marks on fossils from Olduvai Gorge, Tanzania, and Koobi Fora, Kenya. We were working almost side by side at the National Museums of Kenya, in Nairobi, where the fossils are stored. The possibility of cut marks was exciting, since both sites preserve some of the oldest known archaeological materials. Potts and I returned to the United States, manufactured some stone tools, and started "butchering" bones and joints begged from our local butchers. Under the SEM, replicas of these cut marks looked very different from replicas of carnivore tooth scratches, regardless of the species of carnivore or the type of tool involved. By comparing the marks on the fossils with our hundreds of modern bones of known history, we were able to demonstrate convincingly that hominids using stone tools had processed carcasses of many different animals nearly two million years ago. For the first time, there was a firm link between stone tools and at least some of the early fossil animal bones.

This initial discovery persuaded some paleoanthropologists that the hominid hunter scenario was correct. Potts and I were not so sure. Our study had shown that many of the cut-marked fossils also

bore carnivore tooth marks and that some of the cut marks were in places we hadn't expected—on bones that bore little meat in life. More work was needed.

In addition to more data about the Olduvai cut marks and tooth marks, I needed specific information about the patterns of cut marks left by known hunters performing typical activities associated with hunting. If similar patterns occurred on the fossils, then the early hominids probably behaved similarly to more modern hunters; if the patterns were different, then the behavior was probably also different. Three activities related to hunting occur often enough in peoples around the world and leave consistent enough traces to be used for such a test.

First, human hunters systematically disarticulate their kills, unless the animals are small enough to be eaten on the spot. Disarticulation leaves cut marks in a predictable pattern on the skeleton. Such marks cluster near the major joints of the limbs: shoulder, elbow, carpal joint (wrist), hip, knee, and hock (ankle). Taking a carcass apart at the joints is much easier than breaking or cutting through bones. Disarticulation enables hunters to carry food back to a central place or camp, so that they can share it with others or cook it or even store it by placing portions in trees, away from the reach of carnivores. If early hominids were hunters who transported and shared their kills, disarticulation marks would occur near joints in frequencies comparable to those produced by modern human hunters.

Second, human hunters often butcher carcasses, in the sense of removing meat from the bones. Butchery marks are usually found on the shafts of bones from the upper part of the front or hind limb, since this is where the big muscle masses lie. Butchery may be carried out at the kill site—especially if the animal is very large and its bones very heavy—or it may take place at the base camp, during the process of sharing food with others. Compared with disarticulation, butchery leaves relatively few marks. It is hard for a hunter to locate an animal's joints without leaving cut marks on the bone. In contrast, it is easier to cut the meat away from the midshaft of the bone without making such marks. If early hominids shared their food, however, there ought to be a number of cut marks located on the midshaft of some fossil bones.

Finally, human hunters often remove skin or tendons from carcasses, to be used for clothing, bags, thongs, and so on. Hide or tendon must be separated from the bones in many areas where there is little flesh, such as the lower limb bones of pigs, giraffes, antelopes, and zebras. In such cases, it is difficult to cut the skin without leaving a cut mark on the bone. Therefore, one expects to find many more cut marks on such bones than on the flesh-covered bones of the upper part of the limbs.

Unfortunately, although accounts of butchery and disarticulation by modern human hunters are remarkably consistent, quantitative studies are rare. Further, virtually all modern hunter-gatherers use metal tools, which leave more cut marks than stone tools. For these reasons I hesitated to compare the fossil evidence with data on modern hunters. Fortunately, Diane Gifford of the University of California, Santa Cruz, and her colleagues had recently completed a quantitative study of marks and damage on thousands of antelope bones processed by Neolithic (Stone Age) hunters in Kenya some 2,300 years ago. The data from Prolonged Drift, as the site is called, were perfect for comparison with the Olduvai material.

Assisted by my technician, Jennie Rose, I carefully inspected more than 2,500 antelope bones from Bed I at Olduvai Gorge, which is dated to between 1.9 and 1.7 million years ago. We made high-fidelity replicas of every mark that we thought might be either a cut mark or a carnivore tooth mark. Back in the United States, we used the SEM to make positive identifications of the marks. (The replication and SEM inspection was time consuming, but necessary: only about half of the marks were correctly identified by eye or by light microscope.) I then compared the patterns of cut mark and tooth mark distributions on Olduvai fossils with those made by Stone Age hunters at Prolonged Drift.

By their location, I identified marks caused either by disarticulation or meat removal and then compared their frequencies with those from Prolonged Drift. More than 90 percent of the Neolithic marks in these two categories were from disarticulation, but to my surprise, only about 45 percent of the corresponding Olduvai cut marks were from disarticulation. This difference is too great to have occurred by chance; the Olduvai bones did not show the predicted pattern. In fact, the Olduvai cut marks attributable to meat removal and disarticulation showed essentially the same pattern of distribution as the carnivore tooth marks. Apparently, the early hominids were not regularly disarticulating carcasses. This finding casts serious doubt on the idea that early hominids carried their kills back to camp to share with others, since both transport and sharing are difficult unless carcasses are cut up.

When I looked for cut marks attributable to skinning or tendon removal, a more modern pattern emerged. On both the Neolithic and Olduvai bones, nearly 75 percent of all cut marks occurred on bones that bore little meat; these cut marks probably came from skinning. Carnivore tooth marks were much less common on such bones. Hominids were using carcasses as a source of skin and tendon. This made it seem more surprising that they disarticulated carcasses so rarely.

A third line of evidence provided the most tantalizing clue. Occasionally, sets of overlapping marks occur on the Olduvai fossils. Sometimes, these sets include both cut marks and carnivore tooth marks. Still more rarely, I could see under the SEM which mark had been made first, because its features were overlaid by those of the later mark, in much the same way as old tire tracks on a dirt road are obscured by fresh ones. Although only thirteen such sets of marks were found, in eight cases the hominids made the cut marks after the carnivores made their tooth marks. This finding suggested a new hypothesis. Instead of hunting for prey and leaving the remains behind for carnivores to scavenge, perhaps hominids were scavenging from the carnivores. This might explain the hominids' apparently unsystematic use of carcasses: they took what they could get, be it skin, tendon, or meat.

Man the Scavenger is not nearly as attractive an image as Man the Hunter, but it is worth examining. Actually, although hunting and scavenging are different ecological strategies, many mammals do both. The only pure scavengers alive in Africa today are vultures; not one of the modern African mammalian carnivores is a pure scavenger. Even spotted hyenas, which have massive, bone-crushing teeth well adapted for eating the bones left behind by others, only scavenge about 33 percent of their food. Other carnivores that scavenge when there are enough carcasses around include lions, leopards, striped hyenas, and jackals. Long-term behavioral studies suggest that these carnivores scavenge when they can and kill when they must. There are only two nearly pure predators, or hunters—the cheetah and the wild dog—that rarely, if ever, scavenge.

What are the costs and benefits of scavenging compared with those of predation? First of all, the scavenger avoids the task of making sure its meal is dead: a predator has already endured the energetically costly business of chasing or stalking animal after animal until one is killed. But while scavenging may be cheap, it's risky. Predators rarely give up their prey to scavengers without defending it. In such disputes, the larger animal, whether a scavenger or a predator, usually wins, although smaller animals in a pack may defeat a lone, larger animal. Both predators and scavengers suffer the dangers inherent in fighting for posses-

Flight

sion of a carcass. Smaller scavengers such as jackals or striped hyenas avoid disputes to some extent by specializing in darting in and removing a piece of a carcass without trying to take possession of the whole thing. These two strategies can be characterized as that of the bully or that of the sneak: bullies need to be large to be successful, sneaks need to be small and quick.

Because carcasses are almost always much rarer than live prey, the major cost peculiar to scavenging is that scavengers must survey much larger areas than predators to find food. They can travel slowly, since their "prey" is already dead, but endurance is important. Many predators specialize in speed at the expense of endurance, while scavengers do the opposite.

The more committed predators among the East African carnivores (wild dogs and cheetahs) can achieve great top speeds when running, although not for long. Perhaps as a consequence, these "pure" hunters enjoy a much higher success rate in hunting (about three-fourths of their chases end in kills) than any of the scavenger-hunters do (less than half of their chases are successful). Wild dogs and cheetahs are efficient hunters, but they are neither big enough nor efficient enough in their locomotion to make good scavengers. In fact, the cheetah's teeth are so specialized for meat slicing that they probably cannot withstand the stresses of bone crunching and carcass dismembering carried out by scavengers. Other carnivores are less successful at hunting, but have specializations of size, endurance, or (in the case of the hyenas) dentition that make successful scavenging possible. The small carnivores seem to have a somewhat higher hunting success rate than the large ones, which balances out their difficulties in asserting possession of carcasses.

In addition to endurance, scavengers need an efficient means of locating carcasses, which, unlike live animals, don't move or make noises. Vultures, for example, solve both problems by flying. The soaring, gliding flight of vultures expends much less energy than walking or cantering as performed by the part-time mammalian scavengers. Flight enables vultures to maintain a foraging radius

two to three times larger than that of spotted hyenas, while providing a better vantage point. This explains why vultures can scavenge all of their food in the same habitat in which it is impossible for any mammal to be a pure scavenger. (In fact, many mammals learn where carcasses are located from the presence of vultures.)

Since mammals can't succeed as full-time scavengers, they must have another source of food to provide the bulk of their diet. The large carnivores rely on hunting large animals to obtain food when scavenging doesn't work. Their size enables them to defend a carcass against others. Since the small carnivores—jackals and striped hyenas—often can't defend carcasses successfully, most of their diet is composed of fruit and insects. When they do hunt, they usually prey on very small animals, such as rats or hares, that can be consumed in their entirety before the larger competitors arrive.

The ancient habitat associated with the fossils of Olduvai and Koobi Fora would have supported many herbivores and carnivores. Among the latter were two species of large saber-toothed cats, whose teeth show extreme adaptations for meat slicing. These were predators with primary access to carcasses. Since their teeth were unsuitable for bone crushing, the saber-toothed cats must have left behind many bones covered with scraps of meat, skin, and tendon. Were early hominids among the scavengers that exploited such carcasses?

All three hominid species that were present in Bed I times (*Homo habilis, Australopithecus africanus, A. robustus*) were adapted for habitual, upright bipedalism. Many anatomists see evidence that these hominids were agile tree climbers as well. Although upright bipedalism is a notoriously peculiar mode of locomotion, the adaptive value of which has been argued for years (See Matt Cartmill's article, "Four Legs Good, Two Legs Bad," *Natural History*, November 1983), there are three general points of agreement.

First, bipedal running is neither fast nor efficient compared to quadrupedal gaits. However, at moderate speeds of 2.5 to 3.5 miles per hour, bipedal *walk-*

ing is more energetically efficient than quadrupedal walking. Thus, bipedal walking is an excellent means of covering large areas slowly, making it an unlikely adaptation for a hunter but an appropriate and useful adaptation for a scavenger. Second, bipedalism elevates the head, thus improving the hominid's ability to spot items on the ground—an advantage both to scavengers and to those trying to avoid becoming a carcass. Combining bipedalism with agile tree climbing improves the vantage point still further. Third, bipedalism frees the hands from locomotive duties, making it possible to carry items. What would early hominids have carried? Meat makes a nutritious, easy-to-carry package; the problem is that carrying meat attracts scavengers. Richard Potts suggests that carrying stone tools or unworked stones for toolmaking to caches would be a more efficient and less dangerous activity under many circumstances.

In short, bipedalism is compatible with a scavenging strategy. I am tempted to argue that bipedalism evolved because it provided a substantial advantage to scavenging hominids. But I doubt hominids could scavenge effectively without tools, and bipedalism predates the oldest known stone tools by more than a million years.

Is there evidence that, like modern mammalian scavengers, early hominids had an alternative food source, such as either hunting or eating fruits and insects? My husband, Alan Walker, has shown that the microscopic wear on an animal's teeth reflects its diet. Early hominid teeth wear more like that of chimpanzees and other modern fruit eaters than that of carnivores. Apparently, early hominids ate mostly fruit, as the smaller, modern scavengers do. This accords with the estimated body weight of early hominids, which was only about forty to eighty pounds—less than that of any of the modern carnivores that combine scavenging and hunting but comparable to the striped hyena, which eats fruits and insects as well as meat.

Would early hominids have been able to compete for carcasses with other carnivores? They were too small to use a bully strategy, but if they scavenged in groups, a combined bully-sneak strategy might have been possible. Perhaps they were able to drive off a primary predator long enough to grab some meat, skin, or marrow-filled bone before relinquishing the carcass. The effectiveness of this strategy would have been vastly improved by using tools to remove meat or parts of limbs, a task at which hominid teeth are poor. As agile climbers, early hominids may have retreated into the trees to eat their scavenged trophies, thus avoiding competition from large terrestrial carnivores.

In sum, the evidence on cut marks, tooth wear, and bipedalism, together with our knowledge of scavenger adaptation in general, is consistent with the hypothesis that two million years ago hominids were scavengers rather than accomplished hunters. Animal carcasses, which contributed relatively little to the hominid diet, were not systematically cut up and transported for sharing at base camps. Man the Hunter may not have appeared until 1.5 to 0.7 million years ago, when we do see a shift toward omnivory, with a greater proportion of meat in the diet. This more heroic ancestor may have been *Homo erectus*, equipped with Acheulean-style stone tools and, increasingly, fire. If we wish to look further back, we may have to become accustomed to a less flattering image of our heritage.

Pat Shipman is an assistant professor in the Department of Cell Biology and Anatomy at The Johns Hopkins University School of Medicine.

UNIT 5
Late Hominid Evolution

Unit Selections

Key Points to Consider

- When, where, and why did *Homo erectus* evolve? Is it one species or two? Explain your reasoning.

- What were Cro-Magnons trying to say or do with their cave art?

- When did language ability arise in our ancestry and why?

- How do we measure evolutionary time?

- Are Neanderthals part of our ancestry?

- How do you assess the evidence for cannibalism?

 **Links: www.dushkin.com/online/**
These sites are annotated in the World Wide Web pages.

Archaeology Links (NC)
http://www.arch.dcr.state.nc.us/links.htm#stuff/
Human Prehistory
http://users.hol.gr/~dilos/prehis.htm

The most important aspect of human evolution is also the most difficult to decipher from the fossil evidence: our development as sentient, social beings, capable of communicating by means of language.

We detect hints of incipient humanity in the form of crudely chipped tools, the telltale signs of a home base, or the artistic achievements of ornaments and cave art. Yet none of these indicators of a distinctly hominid way of life can provide us with the nuances of the everyday lives of these creatures, their social relations, or their supernatural beliefs, if any. Most of what remains is the rubble of bones and stones from which we interpret what we can of their lifestyle, thought processes, and ability to communicate. Our ability to glean from the fossil record is not completely without hope, however. In fact, informed speculation is what makes possible such essays as "Old Masters" by Pat Shipman, "Secrets of the Cave's Art" by Sharon Begley, and "The Gift of Gab" by Matt Cartmill. Each is a fine example of careful, systematic, and thought-provoking work that is based upon an increased understanding of hominid fossil sites as well as the more general environmental circumstances in which our predecessors lived.

Beyond the technological and anatomical adaptations, questions have arisen as to how our hominid forebears organized themselves socially and whether modern-day human behavior is inherited as a legacy of our evolutionary past or is a learned product of contemporary circumstances. Attempts to address these questions have given rise to the technique referred to as the "ethnographic analogy." This is a method whereby anthropologists use "ethnographies" or field studies of modern-day hunters and gatherers whose lives we take to be the best approximations we have to what life might have been like for our ancestors. Granted, these contemporary foragers have been living under conditions of environmental and social change just as industrial peoples have. Nevertheless, it seems that, at least in some aspects of their lives, they have not changed as much as we have. So, if we are to make any enlightened assessments of prehistoric behavior patterns, we are better off looking at them than at ourselves.

As if to show that controversial interpretations of the evidence are not limited to the earlier hominid period in this unit we see how the question of cannibalism has arisen anew ("Archaeologists Rediscover Cannibals" by Ann Gibbons). In addition, how long-held beliefs about *Homo erectus* are being threatened by new fossil evidence (see James Shreeve's essay "*Erectus* Rising" and Pat Shipman's "Doubting Dmanisi") and by new interpretations of old evidence (as in "The Scavenging of 'Peking Man'" by Noel Boaz and Russell Ciochon.) We also consider new evidence bearing upon the fate of the Neanderthals in "Who Were the Neandertals?" For some scientists, the new evidence fits in quite comfortably with previously held positions; for others it seems that reputations, as well as theories, are at stake.

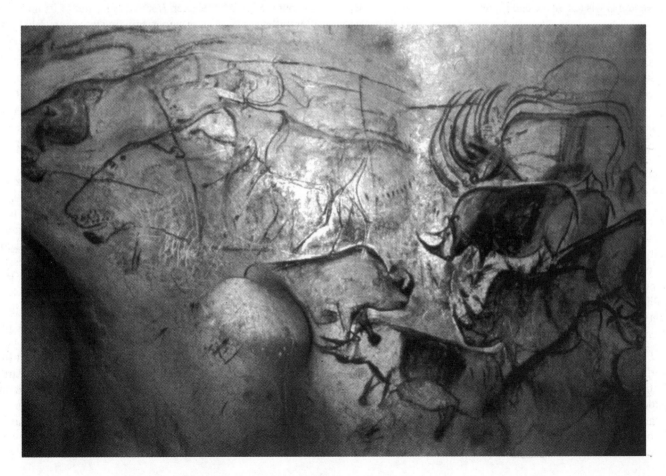

Erectus Rising

Oh No. Not This. The Hominids Are Acting Up Again…

James Shreeve

Just when it seemed that the recent monumental fuss over the origins of modern human beings was beginning to quiet down, an ancient ancestor is once more running wild. Trampling on theories. Appearing in odd places, way ahead of schedule. Demanding new explanations. And shamelessly flaunting its contempt for conventional wisdom in the public press.

The uppity ancestor this time is *Homo erectus*—alias Java man, alias Peking man, alias a mouthful of formal names known only to the paleontological cognoscenti. Whatever you call it, *erectus* has traditionally been a quiet, average sort of hominid: low of brow, thick of bone, endowed with a brain larger than that of previous hominids but smaller than those that followed, a face less apelike and projecting than that of its ancestors but decidedly more simian than its descendants'. In most scenarios of human evolution, *erectus*'s role was essentially to mark time—a million and a half years of it—between its obscure, presumed origins in East Africa just under 2 million years ago and its much more recent evolution into something deserving the name *sapiens*.

Erectus accomplished only two noteworthy deeds during its long tenure on Earth. First, some 1.5 million years ago, it developed what is known as the Acheulean stone tool culture, a technology exemplified by large, carefully crafted tear-shaped hand axes that were much more advanced than the bashed rocks that had passed for tools in the hands of earlier hominids. Then, half a million years later, and aided by those Acheulean tools, the species carved its way out of Africa and established a human presence in other parts of the Old World. But most of the time, *Homo erectus* merely existed, banging out the same stone tools millennium after millennium, over a time span that one archeologist has called "a period of unimaginable monotony."

Asian and African fossils were lumped into one far-flung taxon, a creature not quite like us but human enough to be welcomed into our genus: Homo erectus.

Or so read the old script. These days, *erectus* has begun to ad-lib a more vigorous, controversial identity for itself. Research within the past year has revealed that rather than being 1 million years old, several *erectus* fossils from Southeast Asia are in fact almost 2 million years old. That is as old as the oldest African members of the species, and it would mean that *erectus* emerged from its home continent much earlier than has been thought—in fact, almost immediately after it first appeared. There's also a jawbone, found in 1991 near the Georgian city of Tbilisi, that resembles *erectus* fossils from Africa and may be as old as 1.8 million years, though that age is still in doubt. These new dates—and the debates they've engendered—have shaken *Homo erectus* out of its interpretive stupor, bringing into sharp relief just how little agreement there is on the rise and demise of the last human species on Earth, save one.

"Everything now is in flux," says Carl Swisher of the Berkeley Geochronology Center, one of the prime movers behind the redating of *erectus* outside Africa. "It's all a mess."

The focal point for the flux is the locale where the species was first found: Java. The rich but frustration-soaked history of paleoanthropology on that tropical island began just over 100 years ago, when a young Dutch anatomy professor named Eugène Dubois conceived the idée fixe that the "missing link" between ape and man was to be found in the jungled remoteness of the Dutch East Indies. Dubois had never left Holland, much less traveled to the Dutch East Indies, and his pick for the spot on Earth where humankind first arose owed as much to a large part of the Indonesian archipelago's being a Dutch colony as it did to any scientific evidence. He nevertheless found this missing link—the top of an oddly thick skull with massive browridges—in 1891 on the banks of the Solo River, near a community called Trinil in central Java. About a year later a thighbone that Dubois thought might belong to the same individual was found nearby; it looked so much like a modern human thighbone that Dubois assumed this ancient primate had walked upright. He christened the creature *Pithecanthropus erectus*—"erect ape-man"—and returned home in triumph.

Finding the fossil proved to be the easy part. Though Dubois won popular acclaim, neither he nor his "Java man" received the full approbation of the anatomists of the day, who considered his ape-man either merely an ape or merely a man. In an apparent pique, Dubois cloistered away the fossils for a quarter-century, refusing others the chance to view his prized possessions. Later, other similarly primitive human remains began to turn up in China and East Africa. All shared a collection of anatomical traits, including a long, low braincase with prominent browridges and a flattened forehead; a sharp angle to the back of the skull when viewed in profile; and a deep, robustly built jaw showing no hint of a chin. Though initially given separate regional names, the fossils were eventually lumped together into one far-flung taxon, a creature not quite like us but human enough to be welcomed into our genus: *Homo erectus*.

Over the decades the most generous source of new *erectus* fossils has been the sites on or near the Solo River in Java. The harvest continues: two more skulls, including one of the most complete *erectus* skulls yet known, were found at a famous fossil site called Sangiran just in the past year. Though the Javan yield of ancient humans has been rich, something has always been missing—the crucial element of time. Unless the age of a fossil can be determined, it hangs in limbo, its importance and place in the larger scheme of human evolution forever undercut with doubt. Until researchers can devise better methods for dating bone directly—right now there are no techniques that can reliably date fossilized, calcified bone more than 50,000 years old—a specimen's age

has to be inferred from the geology that surrounds it. Unfortunately, most of the discoveries made on the densely populated and cultivated island of Java have been made not by trained excavators but by sharp-eyed local farmers who spot the bones as they wash out with the annual rains and later sell them. As a result, the original location of many a prized specimen, and thus all hopes of knowing its age, are a matter of memory and word of mouth.

Despite the problems, scientists continue to try to pin down dates for Java's fossils. Most have come up with an upper limit of around 1 million years. Along with the dates for the Peking man skulls found in China and the Acheulean tools from Europe, the Javan evidence has come to be seen as confirmation that *erectus* first left Africa at about that time.

By the early 1970s most paleontologists were firmly wedded to the idea that Africa was the only human-inhabited part of the world until one million years ago.

There are those, however, who have wondered about these dates for quite some time. Chief among them is Garniss Curtis, the founder of the Berkeley Geochronology Center. In 1971 Curtis, who was then at the University of California at Berkeley, attempted to determine the age of a child's skull from a site called Mojokerto, in eastern Java, by using the potassium-argon method to date volcanic minerals in the sediments from which the skull was purportedly removed. Potassium-argon dating had been in use since the 1950s, and Curtis had been enormously successful with it in dating ancient African hominids—including Louis Leakey's famous hominid finds at Olduvai Gorge in Tanzania. The method takes advantage of the fact that a radioactive isotope of potassium found in volcanic ash slowly and predictably decays over time into argon gas, which becomes trapped in the crystalline structure of the

mineral. The amount of argon contained in a given sample, measured against the amount of the potassium isotope, serves as a kind of clock that tells how much time has passed since a volcano exploded and its ash fell to earth and buried the bone in question.

Applying the technique to the volcanic pumice associated with the skull from Mojokerto, Curtis got an extraordinary age of 1.9 million years. The wildly anomalous date was all too easy to dismiss, however. Unlike the ash deposits of East Africa, the volcanic pumices in Java are poor in potassium. Also, not unexpectedly, a heavy veil of uncertainty obscured the collector's memories of precisely where he had found the fossil some 35 years earlier. Besides, most paleontologists were by this time firmly wedded to the idea that Africa was the only human-inhabited part of the world until 1 million years ago. Curtis's date was thus deemed wrong for the most stubbornly cherished of reasons: because it couldn't possibly be right.

In 1992 Curtis—under the auspices of the Institute for Human Origins in Berkeley—returned to Java with his colleague Carl Swisher. This time he was backed up by far more sensitive equipment and a powerful refinement in the dating technique. In conventional potassium-argon dating, several grams' worth of volcanic crystals gleaned from a site are needed to run a single experiment. While the bulk of these crystals are probably from the eruption that covered the fossil, there's always the possibility that other materials, from volcanoes millions of years older, have gotten mixed in and will thus make the fossil appear to be much older than it actually is. The potassium-argon method also requires that the researcher divide the sample of crystals in two. One half is dissolved in acid and passed through a flame; the wavelengths of light emitted tell how much potassium is in the sample. The other half is used to measure the amount of argon gas that's released when the crystals are heated. This two-step process further increases the chance of error, simply by giving the experiment twice as much opportunity to go wrong.

The refined technique, called argon-argon dating, neatly sidesteps most of these difficulties. The volcanic crystals are first placed in a reactor and bombarded with neutrons; when one of these neutrons penetrates the potassium nucleus, it displaces a proton, converting the potassium into an isotope of argon that doesn't occur in nature. Then the artificially created argon and the naturally occurring argon are measured in a single experiment. Because the equipment used to measure the isotopes can look for both types of argon at the same time, there's no need to divide the sample, and so the argon-argon method can produce clear results from tiny amounts of material.

In some cases—when the volcanic material is fairly rich in potassium—all the atoms of argon from a single volcanic crystal can be quick-released by the heat from a laser beam and then counted. By doing a number of such single-crystal experiments, the researchers can easily pick out and discard any data from older, contaminant crystals. But even when the researchers are forced to sample more than one potassium-poor crystal to get any reading at all—as was the case at Mojokerto—the argon-argon method can still produce a highly reliable age. In this case, the researchers carefully heat a few crystals at a time to higher and higher temperatures, using a precisely controlled laser. If all the crystals in a sample are the same age, then the amount of argon released at each temperature will be the same. But if contaminants are mixed in, or if severe weathering has altered the crystal's chemical composition, the argon measurements will be erratic, and the researchers will know to throw out the results.

Curtis and Swisher knew that in the argon-argon step-heating method they had the technical means to date the potassium-poor deposits at Mojokerto accurately. But they had no way to prove that those deposits were the ones in which the skull had been buried: all they had was the word of the local man who had found it. Then, during a visit to the museum in the regional capital, where the fossil was being housed, Swisher noticed something odd. The hardened sedi-

ments that filled the inside of the fossil's braincase looked black. But back at the site, the deposits of volcanic pumice that had supposedly sheltered the infant's skull were whitish in color. How could a skull come to be filled with black sediments if it had been buried in white ones? Was it possible that the site and the skull had nothing to do with each other after all? Swisher suspected something was wrong. He borrowed a penknife, picked up the precious skull, and nicked off a bit of the matrix inside.

"I almost got kicked out of the country at that point," he says. "These fossils in Java are like the crown jewels."

Luckily, his impulsiveness paid off. The knife's nick revealed white pumice under a thin skin of dark pigment: years earlier, someone had apparently painted the surface of the hardened sediments black. Since there were no other deposits within miles of the purported site that contained a white pumice visually or chemically resembling the matrix in the skull, its tie to the site was suddenly much stronger. Curtis and Swisher returned to Berkeley with pumice from that site and within a few weeks proclaimed the fossil to be 1.8 million years old, give or take some 40,000 years. At the same time, the geochronologists ran tests on pumice from the lower part of the Sangiran area, where *erectus* facial and cranial bone fragments had been found. The tests yielded an age of around 1.6 million years. Both numbers obviously shatter the 1-million-year barrier for *erectus* outside Africa, and they are a stunning vindication of Curtis's work at Mojokerto 20 years ago. "That was very rewarding," he says, "after having been told what a fool I was by my colleagues."

While no one takes Curtis or Swisher for a fool now, some of their colleagues won't be fully convinced by the new dates until the matrix inside the Mojokerto skull itself can be tested. Even then, the possibility will remain that the skull may have drifted down over the years into deposits containing older volcanic crystals that have nothing to do with its original burial site, or that it was carried by a river to another, older site. But Swisher contends that the chance of such an occurrence is remote: it would have to

have happened at both Mojokerto and Sangiran for the fossils' ages to be refuted. "I feel really good about the dates," he says. "But it has taken me a while to understand their implications."

The implications that can be spun out from the Javan dates depend on how one chooses to interpret the body of fossil evidence commonly embraced under the name *Homo erectus*. The earliest African fossils traditionally attributed to *erectus* are two nearly complete skulls from the site of Koobi Fora in Kenya, dated between 1.8 and 1.7 million years old. In the conventional view, these early specimens evolved from a more primitive, smaller-brained ancestor called *Homo habilis*, well represented by bones from Koobi Fora, Olduvai Gorge, and sites in South Africa.

If this conventional view is correct, then the new dates mean that *erectus* must have migrated out of Africa very soon after it evolved, quickly reaching deep into the farthest corner of Southeast Asia. This is certainly possible: at the time, Indonesia was connected to Asia by lower sea levels—thus providing an overland route from Africa—and Java is just 10,000 to 15,000 miles from Kenya, depending on the route. Even if *erectus* traveled just one mile a year, it would still take no more than 15,000 years to reach Java—a negligible amount of evolutionary time.

If *erectus* did indeed reach Asia almost a million years earlier than thought, then other, more controversial theories become much more plausible. Although many anthropologists believe that the African and Asian *erectus* fossils all represent a single species, other investigators have recently argued that the two groups are too different to be so casually lumped together. According to paleoanthropologist Ian Tattersall of the American Museum of Natural History in New York, the African skulls traditionally assigned to *erectus* often lack many of the specialized traits that were originally used to define the species in Asia, including the long, low cranial structure, thick skull bones, and robustly built faces. In his view, the African group de-

MEANWHILE, IN SIBERIA...

The presence of *Homo erectus* in Asia twice as long ago as previously thought has some people asking whether the human lineage might have originated in Asia instead of Africa. This long-dormant theory runs contrary to all current thinking about human evolution and lacks an important element: evidence. Although the new Javan dates do place the species in Asia at around the same time it evolved in Africa, all confirmed specimens of other, earlier hominids—the first members of the genus *Homo*, for instance, and the australopithecines, like Lucy—have been found exclusively in Africa. Given such an overwhelming argument, most investigators continue to believe that the hominid line began in Africa.

Most, but not all. Some have begun to cock an ear to the claims of Russian archeologist Yuri Mochanov. For over a decade Mochanov has been excavating a huge site on the Lena River in eastern Siberia—far from Africa, Java, or anywhere else on Earth an ancient hominid bone has ever turned up. Though he hasn't found any hominid fossils in Siberia, he stubbornly believes he's uncovered the next best thing: a trove of some 4,000 stone artifacts—crudely made flaked tools, but tools nonetheless—that he maintains are at least 2 million years old, and possibly 3 million. This, he says, would mean that the human lineage arose not in tropical Africa but in the cold northern latitudes of Asia.

"For evolutionary progress to occur, there had to be the appearance of new conditions: winter, snow, and, accompanying them, hunger," writes Mochanov.

"[The ancestral primates] had to learn to walk on the ground, to change their carriage, and to become accustomed to meat—that is, to become 'clever animals of prey.'" And to become clever animals of prey, they'd need tools.

Although he is a well-respected investigator, Mochanov has been unable to convince either Western anthropologists or his Russian colleagues of the age of his site. Until recently the chipped rocks he was holding up as human artifacts were simply dismissed as stones broken by natural processes, or else his estimate of the age of the site was thought to be wincingly wrong. After all, no other signs of human occupation of Siberia appear until some 35,000 years ago.

But after a lecture swing through the United States earlier this year—in which he brought more data and a few prime examples of the tools for people to examine and pass around—many archeologists concede that it is difficult to explain the particular pattern of breakage of the rocks by any known natural process. "Everything I have heard or seen about the context of these things suggests that they are most likely tools," says anthropologist Rick Potts of the Smithsonian Institution, which was host to Mochanov last January.

They're even willing to concede that the site might be considerably older than they'd thought, though not nearly as old as Mochanov estimates. (To date the site, Mochanov compared the tools with artifacts found early in Africa; he also employed an arcane dating technique little known outside

Russia.) Preliminary results from an experimental dating technique performed on soil samples from the site by Michael Waters of Texas A&M and Steve Forman of Ohio State suggest that the layer of sediment bearing the artifacts is some 400,000 years old. That's a long way from 2 million, certainly, but it's still vastly older than anything else found in Siberia—and the site is 1,500 miles farther north than the famous Peking man site in China, previously considered the most northerly home of *erectus*.

"If this does turn out to be 400,000 years old, it's very exciting," says Waters. "If people were able to cope and survive in such a rigorous Arctic environment at such an early time, we would have to completely change our perception of the evolution of human adaptation."

"I have no problem with hominids being almost anywhere at that age—they were certainly traveling around," says Potts. "But the environment is the critical thing. If it was really cold up there"—temperatures in the region now often reach –50 degrees in deep winter—"we'd all have to scratch our heads over how these early hominids were making it in Siberia. There is no evidence that Neanderthals, who were better equipped for cold than anyone, were living in such climates. But who knows? Maybe a population got trapped up there, went extinct, and Mochanov managed to find it." He shrugs. "But that's just arm waving."

—J. S

serves to be placed in a separate species, which he calls *Homo ergaster*.

Most anthropologists believe that the only way to distinguish between species in the fossil record is to look at the similarities and differences between bones; the age of the fossil should not play a

part. But age is often hard to ignore, and Tattersall believes that the new evidence for what he sees as two distinct populations living at the same time in widely separate parts of the Old World is highly suggestive. "The new dates help confirm that these were indeed two different spe-

cies," he says. "In my view, *erectus* is a separate variant that evolved only in Asia."

Other investigators still contend that the differences between the African and Asian forms of *erectus* are too minimal to merit placing them in separate species.

But if Tattersall is right, his theory raises the question of who the original emigrant out of Africa really was. *Homo ergaster* may have been the one to make the trek, evolving into *erectus* once it was established in Asia. Or perhaps a population of some even more primitive, as-yet-unidentified common ancestor ventured forth, giving rise to *erectus* in Asia while a sister population evolved into *ergaster* on the home continent.

Furthermore, no matter who left Africa first, there's the question of what precipitated the migration, a question made even more confounding by the new dates. The old explanation, that the primal human expansion across the hem of the Old World was triggered by the sophisticated Acheulean tools, is no longer tenable with these dates, simply because the tools had not yet been invented when the earliest populations would have moved out. In hindsight, that notion seems a bit shopworn anyway. Acheulean tools first appear in Africa around 1.5 million years ago, and soon after at a site in the nearby Middle East. But they've never been found in the Far East, in spite of the abundant fossil evidence for *Homo erectus* in the region.

Until now, that absence has best been explained by the "bamboo line." According to paleoanthropologist Geoffrey Pope of William Paterson College in New Jersey, *erectus* populations venturing from Africa into the Far East found the land rich in bamboo, a raw material more easily worked into cutting and butchering tools than recalcitrant stone. Sensibly, they abandoned their less efficient stone industry for one based on the pliable plant, which leaves no trace of itself in the archeological record. This is still a viable theory, but the new dates from Java add an even simpler dimension to it: there are no Acheulean tools in the Far East because the first wave of *erectus* to leave Africa didn't have any to bring with them.

So what *did* fuel the quick-step migration out of Africa? Some researchers say the crucial development was not cultural but physical. Earlier hominids like *Homo habilis* were small-bodied creatures with more apelike limb proportions, notes pa-

leoanthropologist Bernard Wood of the University of Liverpool, while African *erectus* was built along more modern lines. Tall, relatively slender, with long legs better able to range over distance and a body better able to dissipate heat, the species was endowed with the physiology needed to free it from the tropical shaded woodlands of Africa that sheltered earlier hominids. In fact, the larger-bodied *erectus* would have required a bigger feeding range to sustain itself, so it makes perfect sense that the expansion out of Africa should begin soon after the species appeared. "Until now, one was always having to account for what kept *erectus* in Africa so long after it evolved," says Wood. "So rather than raising a problem, in some ways the new dates in Java solve one."

Of course, if those dates are right, the accepted time frame for human evolution outside the home continent is nearly doubled, and that has implications for the ongoing debate over the origins of modern human beings. There are two opposing theories. The "out of Africa" hypothesis says that *Homo sapiens* evolved from *erectus* in Africa, and then—sometime in the last 100,000 years—spread out and replaced the more archaic residents of Eurasia. The "multiregional continuity" hypothesis says that modern humans evolved from *erectus* stock in various parts of the Old World, more or less simultaneously and independently. According to this scenario, living peoples outside Africa should look for their most recent ancestors not in African fossils but in the anatomy of ancient fossils within their own region of origin.

As it happens, the multiregionalists have long claimed that the best evidence for their theory lies in Australia, which is generally thought to have become inhabited around 50,000 years ago, by humans crossing over from Indonesia. There are certain facial and cranial characteristics in modern Australian aborigines, the multiregionalists say, that can be traced all the way back to the earliest specimens of *erectus* at Sangiran—characteristics that differ from and precede those of any more recent, *Homo sapiens* arrival from Africa. But if the new Javan dates are right, then these unique characteristics,

and thus the aborigines' Asian *erectus* ancestors, must have been evolving separately from the rest of humankind for almost 2 million years. Many anthropologists, already skeptical of the multiregionalists' potential 1-million-year-long isolation for Asian *erectus*, find a 2-million-year-long isolation exceedingly difficult to swallow. "Can anyone seriously propose that the lineage of Australian aborigines could go back that far?" wonders paleoanthropologist Chris Stringer of the Natural History Museum in London, a leading advocate of the out-of-Africa theory.

The multiregionalists counter that they've never argued for *complete* isolation—that there's always been some flow of genes between populations, enough interbreeding to ensure that clearly beneficial *sapiens* characteristics would quickly be conferred on peoples throughout the Old World. "Just as genes flow now from Johannesburg to Beijing and from Melbourne to Paris, they have been flowing that way ever since humanity evolved," says Alan Thorne of the Australian National University in Canberra, an outspoken multiregionalist.

Stanford archeologist Richard Klein, another out-of-Africa supporter, believes the evidence actually *does* point to just such a long, deep isolation of Asian populations from African ones. The fossil record, he says, shows that while archaic forms of *Homo sapiens* were developing in Africa, *erectus* was remaining much the same in Asia. In fact, if some *erectus* fossils from a site called Ngandong in Java turn out to be as young as 100,000 years, as some researchers believe, then *erectus* was still alive on Java at the same time that fully modern human beings were living in Africa and the Middle East. Even more important, Klein says, is the cultural evidence. That Acheulean tools never reached East Asia, even after their invention in Africa, could mean the inventors never reached East Asia either. "You could argue that the new dates show that until very recently there was a long biological and cultural division between Asia on one hand, and Africa and Europe on the other," says Klein. In other words, there must have been two separate lineages of *erectus*, and since there aren't two separate lineages of modern humans, one of those must have gone extinct: presumably the Asian lineage, hastened into oblivion by the arrival of the more culturally adept, tool-laden *Homo sapiens*.

Naturally this argument is anathema to the multiregionalists. But this tenacious debate is unlikely to be resolved without basketfuls of new fossils, new ways of interpreting old ones—and new dates. In Berkeley, Curtis and Swisher are already busy applying the argon-argon method to the Ngandong fossils, which could represent some of the last surviving *Homo erectus* populations on Earth. They also hope to work their radiometric magic on a key *erectus* skull from Olduvai Gorge. In the meantime, at least one thing has become clear: *Homo erectus*, for so long the humdrum hominid, is just as fascinating, contentious, and elusive a character as any other in the human evolutionary story.

FURTHER READING

Eugène Dubois & the Ape-Man from Java. Bert Theunissen. Kluwer Academic, 1989. When a Dutch army surgeon, determined to prove Darwin right, traveled to Java in search of the missing link between apes and humans, he inadvertently opened a paleontological Pandora's box. This is Dubois's story, the story of the discovery of *Homo erectus*.

James Shreeve is the coauthor, with anthropologist Donald Johanson, of Lucy's Child: The Discovery of a Human Ancestor. *His book,* The Neandertal Enigma: Solving the Mystery of Modern Human Origins, *was published in 1995, and he is at work on a novel that a reliable source calls "a murder thriller about the species question."*

Reprinted with permission from *Discover* magazine, September 1994, pp. 80–84, 86, 88–89. © 1994 by The Walt Disney Company.

DOUBTING DMANISI

Pat Shipman

Why are some discoveries welcomed, whereas others are received with skepticism? I am prompted to ask this by recent developments in paleoanthropology. On the face of things, the story is an old one: International team finds startling new fossil human, oldest of its type in the region; experts agog. The catch is that the new find now being hailed merely echoes an earlier one in the same place, by many of the same researchers—but the early find was received with a "wait and see" attitude, if not outright disbelief. What makes the difference?

The original find, in 1991, was a primitive human mandible or jaw found at the then newly discovered fossil site of Dmanisi in the Republic of Georgia. A joint German-Georgian team of scientists and students excavated there for some months, recovering beautiful fossils of extinct species like saber-toothed cats, elephants and rhinos, along with some crude stone tools. On the last day—similar episodes are so common that the Last Day Find is practically a cliché—Antje Justus, a German graduate student, freed a partial skeleton of a saber-tooth cat from the sediments in her area of the dig. Lying directly underneath the extinct cat was the fossilized jaw of a primitive human, with a complete set of teeth. This was the find everyone had been hoping for all summer long.

In that moment, Dmanisi was transformed from being an interesting site to being one of major significance for human origins. Although the jaw itself could not be dated directly (as is often the case), its inferred age was impressive. The most recent record of the extinct animals found at Dmanisi turned out to be about 1.2 million years ago, while the fresh-looking lava lay underneath the fossil-bearing sediments was estimated to be about 1.8 million years old, according to preliminary radiometric dating. That meant that the owner of the Dmanisi mandible lived in the interval between 1.2 and 1.8 million years ago, making it the earliest evidence of *Homo erectus* from the Eurasian continent by a significant margin.

The first I heard of the find was in December of 1991, when Justus, paleontologist Leo Gabunia of the Republic of Georgia National Academy of Sciences, and dig director David Lordkipanidze of the Georgia State Museum traveled to a conference on *Homo erectus* at the Senckenberg Museum in Frankfurt, Germany. Gabunia and Justus gave a joint presentation briefly describing the site, the fauna, the tools, the jaw and the preliminary dates. They generously brought the original fossil with them, so that colleagues could examine it firsthand during the workshop portion of the conference.

I knew most of the conference participants, but Gabunia, Justus and Lordkipanidze seemed to have come out of nowhere, speaking of a site I couldn't find without an atlas. Gabunia is a quiet, silver-haired man who spoke in French so clear that even I understood the jaw's anatomy. Justus put the find in context, speaking in articulate English and looking even younger than she was. Lordkipanidze fell somewhere in the middle in terms of age and personality; his English was excellent, his enthusiasm palpable, and he was obviously knowledgeable. If they were even half right in what they were saying, this was a very important new find indeed.

Separated at Birth?

Like everyone else, I was eager to look at the jaw. I knew the African *erectus* specimens well, for my husband, Alan Walker, had co-directed the dig at Nariokotome, Kenya, which had yielded the most complete known skeleton of *Homo erectus* a few years before. (In 1991, as now, some researchers would call the Nariokotome and other early African specimens *Homo ergaster* to distinguish them from their presumed descendants in Eurasia, the fossils originally dubbed *Homo erectus*.) Whatever you want to call them, the specimens from Dmanisi and Nariokotome needed close comparison. When Gabunia put his fossil next to the cast of the Nariokotome jaw that Alan had brought, there was an almost visible spark of recognition. The two jaws were not just *similar*; they might have come from twins. Impulsively, Alan gave Gabunia the Nariokotome cast to take home with him, knowing there was none in the Republic of Georgia.

From then on, I was convinced the new jaw was *Homo erectus* and probably a very old one. The morphology, the date, the fauna were all right. No other Eurasian site had yielded hominids (human ancestors) anywhere near as old as the Dmanisi jaw; most were less than half a million years old. Only in Africa were there hominids dated to more than 1 million years, and the oldest *Homo erectus* (or *ergaster*, for those who preferred that term) in Africa was about 2 million years ago. By about 1 million years, *Homo erectus* had massively expanded its geographic range and was found in Java, somewhat later in China and later still in Europe. What propelled *Homo erectus* out of Africa into such a stunning dispersal? And why was there a time lag of almost 1 million years between the species' first evolutionary appearance in Africa and its invasion of Eurasia? It was an intriguing mystery.

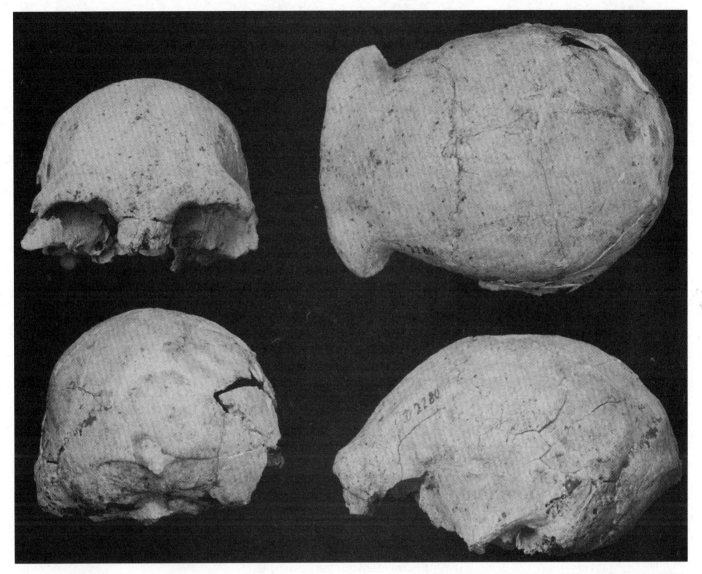

Figure 1. Partial skull *(above four perspectives)* and full skull *(next page)* found in Dmanisi, the Republic of Georgia, confirm earlier claims for a 1.7-million-year-old dispersal of *Homo erectus* out of Africa. Many anthropologists were surprised by the fossils' antiquity and by their close anatomical resemblance to early African specimens of *Homo erectus*.

In 1989, my husband and I had tackled this problem in a paper published in the *Journal of Human Evolution*. We interpreted *Homo erectus*'s expanded brain size, increased body size and powerful strength relative to those of previous hominids as evidence that *Homo erectus* had a strikingly different diet from its predecessors. Earlier hominids were largely or exclusively vegetarian; we hypothesized that *Homo erectus* was the first efficient, regular hunter in human evolution. Only consistent access to very high-quality food would have enabled *erectus* mothers to bear and raise offspring with such nutritionally expensive characteristics.

Diets and Dates

To test our hypothesis, we made a prediction based on the energetic and ecological "rules" that govern the animal kingdom. If *Homo erectus* had indeed undergone a dietary shift from a plant- to an animal-based diet, then the ecological consequences of becoming a predator should be visible in the fossil record. The most obvious repercussion of this dietary shift would have been a density dilemma. Predators must be much more rare (less densely distributed across the landscape) than their prey. Violate this principle and you, as predator, risk starvation. There are two basic solutions to this problem. First, predators may, if time permits, evolve smaller bodies that require fewer or smaller bodies that require fewer or smaller prey. Second, the

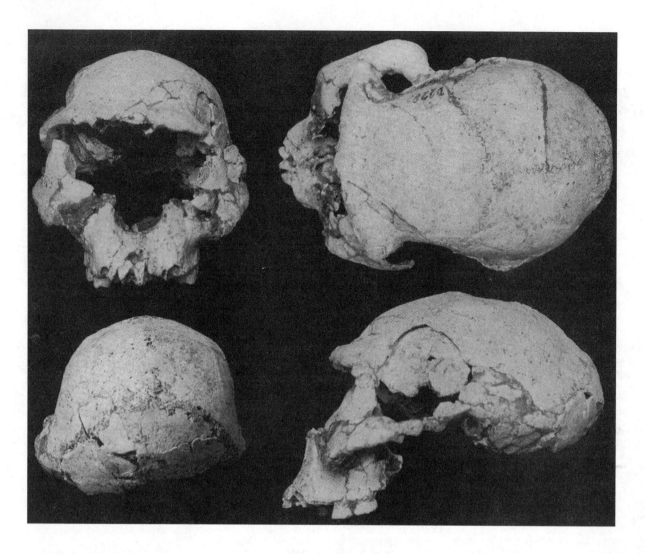

predators may lower their population density if they greatly expand their territory, in which case their depredations are spread across a wider range of prey populations. Could we see one of these solutions in the fossil record? Yes, gratifyingly, we could, for by spreading out of Africa across the Old World, *Homo erectus* had behaved just exactly as a newly predatory species ought to.

What we could not explain or understand was the troublesome time lag *before* the geographic expansion took place. Other colleagues suggested that perhaps *Homo erectus* was confined to Africa until some technological breakthrough occurred, the favorite being the invention of the Acheulian tool culture. We didn't like this idea much, for there is no obvious functional property of Acheulian tools that makes them superior to the earliest Oldowan tools, but we had no better alternative.

Thus, when Gabunia and Justus presented their finds at Senckenberg, every listener in the audience knew that the *Homo erectus* lineage hadn't gotten out of Africa until 1 million years ago. Many scholars concluded that the Dmanisi jaw was not *Homo erectus* but a later species of *Homo* and figured that the date was wrong. What should have made us all suspicious was that proof that *Homo erectus* was confined to Africa prior to 1 million years ago was nothing more than a flimsy absence of evidence of the species in Eurasia.

I wonder, too, whether the identity of those presenting the work contributed to the general skepticism. Had three of the well-known and highly respected leaders of the field announced the Dmanisi finds, the general response might have been more favorable. As it was, Justus was only a student, and students are notoriously prone to oversell the importance of

their finds; Gabunia and Lordkipanidze were mature scientists, but they had no reputation in paleoanthropology as far as Western Europeans and Americans were concerned.

Instead of focusing on the new Dmanisi material, most of the participants at the Senckenberg conference got drawn into a flaming debate over the taxonomic status of *Homo erectus* started by Milford Wolpoff of the University of Michigan, Alan Thorne of the University of Canberra and their colleagues. They argued forcefully that *Homo erectus* had no validity as a species and should be eliminated altogether. All members of the genus *Homo*, from about 2 million years ago to the present, were one highly variable, widely spread species, *Homo sapiens*, with no natural breaks or subdivisions. The subject of the conference, *Homo erectus*, didn't exist. It was a radical suggestion.

Tempers flared and voices grew loud. One European, shocked by the vehemence, said quietly to me that, in his country, such insults would be resolved with pistols at dawn.

Skulls

Although the Dmanisi jaw and its significance were largely overshadowed in 1991, excavations continued. In the summer of 1999, David Lordkipanidze sent word that there was something new and special from Dmanisi: "Skulls," he said enigmatically. We waited eagerly for more information. In May of 2000, a wonderful new paper appeared in *Science* by Gabunia and a host of colleagues, including Justus, Lordkipanidze and the German researchers who had worked with them from the beginning. Enlarging the team were two Americans—Carl Swisher III, and dating specialist, and Susan Antón, an expert on the skull of *Homo erectus*—and Marie-Antoinette de Lumley, a renowned archaeologist from the Laboratoire Museum National d'Histoire Naturelle.

Skulls it was. The paper announced two new skulls of *Homo erectus* from Dmanisi, one very complete and the other a partial skull missing the face. Anatomically, these specimens were very similar to the older, African specimens like Nariokotome, which the Dmanisi team called *Homo ergaster*, meaning the *ergaster* was no longer a strictly African form. The antiquity of Dmanisi was now firmly established at 1.7 million years, based on state-of-the-art radiometric and paleomagnetic studies by Swisher and colleagues; the date was supported by additional study of the faunal material. Finally, more than 1,000 stone artifacts excavated from Dmanisi confirmed that the tools were part of the Oldowan (or Mode I) culture.

This time, the new Dmanisi discoveries were widely hailed by the media who garnered many catchy quotes from major figures in paleoanthropology. "Fossil signs of first human migration are found," *The New York Times* cheered. "This has doubled again the age of humans in Europe, or at least at the gates of Europe," declared Giacomo Giacobini of the University of Turin, echoing an endorsement of Ofer Bar-Yosef of Harvard University, who has visited Dmanisi. "As soon as *Homo erectus* evolves in Africa, they're out," remarked Walker to a reporter. Ian Tattersall of the American Museum of Natural History added, "these guys [were] moving very, very fast." The million-year time lag simply evaporated, leaving in its place and impressively rapid outward dispersal from Africa.

Why are the claims for Dmanisi accepted now, when they were not in 1991? For one thing, the evidence itself is stronger. Skulls are more readily identifiable to species than are jaws when hominids are at issue. Bringing new experts onto the team, well known for their work in dating, morphology and archaeology, has also enhanced the credibility of the work.

Since 1991 the field's focus has shifted. The move to eliminate *Homo erectus* is largely defunct, and many anthropologists use *Homo ergaster* as an informal shorthand for "the earliest part of the evolving *ergaster/erectus* lineage." Moreover, the simple dichotomy that once linked early Africa-Oldowan and contrasted that complex with the late Eurasian-Acheulian has been dismantled. In 1994, Carl Swisher and colleagues produced evidence that the Javan *Homo erectus* sites may range in age from as much as 1.8 million years to roughly 50,000 years, making them both younger and older than previously thought. Scrappy fossils that may be

Homo erectus have been found in China, too, dating to about 1.9 million years. Thus, "early" no longer implies "African." Similarly, though Oldowan tools once suggested great antiquity, they too have been found at younger sites, such as Gran Dolina at Atapuerca, Spain, some 780,000 years ago, whereas the oldest Acheulian sites in Eurasia are now as old as 1.5 million years. A whole series of finds and analyses has contributed to a new paradigm that makes the Dmanisi find more palatable.

This episode offers an important lesson about how science is done. When we scrutinize a colleague's work, we try to make an objective judgement. We evaluate the work against the holy grails of Replicability and Causality, but these are largely unattainable goals, at least for those working with fossils. Like most scientists, we tend to accord an extra dollop of credibility to studies conducted by colleagues known to have done reputable work.

But should the work of the young or the less known be held to higher standards than that of the great matriarchs and silverbacked males of the field? Skepticism is a cheap stance to adopt, for it is easier to cast doubt than to substantiate, especially if new techniques and new paradigms must be forged along the way. Science is a process of discovery, not confirmation. Let us allow for the occasional, delicious surprise that makes us rethink all we thought we knew.

Pat Shipman is an adjunct professor of anthropology at the Pennsylvania State University. In January of 2001, her book about Eugene Dubois's initial discovery of Homo erectus—*entitled* The Man Who Found the Missing Link—*was published by Simon and Schuster. Address: Department of Anthropology, 315 Carpenter Building, Pennsylvania State University, University Park, PA 16801. Internet: pls10@psu.edu*

From *American Scientist*, November/December 2000, pp. 491–494. © 2000 by American Scientist. Reprinted by permission.

The Scavenging of "Peking Man"

New evidence shows that a venerable cave was neither hearth nor home.

By Noel T. Boaz and Russell L. Ciochon

China is filled with archaeological wonders, but few can rival the Peking Man Site at Zhoukoudian, which has been inscribed on UNESCO's World Heritage List. Located about thirty miles southwest of Beijing, the town of Zhoukoudian boasts several attractions, including ruins of Buddhist monasteries dating from the Ming Dynasty (1368–1644). But the town's main claim to fame is Longgushan, or Dragon Bone Hill, the site of the cave that yielded the first (and still the largest) cache of fossils of *Homo erectus pekinensis*, historically known as Peking man—a human relative who walked upright and whose thick skull bones and beetling brow housed a brain three-quarters the size of *H. sapiens*'s.

The remains of about forty-five individuals—more than half of them women and children—along with thousands of stone stools, debris from tool manufacturing, and thousands of animal bones, were contained within the hundred-foot-thick deposits that once completely filled the original cave. The task of excavation, initiated in 1921, was not completed until 1982. Some evidence unearthed at the site suggested that these creatures, who lived from about 600,000 to 300,000 years ago, had mastered the use of fire and practiced cannibalism. But despite years of excavation and analysis, little is certain about what occurred here long ago. In the past two years we have visited the cave site, reexamined the fossils, and

carried out new tests in an effort to sort out the facts.

To most of the early excavators, such as anatomist Davidson Black, paleontologist Pierre Teilhard de Chardin, and archaeologist Henri Breuil, the likely scenario was that these particular early humans lived in the cave where their bones and stone tools were found and that the animal bones were the remains of meals, proof of their hunting expertise. Excavation exposed ash in horizontal patches within the deposits or in vertical patches along the cave's walls; these looked very much like the residue of hearths built up over time.

A more sensational view, first advanced by Breuil in 1929, was that the cave contained evidence of cannibalism. If the animal bones at the site were leftovers from the cave dwellers' hunting forays, he argued, why not the human bones as well? And skulls were conspicuous among the remains, suggesting to him that these might be the trophies of headhunters. Perhaps, Breuil even proposed, the dull-witted *H. erectus* had been prey to a contemporary, advanced cousin, some ancestral form of *H. sapiens*. Most paleoanthropologists rejected this final twist, but the cannibalism hypothesis received considerable support.

In the late 1930s Franz Weidenreich, an eminent German paleoanthropologist working at Peking Union Medical College, described the *H. erectus* remains in

scientific detail. A trained anatomist and medical doctor, he concluded that some of the skulls showed signs of trauma, including scars and fresh injuries from attacks with both blunt and sharp instruments, such as clubs and stone tools. Most convincing to him and others was the systematic destruction of the skulls, apparently at the hands of humans who had decapitated the victims and then broken open the skull bases to retrieve the brains. Weidenreich also believed that the large longitudinal splits seen, for example, in some of the thighbones could only have been caused by humans and were probably made in an effort to extract the marrow.

Others held dissenting views. Chinese paleoanthropologist Pei Wenzhong, who codirected the early Zhoukoudian excavations, disagreed with Breuil and suggested in 1929 that the skulls had been chewed by hyenas. Some Western scientists also had doubts. In 1939 German paleontologist Helmuth Zapfe published his findings on the way hyenas at the Vienna zoo fed on cow bones. Echoing Pei's earlier observations, of which he was aware, Zapfe convincingly argued that many of the bones found at sites like Longgushan closely resembled modern bones broken up by hyenas. In fact, a new term, taphonomy, was coined shortly thereafter for the field Zapfe pioneered: the study of how, after death, animal and plant remains become modi-

Franz Weidenreich, who in the 1930s studied the fossils of Homo erectus *unearthed in China, is caricatured along with Ralph Von Koenigswald (wielding the shovel), who found fossils of* H. erectus *in Java. The fanciful setting is, according to the artist, "any place where the dead are disturbed."*

fied, moved, buried, and fossilized. Franz Weidenreich soon revised his prior interpretation of several *H. erectus* bones whose condition he had attributed to human cannibalistic activity; but he continued to argue that the long-bone splinters and broken skull bases must have resulted from human action.

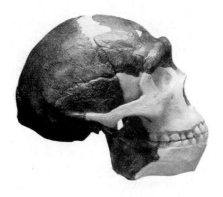

Above: A model of an H. erectus *skull, based on fossils of several individuals from the Peking Man Site at Zhoukoudian. Most of the missing bones, represented in white, mirror existing parts on the opposite side of the skull.*

Following disruptions in fieldwork during World War II (including the loss of all the *H. erectus* fossils collected at Longgushan up to that time, leaving only the casts that had been made of them), Chinese paleoanthropologists resumed investigation of the site. While rejecting the idea of cannibalism, they continued to look upon the cave as a shelter used by early humans equipped with stone tools and fire, as reflected in the title of paleoanthropologist Jia Lampo's book *The Cave Home of Peking Man*, published in 1975.

About this time, Western scientists began to appreciate and develop the field of taphonomy. A few scholars, notably U.S. archaeologist Lewis R. Binford, then reexamined the Longgushan evidence, but only from a distance, concluding that the burning of accumulated bat or bird guano may have accounted for the ash in the cave. With the founding in 1993 of the Zhoukoudian International Paleoanthropological Research Center at Beijing's Institute of Vertebrate Paleontology and Paleoanthropology, a new era of multidisciplinary and international re-

search at Longgushan began. At the institute, we have been able to collaborate with paleontologists Xu Qinqi and Liu Jinyi and with other scholars in a reassessment of the excavations.

> *It looked as if* H. erectus *had smashed open the skulls to cannibalize the brains.*

One of taphonomy's maxims is that the most common animals at a fossil site and/or the animals whose remains there are the most complete are most likely the ones to have inhabited the area in life. Standing in the Beijing institute amid row after row of museum cases filled with mammal fossils from the cave, we were immediately struck by how few belonged to *H. erectus*—perhaps only 0.5 percent. This suggests that most of the time, this species did not live in the cave. Furthermore, none of the *H. erectus* skel-

AMNH

The early investigations at Zhoukoudian were coordinated by the Cenozoic Research Laboratory in Beijing. Staff members there included (left to right in foreground) Teilhard de Chardin, Franz Weidenreich, Yang Zhongjian, Pei Wenzhong, and Bian Meinian.

etons is complete. There is a dearth of limb bones, especially of forearms, hands, lower leg bones, and feet—indicating to us that these individuals died somewhere else and that their partial remains were subsequently brought to the cave. But how?

The answer was suggested by the remains of the most common and complete animal skeletons in the cave deposit: those of the giant hyena, *Pachycrocuta brevirostris*. Had *H. erectus*, instead of being the mighty hunters of anthropological lore, simply met the same ignominious fate as the deer and other prey species in the cave? This possibility, which had been raised much earlier by Pei and Zapfe, drew backing from subsequent studies by others. In 1970, for example, British paleontologist Anthony J. Sutcliffe reported finding a modern hyena den in Kenya that contained a number of human bones, including skulls, which the animals had apparently obtained from a nearby hospital cemetery. In the same year, South African zoologist C. K. Brain published the findings of his extensive feeding experiments with captive carnivores, akin to those of Zapfe three decades earlier. One of Brain's

conclusions was that carnivores tend to chew up and destroy the ends of the extremities, leaving, in the case of primates, very little of the hands and feet.

AMNH

During the 1930s, excavators dug down through the hundred-foot-thick deposits that contained the remains of "Peking man." The deposits, which also yielded animal bones, stone tools, and layers of ash, had completely filled an ancient cave.

To test the giant hyena hypothesis, we examined all the fossil casts and the few actual fossils of *H. erectus* from Longgushan. We looked for both carnivore bite marks and the shallow, V-shaped straight cuts that would be left by stone tools (although we realized that cut marks would probably not be detectable on the casts). We also analyzed each sample's fracture patterns. Breaks at right angles indicate damage long after death, when the bone is fossilized or fossilizing; fractures in fresh bone tend to be irregular, following natural structural lines. Breakage due to crushing by cave rocks is usually massive, and the fracture marks characteristically match rock fragments pushed into the bone.

We were surprised by our findings. Two-thirds of Longgushan's *H. erectus* fossils display what we are convinced are one or more of the following kinds of damage: puncture marks from a carnivore's large, pointed front teeth, most likely the canines of a hyena; long, scraping bite marks, typified by U-shaped grooves along the bone; and fracture patterns comparable to those created by modern hyenas when they chew bone. Moreover, we feel that the longitudinal

Franz Weidenreich at his laboratory at the American Museum of Natural History in the 1940s, with ape and human skulls

veals telltale surface etchings from stomach acid, indicating it was swallowed and then disgorged.

The pattern of damage on some of the skulls sheds light on how hyenas may have handled them. Bite marks on the brow ridge above the eyes indicate that this protrusion had been grasped and bitten by an animal in the course of chewing off the face. Most animals' facial bones are quite thin, and modern hyenas frequently attack or bite the face first; similarly, their ancient predecessors would likely have discovered this vulnerable region in *H. erectus*. Practically no such facial bones, whose structure is known to us from discoveries at other sites, have been found in the Longgushan cave.

The rest of the skull is a pretty tough nut to crack, however, even for *Pachycrocuta*, since it consists of bones half again as thick as those of a modern human, with massive mounds called tori above the eyes and ears and around the back of the skull. Puncture marks and elongated bite marks around the skulls reveal that the hyenas gnawed at and grappled with them, probably in an effort to crack open the cranium and consume the tasty, lipid-rich brain. We concluded that the hyenas probably succeeded best

*A composite image of the skulls of **Pachycrocuta** and **H. erectus**, shows how the giant hyena may have attacked the face. Beneath is a disgorged piece of an **H. erectus** thighbone.*

by chewing through the face, gaining a purchase on the bone surrounding the foramen magnum (the opening in the cranium where the spinal cord enters), and then gnawing away until the skull vault cracked apart or the opening was large enough to expose the brain. This is how we believe the skull bases were destroyed—not by the actions of cannibalistic *H. erectus*.

splitting of large bones—a feature that Weidenreich considered evidence of human activity—can also be attributed to a hyena, especially one the size of the extinct *Pachycrocuta*, the largest hyena known, whose preferred prey was giant elk and woolly rhinoceros. One of the *H. erectus* bones, part of a femur, even re-

*An artist's depiction of the cave shows hyenas consuming the remains of an **H. erectus**.*

*Two-thirds of the
fossils show bite marks
or fractures inflicted
by carnivores.*

We know from geological studies of the cave that the animal bones found there could not have been washed in by rains or carried in by streams: the sediments in which the bones are found are either very fine-grained—indicating gradual deposition by wind or slow-moving water—or they contain angular, sharp-edged shards that would not have survived in a stream or flood. Some of the bones may have belonged to animals that died inside the cave during the course of living in it or frequenting it. Other bones were probably brought in and chewed on by hyenas and other carnivores.

Cut marks we observed on several mammal bones from the cave suggest that early humans did sometimes make use of Longgushan, even if they were not responsible for accumulating most of the bones. Stone tools left near the cave entrance also attest to their presence. Given its long history, the cave may have served a variety of occupants or at times have been configured as several separate, smaller shelters. Another possibility is that, in a form of time-sharing, early humans ventured partway into the cave during the day to scavenge on what the hyenas had not eaten and to find temporary shelter. They may not have realized that the animals, which roamed at twilight and at night, were sleeping in the dark recesses a couple of hundred feet away.

What about the ash in the cave, which has been taken as evidence that *H. erectus* used fire? Recently published work by geochemist Steve Weiner and his team at the Weizmann Institute of Science in Israel suggests that the fires were not from hearths. In detailed studies of the ash levels, they discovered no silica-rich layers, which would be left by the burning of wood. Wood (as well as grass and leaves) contains silica particles known as phytoliths—heat-resistant residues that are ubiquitous in archaeological hearth sites. The results indicate that fire was present in the cave but that its controlled use in hearths was not part of the story.

Still, a human hand may somehow be implicated in these fires. One possibility we are exploring in the next phase of our research is that Longgushan was a place where *Pachycrocuta* and *H. erectus* confronted each other as the early humans sought to snatch some of the meat brought back to the cave by the large hyenas. *Pachycrocuta* would have had the home court advantage, but *H. erectus*, perhaps using fire to hold the carnivore at bay, could have quickly sliced off slivers of meat. Although today we might turn up our noses at such carrion, it may have been a dependable and highly prized source of food during the Ice Age.

From *Natural History*, March 2001, pp. 46–51. © 2001 the American Museum of Natural History

OLD MASTERS

Brilliant paintings brightened the caves of our early ancestors. But were the artists picturing their mythic beliefs or simply showing what they ate for dinner?

Pat Shipman

Fifty years ago, in a green valley of the Dordogne region of southwest France, a group of teenage boys made the first claustrophobic descent into the labyrinthine caverns of Lascaux. When they reached the main chamber and held their lamps aloft, the sight that flickered into view astonished them. There were animals everywhere. A frieze of wild horses, with chunky bodies and fuzzy, crew-cut manes, galloped across the domed walls and ceiling past the massive figure of a white bull-like creature (the extinct aurochs). Running helter-skelter in the opposing direction were three little stags with delicately drawn antlers. They were followed by more bulls, cows, and calves rounding the corner of the chamber.

Thousands have since admired these paintings in Lascaux's Hall of the Bulls, probably the most magnificent example of Ice Age art known to us today. In fact, by 1963 so many tourists wanted to view the cave that officials were forced to close Lascaux to the general public; the paintings were being threatened as the huge influx of visitors warmed the air in the cave and brought in corrosive algae and pollen. (Fortunately, a nearby exhibit called Lascaux II faithfully reproduces the paintings.) After I first saw these powerful images, they haunted me for several months. I had looked at photographs of Lascaux in books, of course, so I knew that the paintings were beautiful; but what I didn't know was that they would reach across 17,000 years to grab my soul.

Lascaux is not an Ice Age anomaly. Other animal paintings, many exquisitely crafted, adorn hundreds of caves throughout the Dordogne and the French Pyrenees and the region known as Cantabria on the northern coast of Spain. All these images were created by the people we commonly call Cro-Magnons, who lived during the Upper Paleolithic Period, between 10,000 and 30,000 years ago, when Europe lay in the harsh grip of the Ice Age.

What did this wonderful art mean, and what does it tell us about the prehistoric humans who created it? These questions have been asked since the turn of the century, when cave paintings in Spain were first definitively attributed to Paleolithic humans. Until recently the dominant answers were based on rather sweeping symbolic interpretations—attempts, as it were, to read the Paleolithic psyche.

These days some anthropologists are adopting a more literal-minded approach. They are not trying to empathize with the artists' collective soul—a perilous exercise in imagination, considering how remote Cro-Magnon life must have been from ours. Rather, armed with the tools of the late twentieth century—statistics, maps, computer analyses of the art's distribution patterns—the researchers are trying to make sense of the paintings by piecing together their cultural context.

This is a far cry from earlier attempts at interpretation. At the beginning of the century, with little more to go on than his intuition, the French amateur archeologist Abbé Henri Breuil suggested that the pictures were a form of hunting magic. Painting animals, in other words, was a magical way of capturing them, in the hope that it would make the beasts vulnerable to hunters. Abstract symbols painted on the walls were interpreted as hunting paraphernalia. Straight lines drawn to the animals' sides represented spears, and V and O shapes on their hides were seen as wounds. Rectangular grids, some observers thought, might have been fences or animal traps.

In the 1960s this view was brushed aside for a much more complex, somewhat Freudian approach that was brought into fashion by anthropologist André Leroi-Gourhan. He saw the cave paintings as a series of mythograms, or symbolic depictions, of how Paleolithic people viewed their world—a world split between things male and female. Femaleness was represented by animals such as the bison and aurochs (which were sometimes juxtaposed with human female figures in the paintings), and maleness was embodied by such animals as the horse and ibex (which, when accompanied by human figures, were shown only with males). Female images, Leroi-Gourhan suggested, were clustered in the central parts of the dark, womblike caves, while male images either consorted with the female ones or encircled them in the more peripheral areas.

Leroi-Gourhan also ascribed sex to the geometric designs on the cave walls. Thin shapes such as straight lines, which often make up barbed, arrowlike structures, were seen as male (phallic) signs. Full shapes such as ovals, V shapes, triangles, and rectangles were female (vulval) symbols. Thus, an arrow stuck into a V-shaped wound on an animal's hide was a male symbol entering a complementary female one.

Leroi-Gourhan was the first to look for structure in the paintings systematically, and his work reinforced the notion that these cave paintings had underlying designs and were not simply idle graffiti or random doodles. Still, some scholars considered his *"perspective sexomaniaque"* rather farfetched; eventually even he played down some of the sexual interpretations. However, a far bigger problem with both his theory and Breuil's was their sheer monolithic scope: a single explanation was assumed to account for 20,000 years of paintings produced by quite widely scattered groups of people.

Yet it is at least as likely that the paintings carried a number of different messages. The images' meaning may have varied depending on who painted them and where. Increasingly, therefore, researchers have tried to relate the content of the paintings to their context—their distribution within a particular cave, the cave's location within a particular region, and the presence of other nearby dwelling sites, tools, and animal bones in the area.

Anthropologist Patricia Rice and sociologist Ann Paterson, both from West Virginia University, made good use of this principle in their study of a single river valley in the Dordogne region, an area that yielded 90 different caves containing 1,955 animal portrayals and 151 dwelling sites with animal bone deposits. They wanted to find out whether the number of times an animal was painted simply reflected how common it was or whether it revealed further information about the animals or the human artists.

By comparing the bone counts of the various animals—horses, reindeer, red deer, ibex, mammoths, bison, and aurochs—Rice and Paterson were able to score the animals according to their abundance. When they related this number to the number of times a species turned up in the art, they found an interesting relationship: Pictures of the smaller animals, such as deer, were proportionate to their bone counts. But the bigger species, such as horses and bison, were portrayed more often than you'd expect from the faunal remains. In fact, it turned out that to predict how often an animal would appear, you

had to factor in not just its relative abundance but its weight as well.

…animals may have been depicted more or less frequently depending on how aggressive they were to humans.

A commonsense explanation of this finding was that an animal was depicted according to its usefulness as food, with the larger, meatier animals shown more often. This "grocery store" explanation of the art worked well, except for the ibex, which was portrayed as often as the red deer yet was only half its size and, according to the bone counts, not as numerous. The discrepancy led Rice and Paterson to explore the hypothesis that animals may have also been depicted more or less frequently depending on how aggressive they were to humans.

To test this idea, the researchers asked wildlife-management specialists to score the animals according to a "danger index." The feisty ibex, like the big animals, was rated as highly aggressive; and like these other dangerous animals, it was painted more often than just the numbers of its remains would suggest. Milder-tempered red deer and reindeer, on the other hand, were painted only about as often as you'd expect from their bones. Rice and Paterson concluded that the local artists may have portrayed the animals for both "grocery store" and "danger index" reasons. Maybe such art was used to impress important information on the minds of young hunters—drawing attention to the animals that were the most worthwhile to kill, yet balancing the rewards of dinner with the risks of attacking a fearsome animal.

One thing is certain: Paleolithic artists knew their animals well. Subtle physical details, characteristic poses, even seasonal changes in coat color or texture, were deftly observed. At Lascaux bison are pictured shedding their dark winter pelts. Five stags are shown swimming across a river, heads held high above the swirling tide. A stallion is depicted with its lip curled back, responding to a mare

in heat. The reddish coats, stiff black manes, short legs, and potbellies of the Lascaux horses are so well recorded that they look unmistakably like the modern Przhevalsky's horses from Mongolia.

New findings at Solutré, in east-central France, the most famous horse-hunting site from the Upper Paleolithic, show how intimate knowledge of the animal's habits was used to the early hunter's advantage. The study, by archeologist Sandra Olsen of the Virginia Museum of Natural History, set out to reexamine how vast numbers of horses—from tens to hundreds of thousands, according to fossil records—came to be killed in the same, isolated spot. The archeological deposits at Solutré are 27 feet thick, span 20,000 years, and provide a record of stone tools and artifacts as well as faunal remains.

The traditional interpretation of this site was lots of fun but unlikely. The Roche de Solutré is one of several high limestone ridges running east-west from the Saône River to the Massif Central plateau; narrow valleys run between the ridges. When the piles of bones were discovered, in 1866, it was proposed that the site was a "horse jump" similar to the buffalo jumps in the American West, where whole herds of bison were driven off cliffs to their death. Several nineteenth-century paintings depict Cro-Magnon hunters driving a massive herd of wild horses up and off the steep rock of Solutré. But Olsen's bone analysis has shown that the horse jump scenario is almost certainly wrong.

For one thing, the horse bones are not at the foot of the steep western end of Solutré, but in a natural cul-de-sac along the southern face of the ridge. For the horse jump hypothesis to work, one of two fairly incredible events had to occur. Either the hunters drove the horses off the western end and then dragged all the carcasses around to the southern face to butcher them or the hunters herded the animals up the steep slope and then forced them to veer off the southern side of the ridge. But behavioral studies show that, unlike bison, wild horses travel not in herds but in small, independent bands. So it would have been extremely difficult for our Cro-Magnons on foot to force lots of horses together and persuade them to jump en masse.

Instead the horse behavior studies suggested to Olsen a new hypothesis. Wild horses commonly winter in the lowlands and summer in the highlands. This migration pattern preserves their forage and lets them avoid the lowland's biting flies and heat in summer and the highland's cold and snow in winter. The Solutré horses, then, would likely have wintered in the Saône's floodplain to the east and summered in the mountains to the west, migrating through the valleys between the ridges. The kill site at Solutré, Olsen notes, lies in the widest of these valleys, the one offering the easiest passage to the horses. What's more, from the hunters' point of view the valley has a convenient cul-de-sac running off to one side. The hunters, she proposes, used a drive lane of brush, twigs, and rocks to divert the horses from their migratory path into the cul-de-sac and then speared the animals to death. Indeed, spear points found at the site support this scenario.

The image of Paleolithic humans moving by flickering lamps, singing, chanting, and drawing their knowledge of their world is hard to resist.

The bottom line in all this is that Olsen's detailed studies of this prehistoric hunting site confirm what the cave art implies: these early humans used their understanding of animals' habits, mating, and migration patterns to come up with extremely successful hunting strategies. Obviously this knowledge must have been vital to the survival of the group and essential to hand down to successive generations. Perhaps the animal friezes in the cave were used as a mnemonic device or as a visual teaching aid in rites of initiation—a means for people to recall or rehearse epic hunts, preserve information, and school their young. The emotional power of the art certainly suggests that this information was crucial to their lives and could not be forgotten.

For all the finely observed animal pictures, we catch only the sketchiest glimpses of humans, in the form of stick figures or stylized line drawings.

The transmission of this knowledge may well have been assisted by more than illustration. French researchers Iégor Reznikoff and Michel Dauvois have recently shown that cave art may well have been used in rituals accompanied by songs or chants. The two studied the acoustic resonances of three caves in the French Pyrenees by singing and whistling through almost five octaves as they walked slowly through each cave. At certain points the caves resonated in response to a particular note, and these points were carefully mapped.

When Reznikoff and Dauvois compared their acoustic map with a map of the cave paintings, they found an astonishing relationship. The best resonance points were all well marked with images, while those with poor acoustics had very few pictures. Even if a resonance point offered little room for a full painting, it was marked in some way—by a set of red dots, for example. It remains to be seen if this intriguing correlation holds true for other caves. In the meantime, the image of Paleolithic humans moving by flickering lamps, singing, chanting, and drawing their knowledge of their world indelibly into their memories is so appealing that I find it hard to resist.

Yet the humans in this mental image of mine are shadowy, strangely elusive people. For all the finely observed animal pictures, we catch only the sketchiest glimpses of humans, in the form of stick figures or stylized line drawings. Still, when Rice and Paterson turned to study these human images in French and Spanish caves, a few striking patterns did emerge. Of the 67 images studied, 52 were male and a mere 15 were female. Only men were depicted as engaged in active behavior, a category that included walking, running, carrying spears, being speared, or falling. Females were a picture of passivity; they stood, sat, or lay prone. Most women were shown in close proximity to another human figure or group of figures, which were always other women. Seldom were men featured in social groups; they were much more likely to be shown facing off with an animal.

These images offer tantalizing clues to Paleolithic life. They suggest a society where males and females led very separate lives. (Male-female couples do not figure at all in Paleolithic art, for all the sexual obsessions of earlier researchers.) Males carried out the only physical activities—or at least the only ones deemed worthy of recording. Their chief preoccupation was hunting, and from all appearances, what counted most was the moment of truth between man and his prey. What women did in Paleolithic society (other than bear children and gather food) remains more obscure. But whatever they did, they mostly did it in the company of other women, which would seem to imply that social interaction, cooperation, and oral communication played an important role in female lives.

If we could learn the sex of the artists, perhaps interpreting the social significance of the art would be easier. Were women's lives so mysterious because the artists were male and chauvinistically showed only men's activities in their paintings? Or perhaps the artists were all female. Is their passive group activity the recording and encoding of the information vital to the group's survival in paintings and carvings? Did they spend their time with other women, learning the songs and chants and the artistic techniques that transmitted and preserved their knowledge? The art that brightened the caves of the Ice Age endures. But the artists who might shed light on its meaning remain as enigmatic as ever.

Pat Shipman wrote about killer bamboo in [Discover,] *February [1990].*

Secrets of the Cave's Art

Finally allowed back into the cave containing the world's oldest rock paintings,
scientists seek clues to the lives and beliefs of ancient artists

BY SHARON BEGLEY

Standing before the hanging rock deep inside the damp cave, archeologist Yanik Le Guillou had a brainstorm: he would mount the digital camera on a 10-foot-long pole, maneuver it around and past the rock, turn the whole contraption just so, and… snap! capture on film whatever was hidden on the wall behind. On the first try, the scientists cut off the head of what looked like a painting of a bison. On the second try they cut off its feet. Finally they captured the whole animal—it was now looking more like a musk ox or a rhinoceros without horns—and the next day bagged even bigger quarry: painted next to the beast were a lion and a mammoth, powerful animals that are almost as rare in Paleolithic cave art as they are on the streets of Paris. It was like peering into the inner sanctum of an art gallery where the dealer kept the best works for his best customers. And although the Grotte Chauvet, in southeast France, was no gathering spot for Stone Agers drinking white wine and nibbling canapés, it came close: for thousands of years, archeologists now think, people returned to the grotto again and again on what seems to have been a spiritual pilgrimage.

The Grotte Chauvet is one of hundreds of natural caverns cut into the pale limestone cliffs that form the Ardèche Gorge. But it is unique. Its stone etchings and 416 paintings—a dozen more were discovered in the 15-day expedition that began last week—are, at 32,000 years, the oldest cave art known to science. The

find consists of mural after mural of bold lions, leaping horses, pensive owls and charging rhinoceroses that together make up a veritable Louvre of Paleolithic art. Although Jean-Marie Chauvet and friends stumbled upon the cave in 1994, for years exploration had been blocked by lawsuits over who owned the rights to the grotto. Finally, archeologist Jean Clottes, a science adviser to France's Ministry of Culture, won permission to lead a team into the cave in 1998. Last week he and a dozen colleagues returned, seeking clues to the social structure, mind-sets and spiritual beliefs of the ancient artists.

They certainly left behind enough clues. A string of three chambers, 1,700 feet long, as well as one connecting gallery and three vestibules, are all covered with masterworks breathtaking in their use of perspective (as in overlapping mammoths) and shading, techniques that

were supposedly not invented until millenniums later. And eons before Seurat got the idea, Stone Age artists had invented pointillism: one animal, probably a bison, is composed of nothing but red dots. Most striking, however, is that the artists had a thing for rhinos, lions, cave bears and mammoths. In contrast, most cave art depicts hunted animals. "Out of these people's whole bestiary, the artists chose predatory, dangerous animals," says archeologist Margaret Conkey of the University of California, Berkeley. By painting species that virtually never wound up on the Paleolithic menu but which "symbolized danger, strength and power," says Clottes, the artists may have been attempting "to capture the essence of" the animals.

Like bemused gallery goers, Clottes's team spends long hours staring at a painting and asking, what does it mean? One clue comes from how the images are integrated into the walls. In the "Goldilocks" chamber, the missing hindquarters of a cave bear drawn in red ocher seem to lie within rather than on the rock. "The bear seems to come out of the wall," says Clottes. And last week Clottes's team discovered two painted ibexes in the same chamber. The horns of one are actually cracks in the wall which the artist scraped and enlarged. "To these people's way of thinking, those animal spirits were in the walls," says Clottes. Painting them, the artists may have believed, allowed the power within to seep into the real world.

Other hints of the cave's spiritual role include engravings of two large pubic triangles—symbols of fertility?—and a creature with human legs but the head and torso of a bison, suggesting that people hoped to incorporate within themselves some of the animals' power. The cave bear in particular may have had special meaning. The presence of 55 ancient bear skulls, including one carefully placed on a fallen rock as if on an altar, suggests a cult of the cave bear. And that may explain why the cave artists chose Chauvet: dozens of hollows in the floor indicate that the enormous bears hibernated there. People returned time and again to view the works. On the 30-foot-long "panel of the horses," the charcoal marks of torches being knocked against the wall were made after the paintings,

says Conkey: the marks are superimposed on the mineral sheen that covers the figures. If painting was the first step in a spiritual quest, perhaps, then paying homage to the works was the second.

Doing cave archeology still means roughing it. Base camp is a 25-foot-deep cave strewn with clothes, equipment and baguettes. But since the discovery of the Lascaux painted caves in 1940, the work has gone high-tech. Clottes's team is photographing the paintings and etchings with a regular 35-mm, a digital camera and an infrared camera, which picks up the red-ocher paint better than standard optical devices. Back at the research base in the valley, the team scans or downloads the photos into computers, which can brighten the colors, pump up the contrast or manipulate the image.

That technique has helped explain two arrays of red dots that seem unique to Chauvet. Using a scanner, the archeologists fed images of the dots into a computer. A program superimposed arrays of hands onto the dots. The best fit to an array of 48 dots is a sequence of handprints made by an adolescent or a short woman. A panel of 92 dots was probably the handiwork of a tall man. The presence of people of different ages and sexes suggests either a communal experience or masters passing their secrets on to apprentices. Even 32,000 years ago, art was created for more than art's sake.

With DANA THOMAS *at the*
Grotte Chauvet

The Gift *of* Gab

Grooves and holes in fossil skulls may reveal when our ancestors began to speak. The big question, though, is what drove them to it?

By Matt Cartmill

People can talk. Other animals can't. They can all communicate in one way or another—to lure mates, at the very least—but their whinnies and wiggles don't do the jobs that language does. The birds and beasts can use their signals to attract, threaten, or alert each other, but they can't ask questions, strike bargains, tell stories, or lay out a plan of action.

Those skills make *Homo sapiens* a uniquely successful, powerful, and dangerous mammal. Other creatures' signals carry only a few limited kinds of information about what's happening at the moment, but language lets us tell each other in limitless detail about what used to be or will be or might be. Language lets us get vast numbers of big, smart fellow primates all working together on a single task—building the Great Wall of China or fighting World War II or flying to the moon. It lets us construct and communicate the gorgeous fantasies of literature and the profound fables of myth. It lets us cheat death by pouring out our knowledge, dreams, and memories into younger people's minds. And it does powerful things for us inside our own minds because we do a lot of our thinking by talking silently to ourselves. Without language, we would be only a sort of upright chimpanzee with funny feet and clever hands. With it, we are the self-possessed masters of the planet.

How did such a marvelous adaptation get started? And if it's so marvelous, why hasn't any other species come up with anything similar? These may be the most important questions we face in studying human evolution. They are also the least understood. But in the past few years, linguists and anthropologists have been making some breakthroughs, and we are now beginning to have a glimmering of some answers.

COULD NEANDERTHALS talk? They seem to have had nimble tongues, but some scientists think the geometry of their throats prevented them from making many clear vowel sounds.

We can reasonably assume that by at least 30,000 years ago people were talking—at any rate, they were producing carvings, rock paintings, and jewelry, as well as ceremonial graves containing various goods. These tokens of art and religion are high-level forms of symbolic behavior, and they imply that the everyday symbol-handling machinery of human language must have been in place then as well.

Language surely goes back further than that, but archeologists don't agree on just how far. Some think that earlier, more basic human behaviors—hunting in groups, tending fires, making tools—also demanded language. Others think

these activities are possible without speech. Chimpanzees, after all, hunt communally, and with human guidance they can learn to tend fires and chip flint.

Paleontologists have pored over the fossil bones of our ancient relatives in search of evidence for speech abilities. Because the most crucial organ for language is the brain, they have looked for signs in the impressions left by the brain on the inner surfaces of fossil skulls, particularly impressions made by parts of the brain called speech areas because damage to them can impair a person's ability to talk or understand language. Unfortunately, it turns out that you can't tell whether a fossil hominid was able to talk simply by looking at brain impressions on the inside of its skull. For one thing, the fit between the brain and the bony braincase is loose in people and other large mammals, and so the impressions we derive from fossil skulls are disappointingly fuzzy. Moreover, we now know that language functions are not tightly localized but spread across many parts of the brain.

Faced with these obstacles, researchers have turned from the brain to other organs used in speech, such as the throat and tongue. Some have measured the fossil skulls and jaws of early hominids, tried to reconstruct the shape of their vocal tracts, and then applied the laws of acoustics to them to see whether they might have been capable of producing human speech.

All mammals produce their vocal noises by contracting muscles that compress the rib cage. The air in the lungs is driven out through the windpipe to the larynx, where it flows between the vocal cords. More like flaps than cords, these structures vibrate in the breeze, producing a buzzing sound that becomes the voice. The human difference lies in what happens to the air after it gets past the vocal cords.

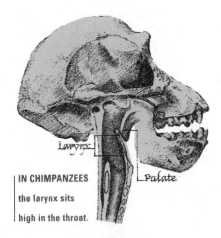

IN CHIMPANZEES
the larynx sits
high in the throat.

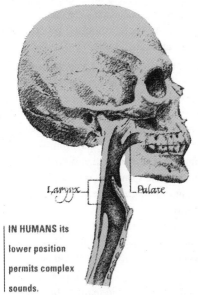

IN HUMANS its
lower position
permits complex
sounds.

ILLUSTRATIONS BY DUGALD STERMER

In people, the larynx lies well below the back of the tongue, and most of the air goes out through the mouth when we talk. We make only a few sounds by exhaling through the nose—for instance, nasal consonants like *m* or *n*, or the so-called nasal vowels in words like the French *bon* and *vin*. But in most mammals, including apes, the larynx sticks farther up behind the tongue, into the back of the nose, and most of the exhaled air passes out through the nostrils. Nonhuman mammals make mostly nasal sounds as a result.

At some point in human evolution the larynx must have descended from its previous heights, and this change had some serious drawbacks. It put the opening of the windpipe squarely in the path of descending food, making it dangerously easy for us to choke to death if a chunk of meat goes down the wrong way—something that rarely happens to a dog or a cat. Why has evolution exposed us to this danger?

Some scientists think that the benefits outweighed the risks, because lowering the larynx improved the quality of our vowels and made speech easier to understand. The differences between vowels are produced mainly by changing the size and shape of the airway between the tongue and the roof of the mouth. When the front of the tongue almost touches the palate, you get the *ee* sound in *beet*; when the tongue is humped up high in the back (and the lips are rounded), you get the *oo* sound in *boot*, and so on. We are actually born with a somewhat apelike throat, including a flat tongue and a larynx lying high up in the neck, and this arrangement makes a child's vowels sound less clearly separated from each other than an adult's.

Philip Lieberman of Brown University thinks that an ape-like throat persisted for some time in our hominid ancestors. His studies of fossil jaws and skulls persuade him that a more modern throat didn't evolve until some 500,000 years ago, and that some evolutionary lines in the genus *Homo* never did acquire modern vocal organs. Lieberman concludes that the Neanderthals, who lived in Europe until perhaps 25,000 years ago, belonged to a dead-end lineage that never developed our range of vowels, and that their speech—if they had any at all—would have been harder to understand than ours. Apparently, being easily understood wasn't terribly important to them—not important enough, at any rate, to outweigh the risk of inhaling a chunk of steak into a lowered larynx. This suggests that vocal communication wasn't as central to their lives as it is to ours.

Many paleoanthropologists, especially those who like to see Neanderthals as a separate species, accept this story. Others have their doubts. But the study of other parts of the skeleton in fossil hominids supports some of Lieberman's conclusions. During the 1980s a nearly complete skeleton of a young *Homo* male was recovered from 1.5-million-year-old deposits in northern Kenya. Examining the vertebrae attached to the boy's rib cage, the English anatomist Ann MacLarnon discovered that his spinal cord was proportionately thinner in this region than it is in people today. Since that part of the cord controls most of the muscles that drive air in and out of the lungs, MacLarnon concluded that the youth may not have had the kind of precise neural control over breathing movements that is needed for speech.

This year my colleague Richard Kay, his student Michelle Balow, and I were able to offer some insights from yet another part of the hominid body. The tongue's movements are controlled almost solely by a nerve called the hypoglossal. In its course from the brain to the tongue, this nerve passes through a hole in the skull, and Kay, Balow, and I found that this bony canal is relatively big in modern humans—about twice as big in cross section as that of a like-size chimpanzee. Our larger canal presumably reflects a bigger hypoglossal nerve, giving us the precise control over tongue movements that we need for speech.

We also measured this hole in the skulls of a number of fossil hominids. Australopithecines have small canals like those of apes, suggesting that they couldn't talk. But later *Homo* skulls, beginning with a 400,000-year-old skull from Zambia, all have big, humanlike hypoglossal canals. These are also the skulls that were the first to house brains as big as our own. On these counts our work supports Lieberman's ideas. We disagree only on the matter of Neanderthals. While he claims their throats couldn't have produced human speech, we find that their skulls also had human-size canals for the hypoglossal nerve, suggesting that they could indeed talk.

THE VERDICT IS STILL out on the language abilities of Neanderthals. I tend to think they must have had fully human language. After all, they had brains larger than those of most humans.

In short, several lines of evidence suggest that neither the australopithecines nor the early, small-brained species of *Homo* could talk. Only around half a million years ago did the first big-brained *Homo* evolve language. The verdict is still out on the language abilities of Neanderthals. I tend to think that they must have had fully human language. After all, they had brains larger than those of most modern humans, made elegant stone tools, and knew how to use fire. But if Lieberman and his friends are right about those vowels, Neanderthals may have sounded something like the Swedish chef on *The Muppet Show*.

We are beginning to get some idea of when human language originated, but the fossils can't tell us how it got started, or what the intermediate stages between animal calls and human language might have been like. When trying to understand the origin of a trait that doesn't fossilize, it's sometimes useful to look for similar but simpler versions of it in other creatures living today. With luck, you can find a series of forms that suggest how simple primitive makeshifts could have evolved into more complex and elegant versions. This is how Darwin attacked the problem of the evolution of the eye. Earlier biologists had pointed to the human eye as an example of a marvelously perfect organ that must have been specially created all at once in its final form by God. But Darwin pointed out that animal eyes exist in all stages of complexity, from simple skin cells that can detect only the difference between light and darkness, to pits lined with such cells, and so on all the way to the eyes of people and other vertebrates. This series,

he argued, shows how the human eye could have evolved from simpler precursors by gradual stages.

Can we look to other animals to find simpler precursors of language? It seems unlikely. Scientists have sought experimental evidence of language in dolphins and chimpanzees, thus far without success. But even if we had no experimental studies, common sense would tell us that the other animals can't have languages like ours. If they had, we would be in big trouble because they would organize against us. They don't. Outside of Gary Larson's *Far Side* cartoons and George Orwell's *Animal Farm*, farmers don't have to watch their backs when they visit the cowshed. There are no conspiracies among cows, or even among dolphins and chimpanzees. Unlike human slaves or prisoners, they never plot rebellions against their oppressors.

Even if language as a whole has no parallels in animal communication, might some of its peculiar properties be foreshadowed among the beasts around us? If so, that might tell us something about how and in what order these properties were acquired. One such property is reference. Most of the units of human languages refer to things—to individuals (like *Fido*), or to types of objects (*dog*), actions (*sit*), or properties (*furry*). Animal signals don't have this kind of referential meaning. Instead, they have what is called instrumental meaning: this is, they act as stimuli that trigger desired responses from others. A frog's mating croak doesn't *refer* to sex. Its purpose is to get some, not to talk about it. People, too, have signals of this purely animal sort—for example, weeping, laughing, and screaming—but these stand outside language. They have powerful meanings for us but not the kind of meaning that words have.

Some animal signals have a focused meaning that looks a bit like reference. For example, vervet monkeys give different warning calls for different predators. When they hear the "leopard" call, vervets climb trees and anxiously look down; when they hear the "eagle" call, they hide in low bushes or look up. But although the vervets' leopard call is in some sense about leopards, it isn't a word for leopard. Like a frog's croak or

human weeping, its meaning is strictly instrumental; it's a stimulus that elicits an automatic response. All a vervet can "say" with it is "*Eeek! A leopard!*"—not "I really hate leopard!" or "No leopards here, thank goodness" or "A leopard ate Alice yesterday."

AUSTRALOPITHECUS africanus and other early hominids couldn't speak.

In these English sentences, such referential words as *leopard* work their magic through an accompanying framework of nonreferential, grammatical words, which set up an empty web of meaning that the referential symbols fill in. When Lewis Carroll tells us in "Jabberwocky" that "the slithy toves did gyre and gimble in the wabe," we have no idea what he is talking about, but we do know certain things—for instance, that all this happened in the past and that there was more than one tove but only one wabe. We know these things because of the grammatical structure of the sentence, a structure that linguists call syntax. Again, there's nothing much like it in any animal signals.

But if there aren't any intermediate stages between animal calls and human speech, then how could language evolve? What was there for it to evolve from? Until recently, linguists have shrugged off these questions—or else concluded that language didn't evolve at all, but just sprang into existence by accident, through some glorious random mutation. This theory drives Darwinians crazy, but the linguists have been content with it because it fits neatly into some key ideas in modern linguistics.

Forty years ago most linguists thought that people learn to talk through the same sort of behavior reinforcement used in training an animal to do tricks: when children use a word correctly or produce a grammatical sentence, they are rewarded. This picture was swept away in the late 1950s by the revolutionary ideas of Noam Chomsky. Chomsky argued that the structures of syntax lie in unconscious linguistic patterns—

so-called deep structures—that are very different from the surface strings of words that come out of our mouths. Two sentences that look different on the surface (for instance, "A leopard ate Alice" and "Alice was eaten by a leopard") can mean the same thing because they derive from a single deep structure. Conversely, two sentences with different deep structures and different meanings can look exactly the same on the surface (for example, "Fleeing leopards can be dangerous"). Any models of language learning based strictly on the observable behaviors of language, Chomsky insisted, can't account for these deep-lying patterns of meaning.

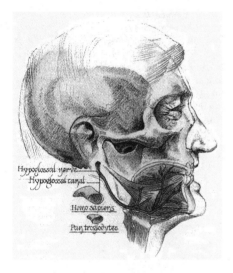

THE TONGUE-CONTROLLING hypoglossal nerve is larger in humans than in chimps.

Chomsky concluded that the deepest structures of language are innate, not learned. We are all born with the same fundamental grammar hard-wired into our brains, and we are preprogrammed to pick up the additional rules of the local language, just as baby ducks are hard-wired to follow the first big animal they see when they hatch. Chomsky could see no evidence of other animals' possessing this innate syntax machinery. He concluded that we can't learn anything about the origins of language by studying other animals and they can't learn language from us. If language learning were just a matter of proper training, Chomsky rea-

soned, we ought to be able to teach English to lab rats, or at least to apes.

As we have seen, apes aren't built to talk. But they can be trained to use sign language or to point to word-symbols on a keyboard. Starting in the 1960s, several experimenters trained chimpanzees and other great apes to use such signs to ask for things and answer questions to get rewards. Linguists, however, were unimpressed. They said that the apes' signs had a purely instrumental meaning: the animals were just doing tricks to get a treat. And there was no trace of syntax in the random-looking jumble of signs the apes produced; an ape that signed "You give me cookie please" one minute might sign "Me cookie please you cookie eat give" the next.

Duane Rumbaugh and Sue Savage-Rumbaugh set to work with chimpanzees at the Yerkes Regional Primate Research Center in Atlanta to try to answer the linguists' criticisms. After many years of mixed results, Sue made a surprising break-through with a young bonobo (or pygmy chimp) named Kanzi. Kanzi had watched his mother, Matata, try to learn signs with little success. When Sue gave up on her and started with Kanzi, she was astonished to discover that he already knew the meaning of 12 of the keyboard symbols. Apparently, he had learned them without any training or rewards. In the years that followed, he learned new symbols quickly and used them referentially, both to answer questions and to "talk" about things that he intended to do or had already done. Still more amazingly, he had a considerable understanding of spoken English—including its syntax. He grasped such grammatical niceties as case structures ("Can you throw a potato to the turtle?") and if-then implication ("You can have some cereal if you give Austin your monster mash to play with"). Upon hearing such sentences, Kanzi behaved appropriately 72 percent of the time—more than a 30-month-old human child given the same tests.

Kanzi is a primatologist's dream and a linguist's nightmare. His language-learning abilities seem inexplicable. He didn't need any rewards to learn language, as the old behaviorists would have predicted; but he also defies the

Chomskyan model, which can't explain why a speechless ape would have an innate tendency to learn English. It looks as though some animals can develop linguistic abilities for reasons unrelated to language itself.

BRAIN ENLARGEMENT in hominids may have been the result of evolutionary pressures that favored intelligence. As a side effect, human evolution crossed a threshold at which language became possible.

Neuroscientist William Calvin of the University of Washington and linguist Derek Bickerton of the University of Hawaii have a suggestion as to what those reasons might be. In their forthcoming book, *Lingua ex Machina*, they argue that the ability to create symbols—signs that refer to things—is potentially present in any animal that can learn to interpret natural signs, such as a trail of footprints. Syntax, meanwhile, emerges from the abstract thought required for a social life. In apes and some other mammals with complex and subtle social relationships, individuals make alliances and act altruistically towards others, with the implicit understanding that their favors will be returned. To succeed in such societies, animals need to choose trustworthy allies and to detect and punish cheaters who take but never give anything in return. This demands fitting a shifting constellation of individuals into an abstract mental model of social roles (debtors, creditors, allies, and so on) connected by social expectations ("If you scratch my back, I'll scratch yours"). Calvin and Bickerton believe that such abstract models of social obligation furnished the basic pattern for the deep structures of syntax.

These foreshadowings of symbols and syntax, they propose, laid the groundwork for language in a lot of social animals but didn't create language itself. That had to wait until our ancestors evolved brains big enough to handle the large-scale operations needed to generate and process complex strings of signs. Calvin and Bickerton suggest that brain enlargement in our ancestry was the result of evolutionary pressures that favored intelligence and motor coordination for making tools and throwing weapons. As a side effect of these selection pressures, which had nothing to do with communication, human evolution crossed a threshold at which language became possible. Big-brained, nonhuman animals like Kanzi remain just on the verge of language.

FOSSILS HINT that language dawned 500,000 years ago.

This story reconciles natural selection with the linguists' insistence that you can't evolve language out of an animal communication system. It is also consistent with what we know about language from the fossil record. The earliest hominids with modern-size brains also seem to be the first ones with modern-size hypoglossal canals. Lieberman thinks that these are also the first hominids with modern vocal tracts. It may be no coincidence that all three of these changes seem to show up together around half a million years ago. If Calvin and Bickerton are right, the enlargement of the brain may have abruptly brought language into being at this time, which would have placed new selection pressures on the evolving throat and tongue.

This account may be wrong in some of its details, but the story in its broad outlines solves so many puzzles and ties up so many loose ends that something like it must surely be correct. It also promises to resolve our conflicting views of the boundary between people and animals. To some people, it seems obvious that human beings are utterly different from any beasts. To others, it's just as obvious that many other animals are essentially like us, only with fewer smarts and more fur. Each party finds the other's view of humanity alien and threatening. The story of language origins sketched above suggests that both parties are right: the human difference is real and profound, but it is rooted in aspects of psychology and biology that we share with our close animal relatives. If the growing consensus on the origins of language can join these disparate truths together, it will be a big step forward in the study of human evolution.

MATT CARTMILL is a professor at Duke, where he teaches anatomy and anthropology and studies animal locomotion. Cartmill is also the author of numerous articles and books on the evolution of people and other animals, including an award-winning book on hunting, A View to a Death in the Morning. *He is the president of the American Association of Physical Anthropologists.*

The Dating Game

*By tracking changes in ancient atoms, archeologists are establishing
the astonishing antiquity of modern humanity.*

James Shreeve

Four years ago archeologists Alison Brooks and John Yellen discovered what might be the earliest traces of modern human culture in the world. The only trouble is, nobody believes them. Sometimes they can't quite believe it themselves.

Their discovery came on a sunsoaked hillside called Katanda, in a remote corner of Zaire near the Ugandan border. Thirty yards below, the Semliki River runs so clear and cool the submerged hippos look like giant lumps of jade. But in the excavation itself, the heat is enough to make anyone doubt his eyes.

Katanda is a long way from the plains of Ice Age Europe, which archeologists have long believed to be the setting for the first appearance of truly modern culture: the flourish of new tool technologies, art, and body ornamentation known as the Upper Paleolithic, which began about 40,000 years ago. For several years Brooks, an archeologist at George Washington University had been pursuing the heretical hypothesis that humans in Africa had invented sophisticated technologies even earlier, while their European counterparts were still getting by with the same sorts of tools they'd been using for hundreds of thousands of years. If conclusive evidence hadn't turned up, it was only because nobody had really bothered to look for it.

"In France alone there must be three hundred well-excavated sites dating from the period we call the Middle Paleolithic," Brooks says. "In Africa there are barely two dozen on the whole continent."

One of those two dozen is Katanda. On an afternoon in 1988 John Yellen— archeology program director at the National Science Foundation and Brooks's husband—was digging in a densely packed litter of giant catfish bones, river stones, and Middle Paleolithic stone tools. From the rubble he extricated a beautifully crafted, fossilized bone harpoon point. Eventually two more whole points and fragments of five others turned up, all of them elaborately barbed and polished. A few feet away, the scientists uncovered pieces of an equally well crafted daggerlike tool. In design and workmanship the harpoons were not unlike those at the very end of the Upper Paleolithic, some 14,000 years ago. But there was one important difference. Brooks and Yellen believe the deposits John was standing in were at least five times that old. To put this in perspective, imagine discovering a prototypical Pontiac in Leonardo da Vinci's attic.

"If the site is as old as we think it is," says Brooks, "it could clinch the argument that modern humans evolved in Africa."

Ever since the discovery the couple have devoted themselves to chopping away at that stubborn little word *if*. In the face of the entrenched skepticism of their colleagues, it is an uphill task. But they do have some leverage. In those same four years since the first harpoon was found at Katanda, a breakthrough has revived the question of modern human origins. The breakthrough is not some new skeleton pulled out of the ground. Nor is it the highly publicized Eve hypothesis, put forth by geneticists, suggesting that all humans on Earth today share a common female ancestor who lived in Africa 200,000 years ago. The real advance, abiding quietly in the shadows while Eve draws the limelight, is simply a new way of telling time.

To be precise, it is a whole smorgasbord of new ways of telling time. Lately they have all converged on the same exhilarating, mortifying revelation: what little we thought we knew about the origins of our own species was hopelessly wrong. From Africa to the Middle East to Australia, the new dating methods are overturning conventional wisdom with insolent abandon, leaving the anthropological community dazed amid a rubble of collapsed certitudes. It is in this shell-shocked climate that Alison Brooks's Pontiac in Leonardo's attic might actually find a hearing.

"Ten years ago I would have said it was impossible for harpoons like these to be so old," says archeologist Michael Mehlman of the Smithsonian's National Museum of Natural History. "Now I'm reserving judgment. Anything can happen."

An archeologist with a freshly uncovered skull, stone tool, or bone Pontiac in hand can take two general approaches to determine its age. The first is called relative dating. Essentially the archeologist places the find in the context of the surrounding geological deposits. If the new discovery is found in a brown sediment lying beneath a yellowish layer of sand, then, all things being equal, it is older than the yellow sand layer or any other deposit higher up. The fossilized remains of extinct animals found near the object also provide a "biostratigraphic" record that can offer clues to a new find's relative age. (If a stone tool is found alongside an extinct species of horse, then it's a fair bet the tool was made while that kind of horse was still running around.) Sometimes the tools themselves can be used as a guide, if they match up in character and style with tools from other, better-known sites. Relative dating methods like these can tell you whether a find is older or younger than something else, but they cannot pin an age on the object in calendar years.

The most celebrated *absolute* method of telling archeological time, radiocarbon dating, came along in the 1940s. Plants take in carbon from the atmosphere to build tissues, and other organisms take in plants, so carbon ends up in everything from wood to woodchucks. Most carbon exists in the stable form of carbon 12. But some is made up of the unstable, radioactive form carbon 14. When an organism dies, it contains about the same ratio of carbon 12 to carbon 14 that exists in the atmosphere. After death the radioactive carbon 14 atoms begin to decay, changing into stable atoms of nitrogen. The amount of carbon 12, however, stays the same. Scientists can look at the amount of carbon 12 and—based on the ratio—deduce how much carbon 14 was originally present. Since the decay rate of carbon 14 is constant and steady (half of it disappears every 5,730 years), the difference between the amount of carbon 14 originally in a charred bit of wood or bone and the amount present now can be used as a clock to determine the age of the object.

Conventional radiocarbon dates are extremely accurate up to about 40,000 years. This is far and away the best method to date a find—as long as it is younger than this cutoff point. (In older materials, the amount of carbon 14 still left undecayed is so small that even the slightest amount of contamination in the

experimental process leads to highly inaccurate results.) Another dating technique, relying on the decay of radioactive potassium rather than carbon, is available to date volcanic deposits *older* than half a million years. When it was discovered in the late 1950s, radiopotassium dating threw open a window on the emergence of the first members of the human family—the australopithecines, like the famous Lucy, and her more advanced descendants, *Homo habilis* and *Homo erectus.* Until now, however, the period between half a million and 40,000 years—a stretch of time that just happens to embrace the origin of *Homo sapiens*—was practically unknowable by absolute dating techniques. It was as if a geochronological curtain were drawn across the mystery of our species' birth. Behind that curtain the hominid lineage underwent an astonishing metamorphosis, entering the dateless, dark centuries a somewhat precocious bipedal ape and emerging into the range of radiocarbon dating as the culturally resplendent, silver-tongued piece of work we call a modern human being.

Fifteen years ago there was some general agreement about how this change took place. First, what is thought of as an *anatomically* modern human being—with the rounded cranium, vertical forehead, and lightly built skeleton of people today—made its presence known in Europe about 35,000 years ago. Second, along with those first modern-looking people, popularly known as the Cro-Magnons, came the first signs of complex human *behavior*, including tools made of bone and antler as well as of stone, and art, symbolism, social status, ethnic identity, and probably true human language too. Finally, in any one region there was no overlap in time between the appearance of modern humans and the disappearance of "archaic" humans such as the classic Neanderthals, supporting the idea that one group had evolved from the other.

"Thanks to the efforts of the new dating methods," says Fred Smith, an anthropologist at Northern Illinois

University, "we now know that each of these ideas was wrong."

The technique doing the most damage to conventional wisdom is called thermoluminescence, TL for short. (Reader take heed: the terrain of geochronology is full of terms long enough to tie between two trees and trip over, so acronyms are a must.) Unlike radiocarbon dating, which works on organic matter, TL pulls time out of stone.

If you were to pick an ordinary rock up off the ground and try to describe its essential rockness, phrases like "frenetically animated" would probably not leap to mind. But in fact minerals are in a state of constant inner turmoil. Minute amounts of radioactive elements, both within the rock itself and in the surrounding soil and atmosphere, are constantly bombarding its atoms, knocking electrons out of their normal orbits. All this is perfectly normal rock behavior, and after gallivanting around for a hundredth of a second or two, most electrons dutifully return to their normal positions. A few, however, become trapped en route—physically captured within crystal impurities or electronic aberrations in the mineral structure itself. These tiny prisons hold on to their electrons until the mineral is heated, whereupon the traps spring open and the electrons return to their more stable position. As they escape, they release energy in the form of light—a photon for every homeward-bound electron.

Thermoluminescence was observed way back in 1663 by the great English physicist Robert Boyle. One night Boyle took a borrowed diamond to bed with him, for reasons that remain obscure. Resting the diamond "upon a warm part of my Naked Body," Boyle noticed that it soon emitted a warm glow. So taken was he with the responsive gem that the next day he delivered a paper on the subject at the Royal Society, noting his surprise at the glow since his "constitution," he felt, was "not of the hottest."

Three hundred years later another Englishman, Martin Aitken of Oxford University, developed the methods to turn thermoluminescence into a geophysical timepiece. The clock works because the radioactivity bombarding a mineral is fairly constant, so electrons become trapped in those crystalline prisons at a steady rate through time. If you crush the mineral you want to date and heat a few grains to a high enough temperature—about 900 degrees, which is more body heat than Robert Boyle's constitution could ever have produced—all the electron traps will release their captive electrons at once, creating a brilliant puff of light. In a laboratory the intensity of that burst of luminescence can easily be measured with a device called a photomultiplier. The higher the spike of light, the more trapped electrons have accumulated in the sample, and thus the more time has elapsed since it was last exposed to heat. Once a mineral is heated and all the electrons have returned "home," the clock is set back to zero.

Now, our lineage has been making flint tools for hundreds of thousands of years, and somewhere in that long stretch of prehistory we began to use fire as well. Inevitably, some of our less careful ancestors kicked discarded tools into burning hearths, setting their electron clocks back to zero and opening up a ripe opportunity for TL timekeepers in the present. After the fire went out, those flints lay in the ground, pummeled by radioactivity, and each trapped electron was another tick of the clock. Released by laboratory heat, the electrons flash out photons that reveal time gone by.

In the late 1980s Hélène Valladas, an archeologist at the Center for Low-Level Radioactivity of the French Atomic Energy Commission near Paris, along with her father, physicist Georges Valladas, stunned the anthropological community with some TL dates on burned flints taken from two archeological sites in Israel. The first was a cave called Kebara, which had already yielded an astonishingly complete Neanderthal skeleton. Valladas dated flints from the Neanderthal's level at 60,000 years before the present.

In itself this was no surprise, since the date falls well within the known range of the Neanderthals' time on Earth. The shock came a year later, when she used the same technique to pin a date on flints from a nearby cave called Qafzeh, which contained the buried remains of early modern human beings. This time, the spikes of luminescence translated into an age of around 92,000 years. In other words, the more "advanced" human types were a full 30,000 years *older* than the Neanderthals they were supposed to have descended from.

If Valladas's TL dates are accurate, they completely confound the notion that modern humans evolved from Neanderthals in any neat and tidy way. Instead, these two kinds of human, equally endowed culturally but distinctly different in appearance, might have shared the same little nook of the Middle East for tens of thousands of years. To some, this simply does not make sense.

"If these dates are correct, what does this do to what else we know, to the stratigraphy, to fossil man, to the archeology?" worries Anthony Marks, an archeologist at Southern Methodist University. "It's all a mess. Not that the dates are necessarily wrong. But you want to know more about them."

Marks's skepticism is not entirely unfounded. While simple in theory, in practice TL has to overcome some devilish complications. ("If these new techniques were easy, we would have thought of them a long time ago," says geochronologist Gifford Miller of the University of Colorado.) To convert into calendar years the burst of luminescence when a flint is heated, one has to know both the sensitivity of that particular flint to radiation and the dose of radioactive rays it has received each year since it was "zeroed" by fire. The sensitivity of the sample can be determined by assaulting it with artificial radiation in the lab. And the annual dose of radiation received from *within* the sample itself can be calculated fairly easily by measuring how much uranium or other radioactive elements the sample contains. But determining the annual dose from the environment *around* the sample—the radioactivity in the surrounding soil, and cosmic rays from the atmosphere itself—is an iffier proposition. At some sites fluctuations in this environmental dose through the millennia can turn the "absolute" date derived from TL into an absolute nightmare.

Fortunately for Valladas and her colleagues, most of the radiation dose for the Qafzeh flints came from within the flints themselves. The date there of 92,000 years for the modern human skeletons is thus not only the most sensational number so far produced by TL, it is also one of the surest.

"The strong date at Qafzeh was just good luck," says Valladas. "It was just by chance that the internal dose was high and the environmental dose was low."

More recently Valladas and her colleague Norbert Mercier turned their TL techniques to the French site of Saint-Césaire. Last summer they confirmed that a Neanderthal found at Saint-Césaire was only 36,000 years old. This new date, combined with a fresh radiocarbon date of about 40,000 years tagged on some Cro-Magnon sites in northern Spain, strongly suggests that the two types of humans shared the same corner of Europe for several thousand years as the glaciers advanced from the north.

While Valladas has been busy in Europe and the Middle East, other TL timekeepers have produced some astonishing new dates for the first human occupation of Australia. As recently as the 1950s, it was widely believed that Australia had been colonized only some five thousand years ago. The reasoning was typically Eurocentric: since the Australian aborigines were still using stone tools when the first white settlers arrived, they must have just recently developed the capacity to make the difficult sea crossing from Indonesia in the first place. A decade later archeologists grudgingly conceded that the date of first entry might have been closer to the beginning of the Holocene period, 10,000 years ago. In the 1970s radiocarbon dates on human occupation sites pushed the date back again, as far as 32,000 years ago. And now TL studies at two sites in northern Australia drop that first human footstep on the continent—and the sea voyage that preceded it—all the way back to 60,000 years before the present. If these dates stand up, then the once-maligned ancestors of modern aborigines were building ocean-worthy craft some 20,000 years *before* the first signs of sophisticated culture appeared in Europe.

"Luminescence has revolutionized the whole period I work in," says Australian National University archeologist

Rhys Jones, a member of the team responsible for the new TL dates. "In effect, we have at our disposal a new machine—a new time machine."

With so much at stake, however, nobody looks to TL—or to any of the other new "time machines"—as a geochronological panacea. Reputations have been too badly singed in the past by dating methods that claimed more than they could deliver. In the 1970s a flush of excitement over a technique called amino acid racemization led many workers to believe that another continent—North America—had been occupied by humans fully 70,000 years ago. Further testing at the same American sites proved that the magical new method was off by one complete goose egg. The real age of the sites was closer to 7,000 years.

"To work with wrong dates is a luxury we cannot afford," British archeologist Paul Mellars intoned ominously earlier this year, at the beginning of a London meeting of the Royal Society to showcase the new dating technologies. "A wrong date does not simply inhibit research. It could conceivably throw it into reverse."

Fear of just such a catastrophe—not to mention the risk that her own reputation could go up in a puff of light—is what keeps Alison Brooks from declaring outright that she has found exquisitely crafted bone harpoons in Zaire that are more than 40,000 years older than such creations are supposed to be. So far the main support for her argument has been her redating of another site, called Ishango, four miles down the Semliki River from the Katanda site. In the 1950s the Belgian geologist Jean de Heinzelin excavated a harpoon-rich "aquatic civilization" at Ishango that he thought was 8,000 years old. Brooks's radiocarbon dating of the site in the mid-1980s pushed the age back to 25,000. By tracing the layers of sediment shared between Ishango and Katanda, Brooks and her colleagues are convinced that Katanda is much farther down in the stratigraphy—twice as old as Ishango, or perhaps even more. But even though Brooks and Yellen talk freely about their harpoons at meetings, they have yet to

utter such unbelievable numbers in the unforgiving forum of an academic journal.

"It is precisely because no one believes us that we want to make our case airtight before we publish," says Brooks. "We want dates confirming dates confirming dates."

Soon after the harpoons were discovered, the team went to work with thermoluminescence. Unfortunately, no burned flints have been found at the site. Nevertheless, while TL works best on materials that have been completely zeroed by such extreme heat as a campfire, even a strong dose of sunlight can spring some of the electron traps. Thus even ordinary sediments surrounding an archeological find might harbor a readable clock: bleached out by sunlight when they were on the surface, their TL timers started ticking as soon as they were buried by natural processes. Brooks and Yellen have taken soil samples from Katanda for TL, and so far the results are tantalizing—but that's all.

"At this point we think the site is quite old," says geophysicist Allen Franklin of the University of Maryland, who with his Maryland colleague Bill Hornyak is conducting the work. "But we don't want to put a number on it."

As Franklin explains, the problem with dating sediments with TL is that while some of the electron traps might be quickly bleached out by sunlight, others hold on to their electrons more stubbornly. When the sample is then heated in a conventional TL apparatus, these stubborn traps release electrons that were captured perhaps millions of years before the sediments were last exposed to sunlight-teasing date-hungry archeologists with a deceptively old age for the sample.

Brooks does have other irons in the dating fire. The most promising is called electron spin resonance—or ESR, among friends. Like TL, electron spin resonance fashions a clock out of the steadily accumulating electrons caught in traps. But whereas TL measures that accumulation by the strength of the light given off when the traps open, ESR literally counts the captive electrons themselves while

they still rest undisturbed in their prisons.

All electrons "spin" in one of two opposite directions—physicists call them up and down. (Metaphors are a must here because the nature of this "spinning" is quantum mechanical and can be accurately described only in huge mathematical equations.) The spin of each electron creates a tiny magnetic force pointing in one direction, something like a compass needle. Under normal circumstances, the electrons are paired so that their opposing spins and magnetic forces cancel each other out. But trapped electrons are unpaired. By manipulating an external magnetic field placed around the sample to be dated, the captive electrons can be induced to "resonate"—that is, to flip around and spin the other way. When they flip, each electron absorbs a finite amount of energy from a microwave field that is also applied to the sample. This loss of microwave energy can be measured with a detector, and it is a direct count of the number of electrons caught in the traps.

ESR works particularly well on tooth enamel, with an effective range from a thousand to 2 million years. Luckily for Brooks and Yellen, some nice fat hippo teeth have been recovered from Katanda in the layer that also held the harpoons. To date the teeth, they have called in Henry Schwarcz of McMaster University in Ontario, a ubiquitous, veteran geochronologist. In the last ten years Schwarcz has journeyed to some 50 sites throughout Europe, Africa, and western Asia, wherever his precious and arcane services are demanded.

Schwarcz also turned up at the Royal Society meeting, where he explained both the power and the problems of the ESR method. On the plus side is that teeth are hardy remains, found at nearly every archeological site in the world, and that ESR can test a tiny sample again and again—with the luminescence techniques, it's a one-shot deal. ESR can also home in on certain kinds of electron traps, offering some refinement over TL, which lumps them all together.

On the minus side, ESR is subject to the same uncertainties as TL concerning the annual soaking of radiation a sample has received from the environment.

What's more, even the radiation from *within* a tooth cannot be relied on to be constant through time. Tooth enamel has the annoying habit of sucking up uranium from its surroundings while it sits in the ground. The more uranium the tooth contains, the more electrons are being bombarded out of their normal positions, and the faster the electron traps will fill up. Remember: you cannot know how old something is by counting filled traps unless you know the rate at which the traps were filled, year by year. If the tooth had a small amount of internal uranium for 50,000 years but took in a big gulp of the hot stuff 10,000 years ago, calculations based on the tooth's current high uranium level would indicate the electron traps were filled at a much faster rate than they really were. "The big question is, When did the uranium get there?" Schwarcz says. "Did the tooth slurp it all up in three days, or did the uranium accumulate gradually through time?"

One factor muddying the "big question" is the amount of moisture present around the sample during its centuries of burial: a wetter tooth will absorb uranium faster. For this reason, the best ESR sites are those where conditions are driest. Middle Eastern and African deserts are good bets. As far as modern human origins go, the technique has already tagged a date of about 100,000 years on some human fossils from an Israeli cave called Skhul, neatly supporting the TL date of 92,000 from Qafzeh, a few miles away. If a new ESR date from a Neanderthal cave just around the corner from Skhul is right, then Neanderthals were also in the Middle East at about the same time. Meanwhile, in South Africa, a human jawbone from the site of Border Cave—"so modern it boggles the mind," as one researcher puts it—has now been dated with ESR at 60,000 years, nearly

twice as old as any fossil like it in Europe.

But what of the cultural change to modern human behavior—such as the sophisticated technological development expressed by the Katanda harpoons? Schwarcz's dating job at Katanda is not yet finished, and given how much is at stake, he too is understandably reluctant to discuss it. "The site has good potential for ESR," he says guardedly. "Let's put it this way: if the initial results had indicated that the harpoons were not very old after all, we would have said 'So what?' to them and backed off. Well, we haven't backed off."

There are other dating techniques being developed that may, in the future, add more certainty to claims of African modernity. One of them, called uranium-series dating, measures the steady decay of uranium into various daughter elements inside anything formed from carbonates (limestone and cave stalactites, for instance). The principle is very similar to radiocarbon dating—the amount of daughter elements in a stalactite, for example, indicates how long that stalactite has been around—with the advantage that uranium-series dates can stretch back half a million years. Even amino acid racemization, scorned for the last 15 years, is making a comeback, thanks to the discovery that the technique, unreliable when applied to porous bone, is quite accurate when used on hard ostrich eggshells.

In the best of all possible worlds, an archeological site will offer an opportunity for two or more of these dating techniques to be called in so they can be tested against each other. When asked to describe the ideal site, Schwarcz gets a dreamy look on his face. "I see a beautiful human skull sandwiched between two layers of very pure flow-stone," he says, imagining uranium-series dating

turning those cave limestones into time brackets. "A couple of big, chunky hippo teeth are lying next to it, and a little ways off, a bunch of burned flints."

Even without Schwarcz's dream site, the dating methods used separately are pointing to a common theme: the alarming antiquity of modern human events where they are not supposed to be happening in the first place. Brooks sees suggestive traces of complexity not just at Katanda but scattered all over the African continent, as early as 100,000 years before the present. A classic stone tool type called the blade, long considered a trademark of the European Upper Paleolithic, appears in abundance in some South African sites 40,000 to 50,000 years before the Upper Paleolithic begins. The continent may even harbor the earliest hints of art and a symbolic side to human society: tools designed with stylistic meaning; colorful, incandescent minerals, valueless but for their beauty, found hundreds of miles away from their source. More and more, the Cro-Magnons of Europe are beginning to look like the last modern humans to show themselves and start acting "human" rather than the first.

That's not an easy notion for anthropologists and archeologists to swallow. "It just doesn't fit the pattern that those harpoons of Alison's should be so old," says Richard Klein, a paleoanthropologist at the University of Chicago. Then he shrugs. "Of course, if she's right, she has made a remarkable discovery indeed."

Only time will tell.

James Shreeve wrote fiction before turning to science writing. He is the coauthor (with anthropologist Donald Johanson) of Lucy's Child: The Discovery of a Human Ancestor *and the author of* Nature: The Other Earthlings.

Who Were the Neandertals?

Controversial evidence indicates that these hominids interbred with anatomically modern humans and sometimes behaved in surprisingly modern ways

by Kate Wong, *staff writer*

It was such a neat and tidy story. No match for the anatomically modern humans who swept in with a sophisticated culture and technology, the Neandertals—a separate species—were quickly driven to extinction by the invading moderns. But neat and tidy stories about the past have a way of unraveling, and the saga of the Neandertals, it appears, is no exception. For more than 200,000 years, these large-brained hominids occupied Europe and western Asia, battling the bitter cold of glacial maximums and the daily perils of prehistoric life. Today they no longer exist. Beyond these two facts, however, researchers fiercely debate who the Neandertals were, how they lived and exactly what happened to them.

The steadfast effort to resolve these elusive issues stems from a larger dispute over how modern humans evolved. Some researchers posit that our species arose recently (around 200,000 years ago) in Africa and subsequently replaced archaic hominids around the world, whereas others propose that these ancient populations contributed to the early modern human gene pool. As the best known of these archaic groups, Neandertals are critical to the origins contro-

versy. Yet this is more than an academic argument over certain events of our primeval past, for in probing Neandertal biology and behavior, researchers must wrestle with the very notion of what it means to be fully human and determine what, if anything, makes us moderns unique. Indeed, spurred by recent discoveries, paleoanthropologists and archaeologists are increasingly asking, How much like us were they?

Comparisons of Neandertals and modern humans first captured the attention of researchers when a partial Neandertal skeleton turned up in Germany's Neander Valley in 1856. Those remains—a heavily built skull with the signature arched browridge and massive limb bones—were clearly different, and Neandertals were assigned to their own species, *Homo neanderthalensis* (although even then there was disagreement: several German scientists argued that these were the remains of a crippled Cossack horseman). But it was the French discovery of the famous "Old Man" of La Chapelle-aux-Saints some 50 years later that led to the characterization of Neandertals as primitive protohumans. Reconstructions showed them as stooped, lumbering, apelike brutes, in

stark contrast to upright, graceful *Homo sapiens*. The Neandertal, it seemed, represented the ultimate "other," a dim-witted ogre lurking behind the evolutionary threshold of humanity.

Decades later reevaluation of the La Chapelle individual revealed that certain anatomical features had been misinterpreted. In fact, Neandertal posture and movement would have been the same as ours. Since then, paleoanthropologists have struggled to determine whether the morphological features that do characterize Neandertals as a group—such as the robustness of their skeletons, their short limbs and barrel chests, prominent browridges and low, sloping foreheads, protruding midfaces and chinless jaws—warrant designating them as a separate species. Researchers agree that some of these characteristics represent environment adaptations. The Neandertals' stocky body proportions, for example, would have allowed them to retain heat more effectively in the extremely cold weather brought on by glacial cycles. But other traits, such as the form of the Neandertal browridge, lack any clear functional significance and seem to reflect the genetic drift typical of isolated populations.

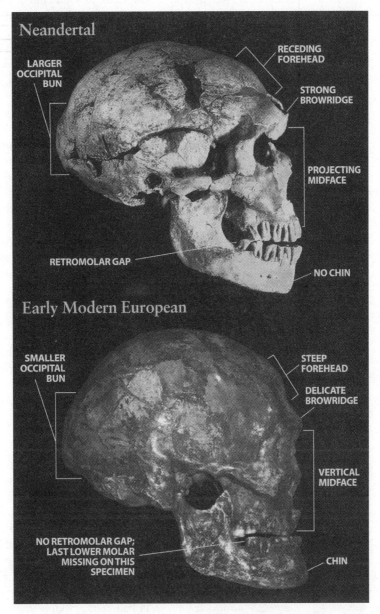

Neandertal

LARGER OCCIPITAL BUN

RECEDING FOREHEAD

STRONG BROWRIDGE

PROJECTING MIDFACE

RETROMOLAR GAP

NO CHIN

Early Modern European

SMALLER OCCIPITAL BUN

STEEP FOREHEAD

DELICATE BROWRIDGE

VERTICAL MIDFACE

NO RETROMOLAR GAP; LAST LOWER MOLAR MISSING ON THIS SPECIMEN

CHIN

ERIK TRINKAUS/MUSÉE DE L'HOMME (TOP);
ARCHEOLOGICKY ÚSTAV AV CR (BOTTOM)

CHARACTERISTIC DIFFERENCES are shown between a Neandertal, represented by a French specimen, La Ferrassie 1, and an early modern, Dolní Vestonice 16, from the Czech Republic. Each aspect can be found in both groups, varying in degree and frequency, but they tend to appear as suites of features.

For those scholars who subscribe to the replacement model of modern human origins, the distinctive Neandertal morphology clearly resulted from following an evolutionary trajectory separate from that of moderns. But for years, another faction of researchers has challenged this interpretation, arguing that many of the features that characterize Neandertals are also seen in the early modern Europeans that followed them. "They clearly have a suite of features that are, overall, different, but it's a frequency difference, not an absolute difference," contends David W. Frayer, a paleoanthropologist at the University of Kansas. "Virtually everything you can find in Neandertals you can find elsewhere."

He points to one of the earliest-known modern Europeans, a fossil from a site in southwestern Germany called Vogelherd, which combines the skull shape of moderns with features that are typically Neandertal, such as the distinct space between the last molar and the ascending part of the lower jaw known as a retromolar gap, and the form of the mandibular foramen—a nerve canal in the lower jaw. Additional evidence, according to Frayer and Milford H. Wolpoff of the University of Michigan, comes from a group of early moderns discovered in Moravia (Czech Republic) at a site called Mladec. The Mladec people, they say, exhibit characteristics on their skulls that other scientists have described as uniquely Neandertal traits.

Guide To Terminology

Neandertal can also be spelled Neanderthal. Around 1900 German orthography changed, and the silent "h" in certain words, such as "thal" (meaning "valley"), was dropped. The designation *Homo neanderthalensis* remains the same, but the common name can be spelled either way.

Paleolithic, or Old Stone Age, is the period ranging from the beginning of culture to the end of the last glaciation. It is subdivided into Lower, Middle and Upper stages.

Mousterian is a Middle Paleolithic, stone tool-based cultural tradition associated with Neandertals and with early moderns in the Near East.

Aurignacian is an Upper Paleolithic cultural tradition associated with moderns that includes advanced tools and art objects.

Châtelperronian is an Upper Paleolithic cultural tradition associated with Neandertals. It resembles both the Mousterian and the Aurignacian.

Although such evidence was once used to argue that Neandertals could have independently evolved into modern Europeans, this view has shifted somewhat. "It's quite clear that people entered Europe as well, so the people that are there later in time are a mix of Neandertals and those populations coming into Europe," says Wolpoff, who believes the two groups differed only as much as living Europeans and aboriginal Australians do. Evidence for mixing also

appears in later Neandertal fossils, according to Fred H. Smith, a paleoanthropologist at Northern Illinois University. Neandertal remains from Vindija cave in northwestern Croatia reflect "the assimilation of some early modern features," he says, referring to their more modern-shaped browridges and the slight presence of a chin on their mandibles.

Those who view Neandertals as a separate species, however, maintain that the Vindija fossils are too fragmentary to be diagnostic and that any similarities that do exist can be attributed to convergent evolution. These researchers likewise dismiss the mixing argument for the early moderns from Mladec. "When I look at the morphology of these people, I see robustness, I don't see Neandertal," counters Christopher B. Stringer of the Natural History Museum in London.

Another reason to doubt these claims for interbreeding, some scientists say, is that they contradict the conclusions reached by Svante Pääbo, then at the University of Munich, and his colleagues, who in July 1997 announced that they had retrieved and analyzed mitochondrial DNA (mtDNA) from a Neandertal fossil. The cover of the journal *Cell*, which contained their report, said it all: "Neandertals Were Not Our Ancestors." From the short stretch of mtDNA they sequenced, the researchers determined that the difference between the Neandertal mtDNA and living moderns' mtDNA was considerably greater than the differences found among living human populations. But though it seemed on the surface that the species question had been answered, undercurrents of doubt have persisted [see "Ancestral Quandary," by Kate Wong, News and Analysis, January 1998].

New fossil evidence from western Europe has intensified interest in whether Neandertals and moderns mixed. In January 1999 researchers announced the discovery in central Portugal's Lapedo Valley of a largely complete skeleton from a four-year-old child buried 24,500 years ago in the Gravettian style known from other early modern Europeans. According to Erik Trinkaus of Washington University, Ci-

dália Duarte of the Portuguese Institute of Archaeology in Lisbon and their colleagues, the specimen, known as Lagar Velho 1, bears a combination of Neandertal and modern human traits that could only have resulted from extensive interbreeding between the two populations [see box "The Hybrid Child from Portugal"].

If the mixed ancestry interpretation for Lagar Velho 1 holds up after further scrutiny, the notion of Neandertals as a variant of our species will gain new strength. Advocates of the replacement model do allow for isolated instances of interbreeding between moderns and the archaic species, because some other closely related mammal species interbreed on occasion. But unlike central and eastern European specimens that are said to show a combination of features, the Portuguese child dates to a time when Neandertals are no longer thought to have existed. For Neandertal features to have persisted thousands of years after those people disappeared, Trinkaus and Duarte say, coexisting populations of Neandertals and moderns must have mixed significantly.

Their interpretation has not gone unchallenged. In a commentary accompanying the team's report in the *Proceedings of the National Academy of Sciences USA* last June, paleoanthropologists Ian Tattersall of the American Museum of Natural History in New York City and Jeffrey H. Schwartz of the University of Pittsburgh argued that Lagar Velho 1 is instead most likely "a chunky Gravettian child." The robust body proportions that Trinkaus and his colleagues view as evidence for Neandertal ancestry, Stringer says, might instead reflect adaptation to Portugal's then cold climate. But this interpretation is problematic, according to Jean-Jacques Hublin of France's CNRS, who points out that although some cold-adapted moderns exhibit such proportions, none are known from that period in Europe. Rather Hublin is troubled that Lagar Velho 1 represents a child, noting that "we do not know anything about the variation in children of a given age in this range of time."

The Hybrid Child From Portugal
by Erik Trinkaus and Cidália Duarte

On a chilly afternoon in late November 1998, while inspecting the Abrigo do Lagar Velho rock-shelter in central Portugal's Lapedo Valley, two archaeology scouts spotted loose sediment in a rodent hole along the shelter's back wall. Knowing that burrowing animals often bring deeper materials to the surface, one of the scouts reached in to see what might have been unearthed. When he withdrew his hand, he held in it something extraordinary: bones of a human child buried nearly 25,000 years ago.

Subsequent excavation of the burial, led by one of us (Duarte), revealed that the four-year-old had been ceremonially interred—covered with red ocher and laid on a bed of burnt vegetation, along with pierced deer teeth and a marine shell—in the Gravettian style known from modern humans of that time across Europe. Based on the abrupt cultural transition seen in archaeological remains from the Iberian Peninsula, it seemed likely that when moderns moved into the area after 30,000 years ago, they rapidly replaced the native Neandertals. So it stood to reason that this specimen, called Lagar Velho 1, represented an early modern child. In fact, it didn't occur to us at first that it could be anything else.

This wonderfully complete skeleton does have a suite of features that align it predominantly with early modern Europeans. These include a prominent chin and certain other details of the mandible (lower jaw), small front teeth, characteristic proportions and muscle markings on the thumb, the narrowness of the front of the pelvis, and several aspects of the shoulder blade and forearm bones. Yet intriguingly, a number of features also suggest Neandertal affinities—specifically the front of the mandible (which slopes backward despite the chin), details of the incisor teeth, the pectoral muscle markings, the knee proportions and the short, strong lower-leg bones. Thus, the Lagar Velho child appears to exhibit a complex mosaic of Neandertal and early modern human features.

This anatomical amalgam is not the result of any abnormalities. Taking normal human growth patterns into consideration, our analysis indicates that except for a bruised forearm, a couple of lines on the bones indicating times when growth was trivially arrested (by sickness or lack of food) and the fact that it died as a child, Lagar Velho 1 developed normally. The combination can only have resulted from a mixed ancestry—something that had not been previously documented for western Europe. We therefore conclude that Lagar Velho 1 resulted from interbreeding between indigenous Iberian Neandertals and early modern humans dispersing throughout Iberia sometime after 30,000 years ago. Because the child lived several millennia after Neandertals are thought to have disappeared, its anatomy probably reflects a true mixing of these populations during the period when they coexisted and not a rare chance mating between a Neandertal and an early modern human.

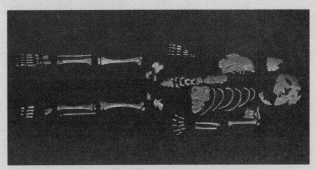

JOSÉ PAULO B. RUAS/PORTUGUESE INSTITUTE OF ARCHAEOLOGY

MORPHOLOGICAL MOSAIC found on this 24,000-year-old skeleton from Portugal indicates that Neandertals and modern humans are members of the same species who interbred freely. The child—Lagar Velho 1—is modern overall but bears some Neandertal traits, such as short lower-limbs bones and a backward-sloping mandible.

Fieldwork conducted last summer yielded major portions of the skull and most of the remaining teeth, along with more archaeological material. And in an effort to fully understand this remarkable specimen, we have organized a team of specialists to examine the skeleton further. Among the projects planned are CT scan analyses of the skull and limb bones and computer-based virtual reconstruction of the damaged skull. Rigorous study is necessary because the discovery of an individual with such a mosaic of features has profound implications. First, it rejects the extreme Out of Africa model of modern human emergence, which proposes that early moderns originating in Africa subsequently displaced all archaic humans in other regions. Instead the Lagar Velho child's anatomy supports a scenario that combines a dispersal of anatomically modern humans out of Africa with mixing between that population and the archaic populations it encountered. (The African ancestry of early modern Europeans is reflected in their relatively long lower-leg bones, a tropical adaptation. Lagar Velho 1, however, has the short shins of the cold-adapted Neandertals.)

Lagar Velho 1 also provides insights into the behavioral similarities of Neandertals and early modern humans. Despite the paleontological evidence indicating anatomical differences between these two groups, their overall adaptive patterns, social behaviors and means of communication (including language) cannot have contrasted greatly. To their contemporaries, the Neandertals were just another group of Pleistocene hunter-gatherers, fully as human as themselves.

ERIK TRINKAUS is a paleoanthropologist at Washington University.

CIDÁLIA DUARTE is completing her Ph.D. in physical anthropology at the University of Alberta in Canada and is the human osteologist at the Portuguese Institute of Archaeology in Lisbon.

SURVIVAL SKILLS

Taxonomic issues aside, much research has focused on Neandertal behavior, which remained largely misunderstood until relatively recently. Neandertals were often portrayed as incapable of hunting or planning ahead, recalls archaeologist John J. Shea of the State University of New York at Stony Brook. "We've got reconstructions of Neandertals as people who couldn't survive a single winter, let alone a quarter of a million years in the worst environments in which humans ever lived," he observes. Analysis of animal remains from the Croatian site of Krapina, however, indicates that Neandertals were skilled hunters capable of killing even large animals such as rhinoceroses, according to University of Cambridge archaeologist Preston T. Miracle. And Shea's studies suggest that some Neandertals employed sophisticated stone-tipped spears to conquer their quarry—a finding supported last year when researches reported the discovery in Syria of a Neandertal-made stone point lodged in a neckbone of a prehistoric wild ass. Moreover, additional research conducted by Shea and investigations carried out by University of Arizona archaeologists Mary C. Stiner and Steven L. Kuhn have shown that Neandertal subsistence strategies varied widely with the environment and the changing seasons.

Such demonstrations refute the notion that Neandertals perished because they could not adapt. But it may be that moderns were better at it. One popular theory posits that modern humans held some cognitive advantage over Neandertals, perhaps a capacity for the most human trait of all: symbolic thought, including language. Explanations such as this one arose from observations that after 40,000 years ago, whereas Neandertal culture remained relatively static, that of modern Europeans boasted a bevy of new features, many of them symbolic. It appeared that only moderns performed elaborate burials, expressed themselves through body ornaments, figurines and cave paintings, and crafted complex bone and antler tools—an industry broadly referred to as Upper Paleolithic.

Neandertal assemblages, in contrast, contained only Middle Paleolithic stone tools made in the Mousterian style.

Yet hints that Neandertals thought symbolically had popped up. Neandertal burials, for example, are well known across Europe, and several, it has been argued, contain grave goods. (Other researchers maintain that for Neandertals, interment merely constituted a way of concealing the decomposing body, which might have attracted unwelcome predators. They view the purported grave goods as miscellaneous objects that happened to be swept into the grave.) Evidence for art, in the form of isolated pierced teeth and engraved bone fragments, and red and yellow ocher, has been reported from a few sites, too, but given their relative rarity, researchers tend to assign alternative explanations to these items.

The possibility that Neandertals might have engaged in modern practices was taken more seriously in 1980, when researchers reported a Neandertal from the Saint-Césaire rock-shelter in Charente-Maritime, France, found in association with stone tools manufactured according to a cultural tradition known as the Châtelperronian, which was assumed to have been the handiwork of moderns. Then, in 1996, Hublin and his colleagues made an announcement that catapulted the Châtelperronian into the archaeological limelight. Excavations that began in the late 1940s at a site called the Grotte du Renne at Arcysur-Cure near Auxerre, France, had yielded numerous blades, body ornaments and bone tools and revealed evidence of huts and hearths—all hallmarks of the Upper Paleolithic. The scant human remains found amid the artifacts were impossible to identify initially, but using computer tomography to examine the hidden inner-ear region preserved inside an otherwise uninformative skull fragment, Hublin's team identified the specimen as Neandertal.

In response, a number of scientists suggested that Neandertals had acquired the modern-looking items either by stealing them, collecting artifacts discarded by moderns or perhaps trading for them. But this view has come under fire,

most recently from archaeologists Francesco d'Errico of the University of Bordeaux and João Zilhão of the Portuguese Institute of Archaeology, who argue that the Châtelperronian artifacts at the Grotte du Renne and elsewhere, though superficially similar to those from the Aurignacian, reflect an older, different method of manufacture [see box "A Case for Neandertal Culture"].

Most researchers are now convinced that Neandertals manufactured the Châtelperronian tools and ornaments, but what prompted this change after hundreds of thousands of years is unclear. Cast in this light, "it's more economical to see that as a result of imitation or acculturation from modern humans than to assume that Neandertals invented it for themselves," reasons Cambridge archaeologist Paul A. Mellars. "It would be an extraordinary coincidence if they invented all these things shortly before the modern humans doing the same things arrived." Furthermore, Mellars disagrees with d'Errico and Zilhão's proposed order of events. "The dating evidence proves to me that [Neandertals] only started to do these things after the modern humans had arrived in western Europe or at least in northern Spain," he asserts. (Unfortunately, because scientists have been unable to date these sites with sufficient precision, researchers can interpret the data differently.)

From his own work on the Grotte du Renne body ornaments, New York University archaeologist Randall White argues that these artifacts reflect manufacturing methods known—albeit at lower frequencies—from Aurignacian ornaments. Given the complicated stratigraphy of the Grotte due Renne site, the modern-looking items might have come from overlying Aurignacian levels. But more important, according to White, the Châtelperronian does not exist outside of France, Belgium, Italy and northern Spain. Once you look at the Upper Paleolithic from a pan-European perspective, he says, "the Châtelperronian becomes post-Aurignacian by a long shot."

A Case For Neandertal Culture
by João Zilhão and Francesco d'Errico

Ever since the discovery nearly 150 years ago of the specimen that defined the Neandertals, researchers have tended to deny Neandertals the behavioral capabilities of modern humans, such as the use of symbols or of complex techniques for tool manufacture. Instead Neandertals were characterized as subhuman, stuck in primitive technical traditions impervious to innovation. And when sophisticated cultural remains were linked to late Neandertals at several sites in western Europe, the evidence was explained away. The most spectacular of these sites, a cave in north-central France named Grotte du Renne (one in a string of sites collectively known as the Arcy-sur-Cure caves), yielded a wealth of complex bone and stone tools, body ornaments and decorated objects, found in association with Neandertal remains. Other sites in France and along the Cantabrian and Pyrenean mountain ranges bore similar artifacts made in this tradition, called the Châtelperronian.

Because early modern Europeans had a comparable industry known as Aurignacian—which often appears at the same sites that contain Châtelperronian materials—some researchers have suggested that the archaeological layers were disrupted, mixing Aurignacian artifacts into the Neandertal-associated levels. Other scholars have interpreted this to mean that Neandertals picked up these ideas from moderns, either collecting or trading for items manufactured by moderns or imitating the newcomers' practices without really grasping the underlying symbolic nature of some of the objects.

Our reassessment of the evidence from the Grotte du Renne shows that the Neandertal-associated personal ornaments and tools found there did not result from a mixing of the archaeological strata, as demonstrated by the presence of finished objects and the by-products of their manufacture in the same stratigraphic level. Moreover, the Châtelperronian artifacts recovered at the Grotte du Renne and other sites, such as Quinçay, in the Poitou-Charentes region of France, were created using techniques different from those favored by Aurignacians. With regard, for example, to the pendants—modified bear, wolf and deer teeth, among others—Neandertals carved a furrow around the tooth root so that a string of some sort could be tied around it for suspension, whereas Aurignacians pierced their pendants. As archaeologist François Lévêque and a colleague have described, even when, as they did on occasion, Neandertals put a hole through a tooth, they took an unusual approach, puncturing the tooth. Moderns, on the other hand, preferred to scrape the tooth thin and then pierce it.

Similarly, the new knapping techniques and tool types that appear among late Neandertals at other sites in France, Italy and Spain fail to show any influence from the Aurignacian. Instead they maintain affinities with the preceding local traditions, of which they seem to represent an autonomous development.

If the Neandertals' Châtelperronian culture was an outcome of contact with moderns, then the Aurignacian should predate the Châtelperronian. Yet our reanalysis of the radiometric dates for the archaeological sequences reveals that apart from a few debatable instances of mixture, wherever both cultures are represented at the same site, the Châtelperronian always underlies the Aurignacian, suggesting its priority. Furthermore, consideration of the hundreds of datings available from this period in Europe and the Near East shows that wherever the context of the dated samples is well known, the earliest occurrences of the Aurignacian are apparently from no earlier than around 36,500 years ago. The same radiometric data, however, indicate that by then Neandertals were already moving toward modernity on their own. In other words, the Châtelperronian and other late Neandertal cultures, such as the Uluzzian of Italy, emerged in Europe around 40,000 years ago, long before any moderns established themselves in those areas.

That this autonomous development included the manufacture and use of symbolic objects created for visual display on the body, as are often observed in traditional societies, reflects various social roles within Neandertal cultures. Thus, "modern" behavior seems to have emerged in different regions and among different groups of humans, as would happen later in history with the invention of agriculture, writing and state society.

An alternative explanation, taking into account the broadly simultaneous appearance of personal ornaments in many parts of the Old World, is that contacts between modern and archaic humans challenged each group's personal, social and biological identities, igniting an explosion of production of symbolic objects by all those involved. On the strength of the available data, however, we favor the hypothesis of independent invention.

Regardless of which is eventually proved correct, the behavioral barrier that seemed to separate moderns from Neandertals and gave us the impression of being a unique and particularly gifted human type—the ability to produce symbolic cultures—has definitively collapsed.

JOÃO ZILHÃO is director of the Portuguese Institute of Archaeology, Ministry of Culture, in Lisbon.

FRANCISCO D'ERRICO is a CNRS researcher at the Institute of Prehistory and Quaternary Geology, University of Bordeaux, in France.

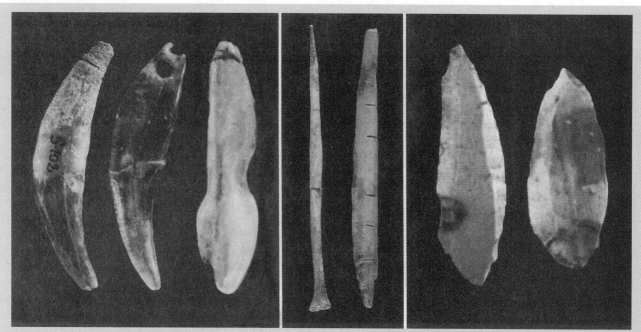

PENDANTS, BONE TOOLS AND KNIVES from the Grotte du Renne site seem to be the handiwork of Neandertals. That the advanced items underlie early modern human cultural remains from the same site and are manufactured according to methods different from those favored by the moderns suggests that some Neandertals independently developed a modern culture.

Still, post-Aurignacian does not necessarily mean after contact with moderns. The earliest Aurignacian sites do not include any human remains. Researchers have assumed that they belonged to moderns because moderns are known from younger Aurignacian sites. But "who the Aurignacians were biologically between 40,000 and 35,000 years ago remains very much an unanswered question," White notes.

He adds that if you look at the Near East around 90,000 years ago, anatomically modern humans and Neandertals were both making Mousterian stone tools, which, though arguably less elaborate than Aurignacian tools, actually require a considerable amount of know-how. "I cannot imagine that Neandertals were producing these kinds of technologically complex tools and passing that on from generation to generation without talking about it," White declares. "I've seen a lot of people do this stuff, and I can't stand over somebody's shoulder and learn how to do it without a lot of verbal hints." Thus, White and others do not buy the argument that moderns were somehow cognitively superior, especially if Neandertals' inferiority meant that they lacked language. Instead it seems that moderns invented a culture that relied more heavily on material symbols.

Researchers have also looked to Neandertal brain morphology for clues to their cognitive ability. According to Ralph L. Holloway of Columbia University, all the brain asymmetries that characterize modern humans are found in Neandertals. "To be able to discriminate between the two," he remarks, "is, at the moment, impossible." As to whether Neandertal anatomy would have permitted speech, studies of the base of the skull conducted by Jeffrey T. Laitman of the Mount Sinai School of Medicine suggest that if they talked, Neandertals had a somewhat limited vocal repertoire. The significance of such physical constraints, however, is unclear.

FADING AWAY

If Neandertals possessed basically the same cognitive ability as moderns, it makes their disappearance additionally puzzling. But the recent redating of Neandertal remains from Vindija cave in Croatia emphasizes that this did not happen overnight. Smith and his colleagues have demonstrated that Neandertals still lived in central Europe 28,000 years ago, thousands of years after moderns had moved in [see box "The Fate of the Neandertals"]. Taking this into consideration, Stringer imagines that moderns, whom he views as a new species, replaced Neandertals in a long, slow process. "Gradually the Neandertals lost out because moderns were a bit more innovative, a bit better able to cope with rapid environmental change quickly, and they probably had bigger social networks," he supposes.

On the other hand, if Neandertals were an equally capable variant of our own species, as Smith and Wolpoff believe, long-term overlap of Neandertals and the new population moving into Europe would have left plenty of time for mingling, hence the mixed morphology that these scholars see in late Neandertals and early moderns in Europe. And if these groups were exchanging genes, they were probably exchanging cultural ideas, which might account for some of the similarity between, say, the Châtelperronian and the Aurignacian. Neandertals as entities disappeared, Wolpoff says, because they were outnumbered by the newcomers. Thousands of years of interbreeding between the small Neandertal population and the larger modern human population, he surmises, diluted the distinctive Neandertal features, which ultimately faded away.

The Fate of the Neandertals

by Fred H. Smith

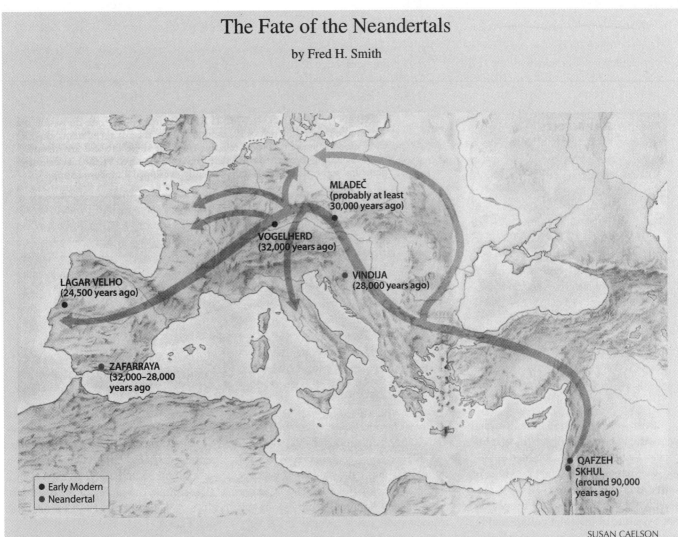

SUSAN CAELSON

MOVEMENT OF MODERNS into Europe did not displace the Neandertals, who were still living in central and western Europe 28,000 years ago. A number of the early modern European specimens bear some Neandertal features, which suggests that during the long period of overlap the two populations mixed.

Strong evidence has accumulated in recent years that the emergence of modern humans in Europe resulted largely from the immigration of peoples into the continent, probably from the Near East, starting sometime between 40,000 and 30,000 years ago. Most researchers envision these early modern populations as having moved into Anatolia and the Balkans, then up through the plains and valleys of central Europe, and finally into northern and western Europe. Meanwhile the indigenous Neandertals, it was thought, were systematically pushed into more peripheral and undesirable parts of the landscape by these expanding populations of moderns. The Neandertals' last bastion appeared to be the Iberian Peninsula, where fossils from a Spanish site called Zafarraya have been dated to 32,000 years ago and tools attributed to Neandertals have been dated to around 28,000 years ago. Many scholars argued that after this time no traces of Neandertals remained in Europe and that Neandertals did not make any biological contributions to early modern humans. It seemed that Neandertals were sent into complete extinction by a superior human species—us.

Now new evidence from an important site in northwestern Croatia calls aspects of this conventional wisdom into question. By performing accelerator mass spectrometry dating directly on two Neandertal specimens from Vindija cave, my colleagues and I have demonstrated that Neandertals were living in some of the most desirable real estate in central Europe as late as 28,000 years ago. These dates, the most recent known for Neandertal fossils, show that these humans were not quickly relegated to the periphery; they competed quite well with intruding modern populations for a long time.

This overlap of Neandertal and early modern peoples for several millennia in the heart of Europe allowed

(Continued on next page)

(Continued from previous page)

some of them. Work by my Croatian colleagues Ivor Karavanic of the University of Zagreb and Jakov Radovic of the Croatian Natural History museum has revealed a combination of Mousterian and Aurignacian tools in the same stratigraphic level as the dated Neandertal fossils, suggesting that Neandertals either made advanced implements or traded with moderns for them. Morphologically, the Vindija Neandertals look more modern than do most other Neandertals, which suggests that their ancestors interbred with early moderns.

The likelihood of gene flow between the groups is also supported by evidence that Neandertals left their mark on early modern Europeans. Fossils representing early modern adults from central European sites such as Vogelherd in southwestern Germany and Mladec in Moravia (Czech Republic) have features that are difficult to explain unless they have some Neandertal contribution to their ancestry. For example, Neandertals and early modern Europeans virtually all exhibit a projection of the back of the skull called an occipital bun (aspects of the shape and position of the buns differ between them because the overall skull shapes are not the same). Yet fossils from the Near Eastern sites of Skhul and Qafzeh, which presumably represent the ancestors of early modern Europeans, do not have this morphology. It is hard to explain how the growth phenomenon responsible for this bunning could reappear independently and could reappear independently and ubiquitously in early modern Europeans. Instead it is far more logical to recognize this morphology as a link to the Neandertals. The Portuguese child discovered recently offers more intriguing clues [see box "The Hybrid Child from Portugal"].

I believe the evidence shows that the behavioral and biological interactions between Neandertal and early modern human populations were very complex—too complex for the origins of modern humans in Europe to have involved a simple, complete biological replacement of the Neandertals. Neandertals as organisms no longer exist, and Neandertal genes may not have persisted to the present day, but those genes were there in the beginnings of modern European biological history.

FRED H. SMITH is chairman of the department of anthropology at Northern Illinois University.

"If we look at Australians a thousand years from now, we will see that the European features have predominated [over those of native Australians] by virtue of many more Europeans," Wolpoff asserts. "Not by virtue of better adaptation, not by virtue of different culture, not by virtue of anything except many more Europeans. And I really think that's what describes what we see in Europe—we see the predominance of more people."

From the morass of opinions in this notoriously contentious field, one consensus emerges: researchers have retired the old vision of the shuffling, culture-less Neandertal. Beyond that, whether these ancient hominids were among the ancestors of living people or a very closely related species that competed formidably with our own for the Eurasian territory and eventually lost remains to be seen. In either case, the details will most likely be extraordinarily complicated. "The more we learn, the more questions arise, the knottier it gets," muses archaeologist Lawrence G. Straus of the University of New Mexico. "That's why simple explanations just don't cut it."

Archaeologists Rediscover Cannibals

At digs around the world, researchers have unearthed strong new evidence that people ate their own kind from the early days of human evolution through recent prehistory

When Arizona State University bioarchaeologist Christy G. Turner II first looked at the jumbled heap of bones from 30 humans in Arizona in 1967, he was convinced that he was looking at the remains of a feast. The bones of these ancient American Indians had cut marks and burns, just like animal bones that had been roasted and stripped of their flesh. "It just struck me that here was a pile of food refuse," says Turner, who proposed in *American Antiquity* in 1970 that these people from Polacca Wash, Arizona, had been the victims of cannibalism.

But his paper was met with "total disbelief," says Turner. "In the 1960s, the new paradigm about Indians was that they were all peaceful and happy. So, to find something like this was the antithesis of the new way we were supposed to be thinking about Indians"—particularly the Anasazi, thought to be the ancestors of living Pueblo Indians. Not only did Turner's proposal fly in the face of conventional wisdom about the Anasazi culture, but it was also at odds with an emerging consensus that earlier claims of cannibalism in the fossil record rested on shaky evidence. Where earlier generations of archaeologists had seen the remains of cannibalistic feasts, current researchers saw bones scarred by ancient burial practices, war, weathering, or scavenging animals.

To Turner, however, the bones from Polacca Wash told a more disturbing tale, and so he set about studying every prehistoric skeleton he could find in the Southwest and Mexico to see if it was an isolated event. Now, 30 years and 15,000 skeletons later, Turner is putting the final touches on a 1500-page book to be published next year by the University of Utah press in which he says, "Cannibalism was practiced intensively for almost four centuries" in the Four Corners region. The evidence is so strong that Turner says "I would bet a year of my salary on it."

He isn't the only one now betting on cannibalism in prehistory. In the past decade, Turner and other bioarchaeologists have put together a set of clear-cut criteria for distinguishing the marks of cannibalism from other kinds of scars. "The analytical rigor has increased across the board," says paleoanthropologist Tim D. White of the University of California, Berkeley. Armed with the new criteria, archaeologists are finding what they say are strong signs of cannibalism throughout the fossil record. This summer, archaeologists are excavating several sites in Europe where the practice may have occurred among our ancestors, perhaps as early as 800,000 years ago. More recently, our brawny cousins, the Neandertals, may have eaten each other. And this behavior wasn't limited to the distant past—strong new evidence suggests that in addition to the Anasazi, the Aztecs of Mexico and the people of Fiji also ate their own kind in the past 2500 years.

These claims imply a disturbing new view of human history, say Turner and others. Although cannibalism is still relatively rare in the fossil record, it is frequent enough to imply that extreme hunger was not the only driving force. Instead of being an aberration, practiced only by a few prehistoric Donner Parties, killing people for food may have been standard human behavior—a means of social control, Turner suspects, or a mob response to stress, or a form of infanticide to thin the ranks of neighboring populations.

Not surprisingly, some find these claims hard to stomach: "These people haven't explored all the alternatives," says archaeologist Paul Bahn, author of the *Cambridge Encyclopedia* entry on cannibalism. "There's no question, for example, that all kinds of weird stuff is done to human remains in mortuary practice"—and in warfare. But even the most prominent skeptic of earlier claims of cannibalism, cultural anthropologist William Arens of the State University of New York, Stony Brook, now admits the case is stronger: "I think the procedures are sounder, and there is more evidence for cannibalism than before."

White learned how weak most earlier scholarship on cannibalism was in 1981, when he first came across what he thought might be a relic of the practice—a massive skull of an early human ancestor from a site called Bodo in Ethiopia. When he got his first look at this 600,000-year-old skull on a museum table, White noticed that it had a series of fine, deep cut marks on its cheekbone and inside its eye socket, as if it had been defleshed. To confirm his suspicions, White wanted to compare the marks with a "type collection" for cannibalism—a carefully studied assemblage of bones showing how the signature of cannibalism differs from damage by animal gnawing, trampling, or excavation.

"We were naïve at the time," says White, who was working with archaeol-

More evidence for cannibalism

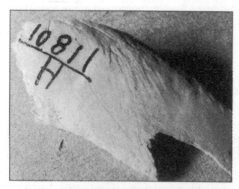

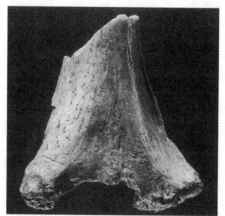

Cannibals house? The Peasco Blanco great house at Chaco Canyon, New Mexico, where some bones bear cut marks (upper left); others were smashed, perhaps to extract marrow.

ogist Nicholas Toth of Indiana University in Bloomington. They learned that although the anthropological literature was full of fantastic tales of cannibalistic feasts among early humans at Zhoukoudian in China, Krapina cave in Croatia, and elsewhere, the evidence was weak—or lost.

Indeed, the weakness of the evidence had already opened the way to a backlash, which was led by Arens. He had deconstructed the fossil and historical record for cannibalism in a book called *The Man-Eating Myth: Anthropology and Anthropophagy* (Oxford, 1979). Except for extremely rare cases of starvation or insanity, Arens said, none of the accounts of cannibalism stood up to scrutiny—not even claims that it took place among living tribes in Papua New Guinea (including the Fore, where cannibalism is thought to explain the spread of the degenerative brain disease kuru). There were no reliable eye witnesses for claims of cannibalism, and the archaeological evidence was circumstantial. "I

didn't deny the existence of cannibalism," he now says, "but I found that there was no good evidence for it. It was bad science."

Unkind cuts. A Neandertal bone from Vindija Cave, Croatia.

Physical anthropologists contributed to the backlash when they raised doubts about what little archaeological evidence there was (*Science*, 20 June 1986, p.

1479). Mary Russell, then at Case Western Reserve University in Cleveland, argued, for example, that cut marks on the bones of 20 Neandertals at Krapina Cave could have been left by Neandertal morticians who were cleaning the bones for secondary burial, and the bones would have been smashed when the roof caved in, for example. In his 1992 review in the *Cambridge Encyclopedia,* Bahn concluded that cannibalism's "very existence in prehistory is hard to swallow."

RISING FROM THE ASHES

But even as some anthropologists gave the ax to Krapina and other notorious cases, a new, more rigorous case for cannibalism in prehistory was emerging, starting in the American Southwest. Turner and his late wife, Jacqueline Turner, had been systematically studying tray after tray of prehistoric bones in museums and private collections in the United States and Mexico. They had identified a pattern of bone processing in several hundred specimens that showed little respect for the dead. "There's no known mortuary practice in the Southwest where the body is dismembered, the head is roasted and dumped into a pit unceremoniously, and other pieces get left all over the floor," says Turner, describing part of the pattern.

White, meanwhile, was identifying other telltale signs. To fill the gap he discovered when he looked for specimens to compare with the Bodo skull, he decided to study in depth one of the bone assemblages the Turners and others had cited. He chose Mancos, a small Anasazi pueblo on the Colorado Plateau from A.D. 1150, where archaeologists had recovered the scattered and broken remains of at least 29 individuals. The project evolved into a landmark book, *Prehistoric Cannibalism at Mancos* (Princeton, 1992). While White still doesn't know why the Bodo skull was defleshed—"it's a black box," he says—he extended the blueprint for identifying cannibalism.

In his book, White describes how he painstakingly sifted through 2106 bone fragments, often using an electron microscope to identify cut marks, burn traces, percussion and anvil damage, disarticulations, and breakages. He reviewed how to distinguish marks left by butchering from those left by animal gnawing, trampling, or other wear and tear. He also proposed a new category of bone damage, which he called "pot polish"—shiny abrasions on bone tips that come from being stirred in pots (an idea he tested by stirring deer bones in a replica of an Anasazi pot). And he outlined how to compare the remains of suspected victims with those of ordinary game animals at other sites to see if they were processed the same way.

When he applied these criteria to the Mancos remains, he concluded that they were the leavings of a feast in which 17 adults and 12 children had their heads cut off, roasted, and broken open on rock anvils. Their long bones were broken—he believes for marrow—and their vertebral bodies were missing, perhaps crushed and boiled for oil. Finally, their bones were dumped, like animal bones.

In their forthcoming book, the Turners describe a remarkably similar pattern

of bone processing in 300 individuals from 40 different bone assemblages in the Four Corners area of the Southwest, dating from A.D. 900 to A.D. 1700. The strongest case, he says, comes from bones unearthed at the Peñasco Blanco great house at Chaco Canyon in New Mexico, which was the highest center of the Anasazi culture and, he argues, the home of cannibals who terrorized victims within 100 miles of Chaco Canyon, where most of the traumatized bones have been excavated. "Whatever drove the Anasazi to eat people, it happened at Chaco," says Turner.

T . D. WHITE/BERKELEY

Close shave. Was flesh stripped from the 600,000-year-old Bodo skull in an act of cannibalism?

The case for cannibalism among the Anasazi that Turner and White have put together hasn't swayed all the critics. "These folks have a nice package, but I don't think it proves cannibalism," says Museum of New Mexico archaeologist Peter Bullock. "It's still just a theory."

But even critics like Bullock acknowledge that Turner and White's studies, along with work by the University of Colorado, Boulder's, Paolo Villa and colleagues at another recent site, Fontbrégoua Cave in southeastern France (*Science,* 25 July 1986, p. 431), have raised the standards for how to investigate a case of cannibalism. In fact, White's book has become the unofficial guidebook for the field, says physical anthropologist Carmen Pijoan at the Museum of Anthropology in Mexico City, who has done a systematic review of sites in Mexico where human bones were defleshed. In a forthcoming book chapter, she singles out three sites where she applied diagnostic criteria outlined by Turner, White, and Villa to bones from Aztec and other early cultures and con-

cludes that all "three sites, spread over 2000 years of Mexican prehistory, show a pattern of violence, cannibalism, and sacrifice through time."

White's book "is my bible," agrees paleontologist Yolanda Fernandez-Jalvo of the Museum of Natural History in Madrid, who is analyzing bones that may be the oldest example of cannibalism in the fossil record—the remains of at least six individuals who died 800,000 years ago in an ancient cave at Atapuerca in northern Spain.

AGE-OLD PRACTICES

The Spanish fossils have caused considerable excitement because they may represent a new species of human ancestor (*Science,* 30 May, pp. 1331 and 1392). But they also show a pattern familiar from the more recent sites: The bones are highly fragmented and are scored with cut marks, which Fernandez-Jalvo thinks were made when the bodies were decapitated and the bones defleshed. A large femur was also smashed open, perhaps for marrow, says Fernandez-Jalvo, and the whole assemblage had been dumped, like garbage. The treatment was no different from that accorded animal bones at the site. The pattern, says Peter Andrews, a paleoanthropologist at The Natural History Museum, London, is "pretty strong evidence for cannibalism, as opposed to ritual defleshing." He and others note, however, that the small number of individuals at the site and the absence of other sites of similar antiquity to which the bones could be compared leave room for doubt.

A stronger case is emerging at Neandertal sites in Europe, 45,000 to more than 130,000 years old. The new criteria for recognizing cannibalism have not completely vindicated the earlier claims about Krapina Cave, partly because few animal bones are left from the excavation of the site in 1899 to compare with the Neandertal remains. But nearby Vindija Cave, excavated in the 1970s, did yield both animal and human remains. When White and Toth examined the bones recently, they found that both sets showed cut marks, breakage, and disarticulation, and had been dumped on the cave floor. It's the same pattern seen at

Neanderthals
Represent [?]

Krapina, and remarkably similar to that at Mancos, says White, who will publish his conclusions in a forthcoming book with Toth. Marseilles prehistorian Alban DeFleur is finding that Neandertals may also have feasted on their kind in the Moula-Guercy Cave in the Ardeche region of France, where animal and Neandertal bones show similar processing. Taken together, says White, "the evidence from Krapina, Vindija, and Moula is strong."

Not everyone is convinced, however. "White does terrific analysis, but he hasn't proved this is cannibalism," says Bahn. "Frankly, I don't see how he can unless you find a piece of human gut [with human bone or tissue in it]." No matter how close the resemblance to butchered animals, he says, the cut marks and other bone processing could still be the result of mortuary practices. Bullock adds that warfare, not cannibalism, could explain the damage to the bones.

or cannibalism

White, however, says such criticism resembles President Clinton's famous claim about marijuana: "Some [although not all] of the Anasazi and Neandertals processed their colleagues. They skinned them, roasted them, cut their muscles off, severed their joints, broke their long bones on anvils with hammerstones, crushed their spongy bones, and put the pieces into pots." Borrowing a line from a review of his book, White says: "To say they didn't eat them is the archaeological equivalent of saying Clinton lit up and didn't inhale."

White's graduate student David DeGusta adds that he has compared human bones at burial sites in Fiji and at a nearby trash midden from the last 2000 years. The intentionally buried bones were less fragmentary and had no bite marks, burns, percussion pits, or other signs of food processing. The human bones in the trash midden, however, were processed like those of pigs. "This site really challenges the claim that these assemblages of bones are the result of mortuary ritual," says DeGusta.

After 30 years of research, Turner says it is a modern bias to insist that cannibalism isn't part of human nature. Many other species eat their own, and our ancestors may have had their own "good" reasons—whether to terrorize subject peoples, limit their neighbors' offspring, or for religious or medicinal purposes. "Today, the only people who eat other people outside of starving are the crazies," says Turner. "We're dealing with a world view that says this is bad and always has been bad.... But in the past, that view wasn't necessarily the group view. Cannibalism could have been an adaptive strategy. It has to be entertained."

—**Ann Gibbons**

UNIT 6

Human Diversity

Unit Selections

Key Points to Consider

- Discuss whether the human species can be subdivided into racial categories. Support your position.

- How and why did the concept of race develop?

- Would you allow archaeologists to study the remains of Kennewick Man, or would you immediately repatriate the bones to Native Americans? Why?

- To what extent is height a barometer of the health of a society, and why?

 **Links: www.dushkin.com/online/**
These sites are annotated in the World Wide Web pages.

Cult Archaeology Topics
http://www.usd.edu/anth/cultarch/culttopics.html

Hominid Evolution Survey
http://www.geocities.com/SoHo/Atrium/1381/index.html

Human Genome Project Information
http://www.ornl.gov/TechResources/Human_Genome/home.html

OMIM Home Page-Online Mendelian Inheritance in Man
http://www3.ncbi.nlm.nih.gov/omim/

Patterns of Human Variability: The Concept of Race
http://www.as.ua.edu/ant/bindon/ant101/lectures/race/race1.htm

The field of biological anthropology has come a long way since the days when one of its primary concerns was the classification of human beings according to racial type. Although human diversity is still a matter of major interest in terms of how and why we differ from one another, most anthropologists have concluded that human beings cannot be sorted into sharply distinct entities. Without denying the fact of human variation throughout the world, the prevailing view today is that the differences between us exist along geographical gradients, as differences in degree, rather than in terms of the separate and discrete reproductive entities perceived in the past.

One of the old ways of looking at human "races" was that each such group was a subspecies of human that, if left reproductively isolated long enough, would eventually

evolve into separate species. While this concept of subspecies, or racial varieties within a species, would seem to apply to some living creatures (such as the dog and wolf or the horse and zebra) and might even be relevant to hominid diversification in the past, the current consensus is that it is not happening today, at least within the human species.

A more recent attempt to salvage the idea of human races has been to perceive them not so much as reproductively isolated entities but as so many clusters of gene frequencies, separable only by the fact that the proportions of traits (such as skin color, hair form, etc.) differ in each artificially constructed group. But, if such "groups" exist only because we say they do and do not have an objective reality of their own, what is to be learned from the exercise? What is its practical value?

It would seem to be more productive to study human traits in terms of their particular adaptiveness (as in "Racial Odyssey" by Boyce Rensberger and "The Tall and the Short of It" by Barry Bogin) or how they help us reconstruct human prehistory (as in "The Lost Man" by Douglas Preston).

Lest anyone think that anthropologists are "in denial" regarding the existence of human races and that the viewpoint expressed here is merely an expression of contemporary political correctness, it should be remembered that serious, scholarly attempts to classify people according to race have been going on now for 200 years and, so far, nothing of value has come of them.

Complicating the matter, as Jonathan Marks elucidates in "Black, White, Other," is that there actually are two concepts of race: the strictly biological one, which was originally set forth by

Linnaeus in the 1700s, and the one of popular culture, which has been around since time immemorial. These "two constantly intersecting ways of thinking about the divisions between us," says Marks, have resulted not only in fuzzy thinking about racial biology, but they have also infected the way we think about people and, therefore, the way we treat each other in the social sense.

What we should recognize, claim most anthropologists, is that, despite the superficial physical and biological differences between us, when it comes to intelligence, all human beings are basically the same. The degrees of variation within our species may be accounted for by the subtle and changing selective forces experienced as one moves from one geographical area to another. However, no matter what the environmental pressures have been, the same intellectual demands have been made upon us all. This is not to say, of course, that we do not vary from each other as individuals. Rather, what is being said is that when we look at these artificially created groups of people called "races," we find the same range of intellectual skills within each group. Indeed, even when we look at traits other than intelligence, we find much greater variation within each group than we find between groups.

It is time, therefore, to put the idea of human races to rest, at least as far as science is concerned. If such notions remain in the realm of social discourse, then so be it. That is where the problems associated with notions of race have to be solved anyway. At least, says Marks, in speaking for the anthropological community: "You may group humans into a small number of races if you want to, but you are denied biology as a support for it."

A REPORTER AT LARGE

The Lost Man

*Is it possible that the first Americans weren't who we think they were?
And why is the government withholding Kennewick Man, who might turn out
to be the most significant archeological find of the decade?*

DOUGLAS PRESTON

On Sunday, July 28, 1996, in the middle of the afternoon, two college students who were watching a hydroplane race on the Columbia River in Kennewick, Washington, decided to take a shortcut along the river's edge. While wading through the shallows, one of them stubbed his toe on a human skull partly buried in the sand. The students picked it up and, thinking it might be that of a murder victim, hid it in some bushes and called the police.

Floyd Johnson, the Benton County coroner, was called in, and the police gave him the skull in a plastic bucket. Late in the afternoon, Johnson called James Chatters, a forensic anthropologist and the owner of a local consulting firm called Applied Paleoscience. "Hey, buddy, I got a skull for you to look at," Johnson said. Chatters had often helped the police identify skeletons and distinguish between those of murder victims and those found in Indian burial sites. He is a small, determined, physically powerful man of forty-eight who used to be a gymnast and a wrestler. His work occasionally involves him in grisly or spectacular murders, where the victims are difficult to identify, such as burnings and dismemberments.

"When I looked down at the skull," Chatters told me, "right off the bat I saw it had a very large number of Caucasoid features"—in particular, a long, narrow braincase, a narrow face, and a slightly projecting upper jaw. But when Chatters took it out of the bucket and laid it on his worktable he began to see some unusual traits. The crowns of the teeth were worn flat, a common characteristic of prehistoric Indian skulls, and the color of the bone indicated that it was fairly old. The skull sutures had fused, indicating that the individual was past middle age. And, for a prehistoric Indian of what was then an advanced age, he or she was in exceptional health; the skull had, for example, all its teeth and no cavities.

As dusk fell, Chatters and Johnson went out to the site to see if they could find the rest of the skeleton. There, working in the dying light, they found more bones, lying around on sand and mud in about two feet of water. The remains were remarkably complete: only the sternum, a few rib fragments, and some tiny hand, wrist, and foot bones were missing. The bones had evidently fallen out of a bank during recent flooding of the Columbia River.

The following day, Chatters and Johnson spread the bones out in Chatters's laboratory. In forensic anthropology, the first order of business is to determine sex, age, and race. Determin-

ing race was particularly important, because if the skeleton turned out to be Native American it fell under a federal law called the Native American Graves Protection and Repatriation Act, or NAGPRA. Passed in 1990, NAGPRA requires the government—in this case, the Army Corps of Engineers, which controls the stretch of the Columbia River where the bones were found—to ascertain if human remains found on federal lands are Native American and, if they are, to "repatriate" them to the appropriate Indian tribe.

Chatters determined that the skeleton was male, Caucasoid, from an individual between forty and fifty-five years old, and about five feet nine inches tall—much taller than most prehistoric Native Americans in the Northwest. In physical anthropology, the term "Caucasoid" does not necessarily mean "white" or "European"; it is a descriptive term applied to certain biological features of a diverse category that includes, for example, some south-Asian groups as well as Europeans. (In contrast, the term "Caucasian" is a culturally defined racial category.) "I thought maybe we had an early pioneer or fur trapper," he said. As he was cleaning the pelvis, he noticed a gray object embedded in the bone, which had partly healed and fused around it. He took the bone to be X-rayed, but the object did not show up, meaning that it was not made of metal. So he requested a CAT scan. To his surprise, the scan revealed the object to be part of a willow-leaf-shaped spear point, which had been thrust into the bone and broken off. It strongly resembled a Cascade projectile point—an Archaic Indian style in wide use from around nine thousand to forty-five hundred years ago.

The Army Corps of Engineers asked Chatters to get a second opinion. He put the skeleton into his car and drove it a hundred miles to Ellensburg, Washington, where an anthropologist named Catherine J. MacMillan ran a forensic consulting business called the Bone-Apart Agency. "He didn't say anything," MacMillan told me. "I examined the bones, and I said 'Male, Caucasian.' He said 'Are you sure?' and I said 'Yeah.' And then he handed me the pelvis and showed me the ancient point embedded in it, and he said, 'What do you think now?' And I said, 'That's extremely interesting, but it still looks Caucasian to me.'" "In her report to the Benton County coroner's office she wrote that in her opinion the skeleton was "Caucasian male."

Toward the end of the week, Chatters told Floyd Johnson and the Army Corps of Engineers that he thought they needed to get a radiocarbon date on Kennewick Man. The two parties agreed, so Chatters sent the left fifth metacarpal bone—a tiny bone in the hand—to the University of California at Riverside.

On Friday, August 23rd, Jim Chatters received a telephone call from the radio-carbon lab. The bone was between ninety-three hundred and ninety-six hundred years old. He was astounded. "It was just a phone call," he said. "I thought, Maybe there's been a mistake. I had to see the report with my own eyes." The report came on Monday, in the form of a fax. "I got very nervous then," Chatters said. He knew that, because of their age, the bones on his worktable had to be one of the most important archeological finds of the decade. "It was just a tremendous responsibility." The following Tuesday, the coroner's office issued a press release on the find, and it was re-ported in the Seattle *Times*, and other local papers.

Chatters called in a third physical anthropologist, Grover S. Krantz, a professor at Washington State University. Krantz looked at the bones on Friday, August 30th. His report noted some characteristics common to both Europeans and Plains Indians but concluded that "this skeleton cannot be racially or culturally associated with any existing American Indian group." He also wrote, "The Native Repatriation Act has no more applicability to this skeleton than it would if an early Chinese expedition had left one of its members there."

Fifteen minutes after Krantz finished looking at the bones, Chatters received a call from Johnson. Apologetically, the coroner said, "I'm going to have to come over and get the bones." The Army Corps of Engineers had demanded that all study of the bones cease, and had required him to put the skeleton in the county sheriff's evidence locker. On the basis of the carbon date, the Corps had evidently decided that the skeleton was Native American and that it fell under NAGPRA.

"When I heard this, I panicked," Chatters said. "I was the only one who'd recorded any information on it. There were all these things I should have done. I didn't even have photographs of the post-cranial skeleton. I thought, Am I going to be the last scientist to see these bones?"

On September 9th, the Umatilla Indians, leading a coalition of five tribes and bands of the Columbia River basin, formally claimed the skeleton under NAGPRA, and the Corps quickly made a preliminary decision to "repatriate" it. The Umatilla Indian Reservation lies just over the border, in northeastern Oregon, and the other tribes live in Washington and Idaho; all consider the Kennewick area part of their traditional territories. The Umatillas announced that they were going to bury the skeleton in a secret site, where it would never again be available to science.

Three weeks later, the *New York Times* picked up the story, and from there it went to *Time* and on around the world. Television crews from as far away as France and Korea descended on Kennewick. The Corps received more than a dozen other claims for the skeleton, including one from a group known as the Asatru Folk Assembly, the California-based followers of an Old Norse religion, who wanted the bones for their own religious purposes.

On September 2nd, the Corps had directed that the bones be placed in a secure vault at the Pacific Northwest National Laboratory, in Richland, Washington. Nobody outside of the Corps has seen them since. They are now at the center of a legal controversy that will likely determine the course of American archeology.

WHAT was a Caucasoid man doing in the New World more than ninety-three centuries ago? In the reams of press reports last fall, that question never seemed to be dealt with. I called up Douglas Owsley, who is the Division Head for Physical Anthropology at the National Museum of Natural History, Smithsonian Institution, in Washington, D.C., and an expert on Paleo-American remains. I asked him how many well-preserved skeletons that old had been found in North America.

He replied, "Including Kennewick, about seven."

Then I asked if any others had Caucasoid features, and there was a silence that gave me the sense that I was venturing onto controversial ground.

He guardedly replied, "Yes."

"How many?"

"Well," he said, "in varying degrees, all of them."

Kennewick Man's bones are part of a growing quantity of evidence that the earliest inhabitants of the New World may have been a Caucasoid people. Other, tentative evidence suggests that these people may have originally come from Europe. The new evidence is fragmentary, contradictory, and controversial. Critical research remains to be done, and many studies are still unpublished. At the least, the new evidence calls into question the standard Beringian Walk theory, which holds that the first human beings to reach the New World were Asians of Mongoloid stock, who crossed from Siberia to Alaska over a land bridge. The new evidence involves three basic questions. Who were the original Americans? Where did they come from? And what happened to them?

"You're dealing with such a black hole," Owsley told me. "It's hard to draw any firm conclusions from such a small sample of skeletons, and there is more than one group represented. That's why Kennewick is so important."

KENNEWICK MAN made his appearance at the dawn of a new age in physical anthropology. Scientists are now able to extract traces of organic material from a person's bone and perform a succession of powerful biochemical assays which can reveal an astonishing amount of information about the person. In March, for example, scientists at Oxford University announced that they had compared DNA extracted from the molar cavity of a nine-thousand-year-old skeleton known as Cheddar Man to DNA collected from fifteen pupils and five adults from old families in the village of Cheddar, in Somersetshire. They had established a blood tie between Cheddar Man and a schoolteacher who lived just half a mile from the cave where the bones were found.

In the few weeks that Kennewick Man was in the hands of scientists, they discovered a great deal about him. Isotopic-carbon studies of the bones indicate that he had a diet high in marine food— that he may have been a fisherman who ate a lot of salmon. He seems to have been a tall, good-looking man, slender and well proportioned. (Studies have shown that "handsomeness" is largely the result of symmetrical features and good health, both of which Kennewick Man had.) Archeological finds of similar age in the area suggest that he was part of a small band of people who moved about, hunting, fishing, and gathering wild plants. He may have lived in a simple sewn tent or mat hut that could be disassembled and carried. Some nearby sites contain large numbers of fine bone needles, indicating that a lot of delicate sewing was going on: Kennewick Man may have worn tailored clothing. For a person at that time to live so long in relatively good health indicates that he was

clever or lucky, or both, or had family and close friends around him.

He appears to have perished from recurring infections caused by the stone point in his hip. Because of the way his bones were found, and the layer of soil from which they presumably emerged, it may be that he was not deliberately buried but died near the river and was swept away and covered up in a flood. He may have perished alone on a fishing trip, far from his family.

Chatters made a cast of the skull before the skeleton was taken from his office. In the months since, he has been examining it to figure out how Kennewick Man may have looked. He plans to work with physical anthropologists and a forensic sculptor to make a facial reconstruction. "On the physical characteristics alone, he could fit on the streets of Stockholm without causing any kind of notice," Chatters told me. "Or on the streets of Jerusalem or New Delhi, for that matter. I've been looking around for someone who matches this Kennewick gentleman, looking for weeks and weeks at people on the street, thinking, This one's got a little bit here, that one a little bit there. And then, one evening, I turned on the TV, and there was Patrick Stewart"—Captain Picard, of "Star Trek"— "and I said, 'My God, there he is! Kennewick Man!'"

IN September, following the requirements of NAGPRA, the Corps advertised in a local paper its intention of repatriating the skeleton secreted in the laboratory vault. The law mandated a thirty-day waiting period after the advertisements before the Corps could give a skeleton to a tribe.

Physical anthropologists and archeologists around the country were horrified by the seizure of the skeleton. They protested that it was not possible to demonstrate a relationship between nine-thousand-year-old remains and any modern tribe of the area. "Those tribes are relatively new," says Dennis Stanford, the chairman of the Department of Anthropology at the Smithsonian's National Museum of Natural History. "They pushed out other tribes that were there." Both Owsley and Richard L.

Jantz, a biological anthropologist at the University of Tennessee, wrote letters to the Army Corps of Engineers in late September saying that the loss to science would be incalculable if Kennewick Man were to be reburied before being studied. They received no response. Robson Bonnichsen, the director of the Center for the Study of the First Americans, at Oregon State University, also wrote to the Corps and received no reply. Three representatives and a United States senator from the state of Washington got in touch with the Corps, pleading that it allow the skeleton to be studied before reburial, or, at least, refrain from repatriating the skeleton until Congress could take up the issue. The Corps rebuffed them.

The Umatillas themselves issued a statement, which was written by Armand Minthorn, a tribal religious leader. Minthorn, a small, well-spoken young man with long braids, is a member of a new generation of Native American activists, who see religious fundamentalism—in this case, the Washat religion—as a road back to Native American traditions and values:

> Our elders have taught us that once a body goes into the ground, it is meant to stay there until the end of time.... If this individual is truly over 9,000 years old, that only substantiates our belief that he is Native American. From our oral histories, we know that our people have been part of this land since the beginning of time. We do not believe that our people migrated here from another continent, as the scientists do.... Scientists believe that because the individual's head measurement does not match ours, he is not Native American. Our elders have told us that Indian people did not always look the way we look today. Some scientists say that if this individual is not studied further, we, as Indians, will be destroying evidence of our history. We already know our history. It is passed on to us through our elders and through our religious practices.

Despite the mounting protests, the Corps refused to reconsider its decision to ban scientific study of the Kennewick skeleton. As the thirty-day waiting period came to a close, anthropologists around the country panicked. Just a week before it ended, on October 23rd, a group of eight anthropologists filed suit against the Corps. The plaintiffs included Douglas Owsley, Robson Bonnichsen, and also Dennis Stanford. Stanford, one of the country's top Paleo-Indian experts, is a formidable opponent. While attending graduate school in New Mexico, he roped in local rodeos, and helped support his family by leasing an alfalfa farm. There's still a kind of laconic, frontier toughness about him. "Kennewick Man has the potential to change the way we view the entire peopling of the Americas," he said to me. "We had to act. Otherwise, I might as well retire."

The eight are pursuing the suit as individuals. Their academic institutions are reluctant to get involved in a lawsuit as controversial as this, particularly at a time when most of them are negotiating with tribes over their own collections.

In the suit, the scientists have argued that Kennewick Man may not meet the NAGPRA definition of "Native American" as being "of, or relating to, a tribe, people, or culture that is indigenous to the United States." The judge trying the case has asked both sides to be prepared to define the word "indigenous" as it is used in NAGPRA. This will be an interesting exercise, since no human beings are indigenous to the New World: we are all immigrants.

The scientists have also argued that the Corps had had no evidence to support its claim that the skeleton had a connection to the Umatillas. Alan Schneider, the scientists' attorney, says, "Our analysis of NAGPRA is that first you have to make a determination if the human remains are Native American. And then you get to the question of cultural affiliation. The Army Corps assumed that anyone who died in the continental United States prior to a certain date is automatically Native American."

The NAGPRA law appears to support the scientists' point of view. It says that when there are no known lineal descendants "cultural affiliation" should be determined using "geographical, kinship, biological, archeological, anthropologi-

cal, linguistic, folkloric, oral traditional, historical," or other "relevant information or expert opinion" before human remains are repatriated. In other words, human remains must often be studied before anyone can say whom they are related to.

The Corps, represented by the Justice Department, has refused to comment on most aspects of the case. "It's really as if the government didn't want to know the truth about Kennewick Man," Alan Schneider told me in late April. "It seems clear that the government will *never* allow this skeleton to be studied, for any reason, unless it is forced to by the courts."

Preliminary oral arguments in the case were heard on June 2nd in the United States District Court for the District of Oregon. The scientists asked for immediate access to study the bones, and the Corps asked for summary judgment. Judge John Jelderks denied both motions, and said that he would have a list of questions for the Corps that it is to answer within a reasonable time. With the likelihood of appeals, the case could last a couple of years longer, and could ultimately go to the Supreme Court.

Schneider was not surprised that the Corps had sided with the Indians. "It constantly has a variety of issues it has to negotiate with Native American tribes," he told me, and he specified, among others, land issues, water rights, dams, salmon fishing, hydroelectric projects, and toxic-waste dumps. The Corps apparently decided, Schneider speculated, that in this case its political interests would be better served by supporting the tribes than by supporting a disgruntled group of anthropologists with no institutional backing, no money, and no political power. There are large constituencies for the Indians' point of view: fundamentalist Christians and liberal supporters of Indian rights. Fundamentalists of all varieties tend to object to scientific research into the origins of humankind, because the results usually contradict their various creation myths. A novel coalition of conservative Christians and liberal activists was important in getting NAGPRA through Congress.

KENNEWICK MAN, early as he is, was not one of the first Americans. But he could be their descendant. There is evidence that those mysterious first Americans were a Caucasoid people. They may have come from Europe and may be connected to the Clovis people of America. Kennewick may provide evidence of a connection between the Old World and the New.

The Clovis mammoth hunters were the earliest widespread culture that we know of in the Americas. They appeared abruptly, seemingly out of nowhere, all over North and South America about eleven thousand five hundred years ago—two thousand years before Kennewick. (They were called Clovis after a town in New Mexico near an early site— a campground beside an ancient spring which is littered with projectile points, tools, and the remains of fires.) We have only a few fragments of human bone from the Clovis people and their immediate descendants, the Folsom, and these remains are so damaged that nothing can be learned from them at present.

The oldest bones that scientists have been able to study are the less than a dozen human remains that are contemporaneous with Kennewick. They date from between eight thousand and nearly eleven thousand years ago—the transition period between the Paleo-Indian and the Archaic Indian traditions. Most of the skeletons have been uncovered accidentally in recent years, primarily because of the building boom in the West. (Bones do not survive well in the East: the soil is too wet and acidic.) Some other ancient skeletons, though, have been discovered gathering dust in museum drawers. Among these oldest remains are the Spirit Cave mummy and Wizard's Beach Willie, both from Nevada; the Hourglass Cave and Gordon's Creek skeletons, from Colorado; the Buhl Burial, from Idaho; and remains from Texas, California, and Minnesota.

Douglas Owsley and Richard Jantz made a special study of several of these ancient remains. The best-preserved specimen they looked at was a partial mummy from Spirit Cave, Nevada, which is more than nine thousand years old. Owsley and Jantz compared the

Faulty

Spirit Cave skull with thirty-four population samples from around the world, including ten Native American groups. In an as yet unpublished letter to the Nevada State Museum, they concluded that the Spirit Cave skull was "very different" from any historic-period Native American groups. They wrote, "In terms of its closest classification, it does have a 'European' or 'Archaic Caucasoid' look, because morphometrically it is most similar to the Ainu from Japan and a Medieval period Norse population." Additional early skeletons that they and others have looked at also show Caucasoid-like traits that, in varying degrees, resemble Kennewick Man's. Among these early skeletons, there are no close resemblances to modern Native Americans.

But, even though the skeletons do look Caucasoid, other evidence indicates that the concept of "race" may not be applicable to human beings of ten or fifteen thousand years ago. Recent studies have discovered that all Eurasians may have looked Caucasoid-like in varying degrees. In addition, some researchers believe that the Caucasoid type first emerged in Western Asia or the Middle East, rather than in Europe. The racial differences we see today may be a late (and trivial) development in human evolution. If this is the case, then Kennewick may indeed be a direct ancestor of today's Native Americans—an idea that some preliminary DNA and dental studies seem to support.

BIOLOGY, however, isn't the whole story. There is some archeological evidence that the Clovis people of America—Kennewick Man's predecessors—came from Europe, which could account for his Caucasoid features. When the Clovis people appeared in the New World, they possessed an advanced stone and bone technology, and employed it in hunting big game. (It is no small feat to kill a mammoth or a mastodon with a hand-held spear or an atlatl.) If the Clovis people—or their precursors—had migrated to North America from Asia, one would expect to find early forms of their distinctive tools, of

the right age, in Alaska or eastern Siberia. We don't. But we do find such artifacts in Europe and parts of Russia.

Bruce Bradley is the country's leading expert on Paleo-Indian flaked-stone technology. In 1970, as a recent college graduate, Bradley spent time in Europe studying paleolithic artifacts, including those of the Solutrean people, who lived in southwestern France and Spain between twenty thousand and sixteen thousand years ago. During his stay in Europe, Bradley learned how to flake out a decent Solutrean point. Then he came back to America and started studying stone tools made by the Clovis people. He noticed not only striking visual similarities between the Old World Solutrean and the New World Clovis artifacts, as many researchers had before, but also a strikingly similar use of flaking technology.

"The artifacts don't just look identical," Bradley told me. "They are *made* the same way." Both the European Solutrean and the American Clovis stone tools are fashioned using the same complex flaking techniques. He went on, "As far as I know, overshot flaking is unique to Solutrean and Clovis, and the only diving flaking that is more than eleven thousand years old is that of Solutrean and Clovis."

To argue his case, he drove from Cortez, Colorado, where he lives, to see me, in Santa Fe, bringing with him a trunkful of Solutrean artifacts, casts of Clovis bone and stone tools, and detailed illustrations of artifacts, along with a two-pound chunk of gray Texas flint and some flaking tools.

Silently, he laid a piece of felt on my desk and put on it a cast of a Clovis knife from Blackwater Draw, New Mexico. On top of that, he put a broken Solutrean knife from Laugerie-Haute, in France. They matched perfectly—in size, shape, thickness, and pattern of flaking. As we went through the collection, the similarities could be seen again and again. "It isn't just the flaking as you see it on the finished piece that is the same," Bradley explained. "Both cultures had a very specific way of preparing the edge before striking it to get a very specific type of flake. I call these deep technologies. These are not mere resemblances—they

are deep, complex, abstract concepts applied to the stone."

I remarked that according to other archeologists I had talked to the resemblances were coincidental, the result of two cultures—one Old World, the other New World—confronting the same problems and solving them in the same way. "Maybe," Bradley said. "But a lot of older archeologists were not trained with technology in mind. They see convergence of form or look, but they don't see the technology that goes into it. I'm not saying this is the final answer. But there is so much similarity that we cannot say, 'This is just coincidence,' and ignore it."

To show me what he meant, he brought out the piece of gray flint, and we went into the back yard. "This isn't just knocking away at a stone," he said, hefting the piece of flint and examining it from various angles with narrowed eyes. "After the initial flaking of a spear point, there comes a stage where you have almost limitless choices on how to continue." He squatted down and began to work on the flint with hammer stones and antler billets, his hands deftly turning and shaping the material—knapping, chipping, scraping, pressing, flaking. The pile of razor-sharp flakes grew bigger, and the chunk of flint began to take on a definite shape. Over the next ninety minutes, Bradley reduced the nodule to a five-inch-long Clovis spear point.

It was a revelation to see that making a Clovis point was primarily an intellectual process. Sometimes ten minutes would pass while Bradley examined the stone and mapped out the next flaking sequence. "After thirty years of intense practice, I'm still at the level of a mediocre Clovis craftsman," he said, wiping his bloodied hands and reviving himself with a cup of cocoa. "This is as difficult and complex as a game of chess."

Those are not the only similarities between the Old World Solutrean and the New World Clovis cultures. As we went through Bradley's casts of Clovis artifacts, he compared them with pictures of similar Solutrean artifacts. The Clovis people, for example, produced enigmatic bone rods that were bevelled on both ends and crosshatched; so did the Solutrean. The Clovis people fashioned distinctive spear points out of mammoth ivory; so did the Solutrean. Clovis and Solutrean shaft wrenches (tools thought to have been used for straightening spears) look almost identical. At the same time, there are significant differences between the Clovis and the Solutrean tool kits; the Clovis people fluted their spear points, for instance, while the Solutrean did not.

"To get to the kind of complexity you find in Clovis tools, I see a long technological development," Bradley said. "It isn't one person in one place inventing something. But there is no evolution in Clovis technology. It just appears, full blown, all over the New World, around eleven thousand five hundred years ago. Where's the evolution? *Where did that advanced Clovis technology come from?*"

When I mentioned the idea of a possible Old World Solutrean origin for the New World Clovis to Lawrence Straus, a Solutrean expert at the University of New Mexico, he said, "There are two gigantic problems with it—thousands of years of separation and thousands of miles of ocean." Pointing out that the Solutrean technology itself appeared relatively abruptly in the South of France, he added, "I think this is a fairly clear case of mankind's ability to reinvent things."

But Bradley and other archeologists have pointed out that these objections may not be quite so insurmountable. Recently, in southern Virginia, archeologists discovered a layer of non-Clovis artifacts beneath a Clovis site. The layer dates from fifteen thousand years ago—much closer to the late Solutrean period, sixteen thousand five hundred years ago. Only a few rough tools have been found, but if more emerge they might provide evidence for the independent development of Clovis—or provide a link to the Solutrean. The as yet unnamed culture may be precisely the precursor to Clovis which archeologists have been looking for since the nineteen-thirties. The gap between Solutrean and Clovis may be narrowing.

The other problem is how the Solutrean people—if they are indeed the ancestors of the Clovis—might have reached America in the first place. Although most of them lived along river-banks and on the seacoast of France and Spain, there is no evidence that they had boats. No Paleo-Indian boats have been found on the American side, either, but there is circumstantial evidence that the Paleo-Indians used boats. The ancestors of the Australian aborigines got to Australia in boats from the Indonesian archipelago at least fifty thousand years ago.

But the Solutrean people may not have needed boats at all: sixteen thousand years ago, the North Atlantic was frozen from Norway to Newfoundland. Seasonal pack ice probably extended as far south as Britain and Nova Scotia. William Fitzhugh, the director of the Arctic Studies Center, at the Smithsonian, points out that if human beings had started in France, crossed the English Channel, then hopped along the archipelago from Scotland to the Faeroes to Iceland to Greenland to Newfoundland, and, finally, Nova Scotia, the biggest distance between landfalls would have been about five hundred miles, which Fitzhugh says could have been done on foot over ice. It would still have been a stupendous journey, but perhaps not much more difficult than the Beringian Walk, across thousands of miles of tundra, muskeg, snow, and ice.

"For a long time, most archeologists have been afraid to challenge the Beringian Walk paradigm," Bradley said. "I don't want to try to convince anybody. But I do want to shake the bushes. You could put all the archeological evidence for the Asian-Clovis connection in an envelope and mail it for thirty-two cents. The evidence for a European-Clovis connection you'd have to send in a U.P.S. box, at least."

Robson Bonnichsen, the director of the Center for the Study of the First Americans, at Oregon State University, is another archeologist whose research is challenging the established theories. "There is a presumption, written into almost every textbook on prehistory, that Paleo-Americans such as Clovis are the direct ancestors of today's Native Americans," he told me. "But now we have a very limited number of skeletons from that early time, and it's not clear that that's true. We're getting some hints from people working with genetic data that these earliest populations might have some shared genetic characteristics with latter-day European populations. A lot more research is needed to sort all this out. Now, for the first time, we have the technology to do this research, especially in molecular biology. Which is why we *must* study Kennewick."

This summer, Bonnichsen hopes to go to France and recover human hair from Solutrean and other Upper Paleolithic sites. He will compare DNA from that hair with DNA taken from naturally shed Paleo-American hair recovered from the United States to see if there is a genetic link. Human hair can survive thousands of years in the ground, and, using new techniques, Bonnichsen and his research team have been finding hair in the places where people worked and camped.

B ONNICHSEN and most other archeologists tend to favor the view that if the ancestors of Clovis once lived in Europe they came to America via Asia—the Beringian Walk theory with somewhat different people doing the walking. C. Vance Haynes, Jr., the country's top Paleo-Indian geochronologist, who is a professor of anthropology at the University of Arizona, and is a plaintiff in the lawsuit, said to me, "When I look at Clovis and ask myself where in the world the culture was derived from, I would say Europe." In an article on the origins of Clovis, Haynes noted that there were extraordinary resemblances between New World Clovis and groups that lived in Czechoslovakia and Ukraine twenty thousand years ago. He noted at least nine "common traits" shared by Clovis and certain Eastern European cultures: large blades, end scrapers, burins, shaft wrenches, cylindrical bone points, knapped bone, unifacial flake tools, red ochre, and circumferentially chopped mammoth tusks. He also pointed out that an eighteen-thousand-year-old burial site of two children near Lake Baikal, in Central Asia, exhibits remarkable similarities to what appears to be a Clovis burial site of two cremated children in Montana. The similarities extend beyond tools and points buried with the remains: red ochre, a kind of iron oxide, was placed in both graves. This suggests a migratory group carrying its technology from Europe across Asia. "If you want to speculate, I see a band moving eastward from Europe through Siberia, and meeting people there, and having cultural differences," Haynes said to me. "Any time there's conflict, it drives people, and maybe it just drove them right across the Bering land bridge. And exploration could have been as powerful a driving force thirteen thousand years ago as it was in 1492."

ONCE the Clovis people or their predecessors reached the New World, what happened to them? This is the second—and equally controversial—half of the theory: that the Clovis people or their immediate successors, the Folsom people, may have been supplanted by the ancestors of today's Native Americans. In this scenario, Kennewick Man may have been part of a remnant Caucasoid population related to Clovis and Folsom. Dennis Stanford, of the Smithsonian, said to me, "For a long time, I've held the theory that the Clovis and the Folsom were overwhelmed by a migration of Asians over the Bering land bridge. It may not just have been a genetic swamping or a pushing aside. The north Asians may have been carrying diseases that the Folsom and the Clovis had no resistance to"—just as European diseases wiped out a large percentage of the Native American population after the arrival of Columbus. Stanford explained that at several sites the Paleo-Indian tradition of Clovis and Folsom was abruptly replaced by Archaic Indian traditions, which had advanced but very different lithic technologies. The abruptness of the transition and the sharp change in technology, Stanford feels, suggest a rapid replacement of Folsom by the Archaic cultural complex, rather than an evolution from one into the other. The Archaic spear point embedded in Kennewick Man's hip could even be evidence of an ancient conflict: the Archaic Indian tradition was just beginning to appear in the Pacific Northwest at the time of Kennewick Man's death.

OWSLEY and other physical anthropologists who have studied the skulls of the earliest Americans say that the living population they most closely match is the mysterious Ainu, the aboriginal inhabitants of the Japanese islands. Called the Hairy People by the Japanese, the Ainu are considered by some researchers to be a Causasoid group who, before mixing with the Japanese, in the late nineteenth and twentieth centuries, had European faces, wavy hair, thick beards, and a European-type distribution of body hair. Early travellers reported that some also had blue eyes. Linguists have not been able to connect the Ainu language with any other on earth. The American Museum of Natural History, in New York, has a collection of nineteenth-century photographs of pure-blood Ainu, which I have examined: they stare from the glass plates like fierce, black-bearded Norwegians.

Historically, the Ainu have been the "Indians" of Japan. After the ancestors of the Japanese migrated from the mainland a couple of thousand years ago, they fought the Ainu and pushed them into the northernmost islands of the Japanese archipelago. The Japanese later discriminated against the Ainu, forcing their children to attend Japanese schools, and suppressing their religion and their language. Today, most Ainu have lost their language and many of their distinct physical characteristics, although there has recently been a movement among them to recapture their traditions, their religion, their language, and their songs. Like the American Indians, the Ainu suffer high rates of alcoholism. The final irony is that the Ainu, like the American Indians for Americans, have become a popular Japanese tourist attraction. Many Ainu now make a living doing traditional dances and selling handicrafts to Japanese tourists. The Japanese are as fascinated by the Ainu as we are by the Indians. The stories are mirror images of each other, with only the races changed.

If the Ainu are a remnant population of those people who crossed into America thirteen or more millennia ago, then they are right where one might expect to find them, in the extreme eastern part of Asia. Stanford says, "That racial type goes all the way to Europe, and I suspect that originally they were the same racial group at both ends. At that point in time, this racial diversification hadn't developed. They could have come into the New World from two directions at once, east and west."

THERE is a suspicion among anthropologists that some of the people behind the effort to rebury Kennewick and other ancient skeletons are afraid that the bones could show that the earliest Americans were Caucasoid. I asked Armand Minthorn about this. "We're not afraid of the truth," he said calmly. "We already know our truth. We're not telling the scientists what *their* truth is".

The Umatillas were infuriated by the research that Chatters did on the skeleton before it was seized by the Corps. "Scientists have dug up and studied Native Americans for decades," Minthorn wrote. "We view this practice as desecration of the body and a violation of our most deeply-held religious beliefs." Chatters told me that he had received "vitriolic" and "abusive" telephone calls from tribe members, accusing him of illegalities and racism. (The latter was an odd charge, since Chatters's wife is of Native American descent.) A client of his, he said, received an unsigned letter from one of the tribes, telling the client not to work with Chatters anymore. "They're going to ruin my livelihood," the forensic consultant said.

In a larger sense, the anger of the Umatillas and other Native American tribes is understandable, and even justified. If you look into the acquisition records of most large, old natural-history museums, you will see a history of unethical, and even grisly, collecting practices. Fresh graves were dug up and looted, sometimes in the dead of night. "It is most unpleasant to steal bones from a grave," the eminent anthropologist Franz Boas wrote in his diary just around the turn of the century, "but what is the use, someone has to do it." Indian skulls were bought and sold among collectors like arrowheads and pots. Skeletons were exhibited with no regard for tribal sensitivities. During the Indian wars, warriors who had been killed on the battlefield were sometimes decapitated by Army doctors so that scientists back in the East could study their heads. The

ANTHROPOLOGY

Anthropologists 1, Army Corps 0

American anthropologists won a round in an important legal battle last week, when a U.S. District Court in Portland, Oregon, ordered the Army Corps of Engineers to reopen the case of 9300-year-old human skeleton found on federal land in Washington state. The corps, which has jurisdiction over the skeleton—one of the oldest in the Americas—had planned to turn it over to American Indian tribes for reburial last October under the 1990 Native American Graves Protection and Repatriation Act (NAGPRA). But scientists sued to prevent the handover until they had studied the bones.

Now, although the court stopped short of allowing study of the skeleton, it opened the door for future research by recognizing that the scientists have a legitimate claim that must be considered. "It's a landmark ruling," exulted Alan Schneider, the Portland attorney for the scientists. "This is the first case where a court has held that a third party like a scientist has standing to challenge a government agency's overenforcement of NAGPRA."

The male skeleton, known as "Kennewick Man" for the town where it was discovered in the bank of the Columbia River last summer, is a rare representative of the earliest people to inhabit the Americas. It also had a projectile point embedded in its pelvis and facial features that may be Caucasoid-like, offering clues about early Americans (*Science,* 11 October 1996, p. 172).

As soon as the skeleton was discovered, Smithsonian Institution skeletal biologist Douglas Owsley sought permission to study it, and a team at the University of California, Davis, extracted ancient DNA from a bit of its finger bone for analysis. Owsley and others say that without scientific study it's impossible to know whether the skeleton has a biological or cultural tie to any living people—knowledge needed to determine which tribe, if any, should receive it.

But Owsley says he was told by the corps "flat-out that there would be no scientific study." The corps ordered a halt to the DNA work as soon as it learned of it in October, and announced that it would hand over the skeleton to the Confederated Tribes of the Umatilla Indian Reservation under the auspices of NAGPRA, which requires remains or cultural objects to be given to a culturally affiliated tribe. It later rescinded that order but has kept the skeleton locked away and unavailable for study. Court documents suggest that corps officials were concerned about alienating the Indians. In an 18 September 1996 e-mail message, a corps official wrote: "All risk to us seems to be associated with not repatriating the remains."

In the new decision, U.S. District Court Magistrate John Jelderks invalidated all the corps' orders in the case and criticized the "flawed" procedures used by the agency, which he said "acted before it had all the evidence or fully appreciated the scope of the problem." Jelderks also asked the corps to report back to him with its decision on the case and to answer several questions, including whether repatriation under NAGPRA required a biological or cultural link between bones and living tribes, and how such a link would be determined.

Corps attorney Daria Zane declined to comment for the record. As for the scientists, although they still can't study the skeleton, they're pleased. "Hopefully, the Army Corps will come to its senses," says Owsley. "They are using government lawyers and taxpayers' dollars to argue against academic freedom."

—**Ann Gibbons**

From *Science,* Vol. 277, July 11, 1997, p. 173. © 1997 by The American Association for the Advancement of Science. Reprinted by permission

American Museum of Natural History "collected" six live Inuits in Greenland and brought them to New York to study; four of them died of respiratory diseases, whereupon the museum macerated their corpses and installed the bones in its collection. When I worked at the museum, in the nineteen-eighties, entire hallways were lined with glass cases containing Indian bones and mummified body parts—a small fraction of the museum's collection, which includes an estimated twenty thousand or more human remains, of all races. Before NAGPRA, the Smithsonian had some thirty-five thousand sets of human remains in storage; around eighteen thousand of them were Native American.

Now angry Native Americans, armed with NAGPRA and various state reburial laws, are emptying such museums of bones and grave goods. Although most anthropologists agree that burials identified with particular tribes should be returned, many have been horrified to discover that some tribes are trying to get everything—even skeletons and priceless funerary objects that are thousands of years old.

An amendment that was introduced in Congress last January would tighten NAGPRA further. The amended law could have the effect of hindering much archeology in the United States involving human remains, and add to the cost of construction projects that inadvertently uncover human bones. (Or perhaps the law would merely guarantee that such remains would be quietly destroyed.)

Native Americans have already claimed and reburied two of the earliest skeletons, the Buhl Burial and the Hourglass Cave skeleton, both of which apparently had some Caucasoid characteristics. The loss of the Buhl Burial was particularly significant to anthropologists, because it was more than ten thousand years old—a thousand years older than Kennewick Man—and had been found buried with its grave goods. The skeleton, of a woman between eighteen and twenty years old, received, in the opinion of some anthropologists, inadequate study before it was turned over to the Shoshone-Bannock tribe. The Northern Paiute have asked that the Spirit Cave mummy be reburied. If these early skeletons are all put back in the ground, anthropologists say, much of the history of the peopling of the Americas will be lost.

WHEN Darwin proposed his theory of natural selection, it was seized upon and distorted by economists, social engineers, and politicians, particularly in England: they used it to justify all sorts of vicious social and economic policies. The scientific argument about the original peopling of the Americas threatens to be distorted in a similar way. Some tabloids and radio talk shows have referred to Kennewick as a "white man" and have suggested that his discovery changes everything with respect to the rights of Native Americans in this country. James Chatters said to me, "There are some less racially enlightened folks in the neighborhood who are saying, 'Hey, our ancestors were here first, so we don't owe the Indians anything.'"

This is clearly racist nonsense: these new theories cannot erase or negate the existing history of genocide, broken treaties, and repression. But it does raise an interesting question: If the original inhabitants of the New World were Europeans who were pushed out by Indians, would it change the Indians' position in the great moral landscape?

"No," Stanford said in reply to this question. "Whose ancestors are the people who were pushed out? And who did the pushing? The answer is that we're all the descendants of those folks. If you go back far enough, eventually we all have a common ancestor—*we're all the same.* When the story is finally written, the peopling of the Americas will turn out to be far more complicated than anyone imagined. There have been a lot of people who came here, at many different times. Some stayed and some left, some made it and some didn't, some got pushed out and some did the pushing. It's the history of humankind: the tough guy gets the ground."

Chatters put it another way. "We didn't go digging for this man. He fell out—he was actually a volunteer. I think it would be wrong to stick him back in the ground without waiting to hear the story he has to tell. We need to look at things as human beings, not as one race or another. The message this man brings to us is one of unification: there may be some commonality in our past that will bring us together."

From *The New Yorker,* June 16, 1997, pp. 70-78, 80-81. © 1997 by Douglas Preston. Reprinted by permission of Janklow, Nesbit, and Associates.

Black, White, Other

Racial categories are cultural constructs masquerading as biology

Jonathan Marks

While reading the Sunday edition of the *New York Times* one morning last February, my attention was drawn by an editorial inconsistency. The article I was reading was written by attorney Lani Guinier. (Guinier, you may remember, had been President Clinton's nominee to head the civil rights division at the Department of Justice in 1993. Her name was hastily withdrawn amid a blast of criticism over her views on political representation of minorities.) What had distracted me from the main point of the story was a photo caption that described Guinier as being "half-black." In the text of the article, Guinier had described herself simply as "black."

How can a person be black and half black at the same time? In algebraic terms, this would seem to describe a situation where $x = \frac{1}{2}x$, to which the only solution is $x = 0$.

The inconsistency in the *Times* was trivial, but revealing. It encapsulated a longstanding problem in our use of racial categories—namely, a confusion between biological and cultural heredity. When Guinier is described as "half-black," that is a statement of biological ancestry, for one of her two parents is black. And when Guinier describes herself as black, she is using a cultural category, according to which one can either be black or white, but not both.

Race—as the term is commonly used—is inherited, although not in a strictly biological fashion. It is passed down according to a system of folk heredity, an all-or-nothing system that is different from the quantifiable heredity

of biology. But the incompatibility of the two notions of race is sometimes starkly evident—as when the state decides that racial differences are so important that interracial marriages must be regulated or outlawed entirely. Miscegenation laws in this country (which stayed on the books in many states through the 1960s) obliged the legal system to define who belonged in what category. The resulting formula stated that anyone with one-eighth or more black ancestry was a "negro." (A similar formula, defining Jews, was promulgated by the Germans in the Nuremberg Laws of the 1930s.)

Applying such formulas led to the biological absurdity that having one black great-grandparent was sufficient to define a person as black, but having seven white great grandparents was insufficient to define a person as white. Here, race and biology are demonstrably at odds. And the problem is not semantic but conceptual, for race is presented as a category of nature.

Human beings come in a wide variety of sizes, shapes, colors, and forms—or, because we are visually oriented primates, it certainly seems that way. We also come in larger packages called populations; and we are said to belong to even larger and more confusing units, which have long been known as races. The history of the study of human variation is to a large extent the pursuit of those human races—the attempt to identify the small number of fundamentally distinct kinds of people on earth.

This scientific goal stretches back two centuries, to Linnaeus, the father of bio-

logical systematics, who radically established *Homo sapiens* as one species within a group of animals he called Primates. Linnaeus's system of naming groups within groups logically implied further breakdown. He consequently sought to establish a number of subspecies within *Homo sapiens.* He identified five: four geographical species (from Europe, Asia, Africa, and America) and one grab-bag subspecies called *monstrosus.* This category was dropped by subsequent researchers (as was Linnaeus's use of criteria such as personality and dress to define his subspecies).

While Linnaeus was not the first to divide humans on the basis of the continents on which they lived, he had given the division a scientific stamp. But in attempting to determine the proper number of subspecies, the heirs of Linnaeus always seemed to find different answers, depending upon the criteria they applied. By the mid-twentieth century, scores of anthropologists—led by Harvard's Earnest Hooton—had expended enormous energy on the problem. But these scholars could not convince one another about the precise nature of the fundamental divisions of our species.

Part of the problem—as with the *Times's* identification of Lani Guinier—was that we humans have two constantly intersecting ways of thinking about the divisions among us. On the one hand, we like to think of "race"—as Linnaeus did—as an objective, biological category. In this sense, being a member of a race is supposed to be the equivalent of being a member of a species or of a phy-

Cultural
Label

lum—except that race, on the analogy of subspecies, is an even narrower (and presumably more exclusive and precise) biological category.

The other kind of category into which we humans allocate ourselves—when we say "Serb" or "Hutu" or "Jew" or "Chicano" or "Republican" or "Red Sox fan"—is cultural. The label refers to little or nothing in the natural attributes of its members. These members may not live in the same region and may not even know many others like themselves. What they share is neither strictly nature nor strictly community. The groupings are constructions of human social history.

Membership in these unbiological groupings may mean the difference between life and death, for they are the categories that allow us to be identified (and accepted or vilified) socially. While membership in (or allegiance to) these categories may be assigned or adopted from birth, the differentia that mark members from nonmembers are symbolic and abstract; they serve to distinguish people who cannot be readily distinguished by nature. So important are these symbolic distinctions that some of the strongest animosities are often expressed between very similar-looking peoples. Obvious examples are Bosnian Serbs and Muslims, Irish and English, Huron and Iroquois.

Obvious natural variation is rarely so important as cultural difference. One simply does not hear of a slaughter of the short people at the hands of the tall, the glabrous at the hands of the hairy, the red-haired at the hands of the brown-haired. When we do encounter genocidal violence between different looking peoples, the two groups are invariably socially or culturally distinct as well. Indeed, the tragic frequency of hatred and genocidal violence between biologically indistinguishable peoples implies that biological differences such as skin color are not motivations but, rather, excuses. They allow nature to be invoked to reinforce group identities and antagonisms that would exist without these physical distinctions. But are there any truly "racial" biological distinctions to be found in our species?

Obviously, if you compare two people from different parts of the world (or whose ancestors came from different parts of the world), they will differ physically, but one cannot therefore define three or four or five basically different kinds of people, as a biological notion of race would imply. The anatomical properties that distinguish people—such as pigmentation, eye form, body build—are not clumped in discrete groups, but distributed along geographical gradients, as are nearly all the genetically determined variants detectable in the human gene pool.

These gradients are produced by three forces. Natural selection adapts populations to local circumstances (like climate) and thereby differentiates them from other populations. Genetic drift (random fluctuations in a gene pool) also differentiates populations from one another, but in non-adaptive ways. And gene flow (via intermarriage and other child-producing unions) acts to homogenize neighboring populations.

In practice, the operations of these forces are difficult to discern. A few features, such as body build and the graduated distribution of the sickle cell anemia gene in populations from western Africa, southern Asia, and the Mediterranean can be plausibly related to the effects of selection. Others, such as the graduated distribution of a small deletion in the mitochondrial DNA of some East Asian, Oceanic, and Native American peoples, or the degree of flatness of the face, seem unlikely to be the result of selection and are probably the results of random bio-historical factors. The cause of the distribution of most features, from nose breadth to blood group, is simply unclear.

The overall result of these forces is evident, however. As Johann Friedrich Blumenbach noted in 1775, "you see that all do so run into one another, and that one variety of mankind does so sensibly pass into the other, that you cannot mark out the limits between them." (Posturing as an heir to Linnaeus, he nonetheless attempted to do so.) But from humanity's gradations in appearance, no defined groupings resembling races readily emerge. The racial categories with which we have become so familiar are the result of our imposing arbitrary cultural boundaries in order to partition gradual biological variation.

Unlike graduated biological distinctions, culturally constructed categories are ultrasharp. One can be French or German, but not both; Tutsi or Hutu, but not both; Jew or Catholic, but not both; Bosnian Muslim or Serb, but not both; black or white, but not both. Traditionally, people of "mixed race" have been obliged to choose one and thereby identify themselves unambiguously to census takers and administrative bookkeepers—a practice that is now being widely called into question.

A scientific definition of race would require considerable homogeneity within each group, and reasonably discrete differences between groups, but three kinds of data militate against this view: First, the groups traditionally described as races are not at all homogeneous. Africans and Europeans, for instance, are each a collection of biologically diverse populations. Anthropologists of the 1920s widely recognized *three* European races: Nordic, Alpine, and Mediterranean. This implied that races could exist within races. American anthropologist Carleton Coon identified *ten* European races in 1939. With such protean use, the term race came to have little value in describing actual biological entities within *Homo sapiens*. The scholars were not only grappling with a broad north-south gradient in human appearance across Europe, they were trying to bring the data into line with their belief in profound and fundamental constitutional differences between groups of people.

But there simply isn't one European race to contrast with an African race, nor three, nor ten: the question (as scientists long posed it) fails to recognize the actual patterning of diversity in the human species. Fieldwork revealed, and genetics later quantified, the existence of far more biological diversity within any group than between groups. Fatter and thinner people exist everywhere, as do people with type O and type A blood. What generally varies from one population to the next is the *proportion* of people in these groups expressing the trait or gene. Hair color varies strikingly among Europeans and native Australians, but little among other peoples. To focus on discovering differences between presumptive races, when the vast majority of detectable variants do not help differentiate them, was thus to define a very narrow—if not largely illusory—problem in human biology. (The fact that Africans are biologically more diverse than Europeans, but have rarely been split into so many races, attests to the cultural basis of these categorizations.)

Second, differences between human groups are only evident when contrasting geographical extremes. Noting these extremes, biologists of an earlier era sought to identify representatives of "pure," primordial races presumably located in Norway, Senegal, and Thailand. At no time, however, was our species composed of a few populations within which everyone looked pretty much the same. Ever since some of our ancestors left Africa to spread out through the Old World, we humans have always lived in the "in-between" places. And human populations have also always been in genetic contact with one another. Indeed, for tens of thousands of years, humans have had trade networks; and where goods flow, so do genes. Consequently, we have no basis for considering *extreme* human forms the most pure, or most representative, of some ancient primordial populations. Instead, they represent populations adapted to the most disparate environments.

And third, between each presumptive "major" race are unclassifiable populations and people. Some populations of India, for example, are darkly pigmented (or "black"), have Europeanlike ("Caucasoid") facial features, but inhabit the continent of Asia (which should make them "Asian"). Americans might tend to ignore these "exceptions" to the racial categories, since immigrants to the United States from West Africa, Southeast Asia, and northwest Europe far outnumber those from India. The very existence of unclassifiable peoples undermines the idea that there are just three human biological groups in the Old World. Yet acknowledging the biological distinctiveness of such groups leads to a rapid proliferation of categories. What about Australians? Polynesians? The Ainu of Japan?

Categorizing people is important to any society. It is, at some basic psychological level, probably necessary to have group identity about who and what you are, in contrast to who and what you are not. The concept of race, however, specifically involves the recruitment of biology to validate those categories of self-identity.

Mice don't have to worry about that the way humans do. Consequently, classifying them into subspecies entails less of a responsibility for a scientist than classifying humans into sub-species does. And by the 1960s, most anthropologists realized they could not defend any classification of *Homo sapiens* into biological subspecies or races that could be considered reasonably objective. They therefore stopped doing it, and stopped identifying the endeavor as a central goal of the field. It was a biologically intractable problem—the old square-peg-in-a-round-hole enterprise; and people's lives, or welfares, could well depend on the ostensibly scientific pronouncement. Reflecting on the social history of the twentieth century, that was a burden anthropologists would no longer bear.

This conceptual divorce in anthropology—of cultural from biological phenomena was one of the most fundamental scientific revolutions of our time. And since it affected assumptions so rooted in our everyday experience, and resulted in conclusions so counterintuitive—like the idea that the earth goes around the sun, and not vice-versa—it has been widely underappreciated.

Kurt Vonnegut, in *Slaughterhouse Five*, describes what he remembered being taught about human variation: "At that time, they were teaching that there was absolutely no difference between anybody. They may be teaching that still." Of course there are biological differences between people, and between populations. The question is: How are those differences patterned? And the answer seems to be: Not racially. Populations are the only readily identifiable units of humans, and even they are fairly fluid, biologically similar to populations nearby, and biologically different from populations far away.

In other words, the message of contemporary anthropology is: You may group humans into a small number of races if you want to, but you are denied biology as a support for it.

New York-born Jonathan Marks earned an undergraduate degree in natural science at Johns Hopkins. After getting his Ph.D. in anthropology, Marks did a post-doc in genetics at the University of California at Davis and is now an associate professor of anthropology at Yale University. He is the coauthor, with Edward Staski, of the introductory textbook Evolutionary Anthropology *(San Diego: Harcourt, Brace Jovanovich, 1992). His new book,* Human Biodiversity: Genes, Race, and History *is published (1995) by Aldine de Gruyter.*

Racial Odyssey

Boyce Rensberger

The human species comes in an artist's palette of colors: sandy yellows, reddish tans, deep browns, light tans, creamy whites, pale pinks. It is a rare person who is not curious about the skin colors, hair textures, bodily structures and facial features associated with racial background. Why do some Africans have dark brown skin, while that of most Europeans is pale pink? Why do the eyes of most "white" people and "black" people look pretty much alike but differ so from the eyes of Orientals? Did one race evolve before the others? If so, is it more primitive or more advanced as a result? Can it be possible, as modern research suggests, that there is no such thing as a pure race? These are all honest, scientifically worthy questions. And they are central to current research on the evolution of our species on the planet Earth.

Broadly speaking, research on racial differences has led most scientists to three major conclusions. The first is that there are many more differences among people than skin color, hair texture and facial features. Dozens of other variations have been found, ranging from the shapes of bones to the consistency of ear wax to subtle variations in body chemistry.

The second conclusion is that the overwhelming evolutionary success of the human species is largely due to its great genetic variability. When migrating bands of our early ancestors reached a new environment, at least a few already had physical traits that gave them an edge in surviving there. If the coming centuries bring significant environmental changes, as many believe they will, our chances of surviving them will be immeasurably enhanced by our diversity as a species.

There is a third conclusion about race that is often misunderstood. Despite our wealth of variation and despite our constant, everyday references to race, no one has ever discovered a reliable way of distinguishing one race from another. While it is possible to classify a great many people on the basis of certain physical features, there are no known feature or groups of features that will do the job in all cases.

Skin color won't work. Yes, most Africans from south of the Sahara and their descendants around the world have skin that is darker than that of most Europeans. But there are millions of people in India, classified by some anthropologists as members of the Caucasoid, or "white," race who have darker skins than most Americans who call themselves black. And there are many Africans living in sub-Sahara Africa today whose skins are no darker than the skins of many Spaniards, Italians, Greeks or Lebanese.

What about stature as a racial trait? Because they are quite short, on the average, African Pygmies have been considered racially distinct from other dark-skinned Africans. If stature, then, is a racial criterion, would one include in the same race the tall African Watusi and the Scandinavians of similar stature?

The little web of skin that distinguishes Oriental eyes is said to be a particular feature of the Mongoloid race. How, then, can it be argued that the American Indian, who lacks this epicanthic fold, is Mongoloid?

Even more hopeless as racial markers are hair color, eye color, hair form, the shapes of noses and lips or any of the other traits put forth as typical of one race or another.

NO NORMS

Among the tall people of the world there are many black, many white and many in between. Among black people of the world there are many with kinky hair, many with straight or wavy hair, and many in between. Among the broad-nosed, full-lipped people of the world there are many with dark skins, many with light skins and many in between.

How did our modern perceptions of race arise? One of the first to attempt a scientific classification of peoples was Carl von Linné, better known as Linnaeus. In 1735, he published a classification that remains the standard today. As Linnaeus saw it there were four races, classifiable geographically and by skin color. The names Linnaeus gave them were *Homo sapiens Africanus nigrus* (black African human being), *H. sapiens Americanus rubescens* (red American human being), *H. sapiens Asiaticus fuscusens* (brownish Asian human being), and *H. sapiens Europaeus albescens* (white European human being). All, Linnaeus recognized, were members of a single human species.

A species includes all individuals that are biologically capable of interbreeding and producing fertile offspring. Most matings between species are fruitless, and even when they succeed, as when a horse and a donkey interbreed and produce a mule, the progeny are sterile. When a poodle mates with a collie, however, the offspring are fertile, showing that both dogs are members of the same species.

DISEASE ORIGINS

The gene for sickle cell anemia, a disease found primarily among black people, appears to have evolved because its presence can render its bearer resistant to malaria. Such a trait would have obvious value in tropical Africa.

A person who has sickle cell anemia must have inherited genes for the disease from both parents. If a child inherits only one sickle cell gene, he or she will be resistant to malaria but will not have the anemia. Paradoxically, inheriting genes from both parents does not seem to affect resistance to malaria.

In the United States, where malaria is practically nonexistent, the sickle cell gene confers no survival advantage and is disappearing. Today only about 1 out of every 10 American blacks carries the gene.

Many other inherited diseases are found only in people from a particular area. Tay-Sachs disease, which often kills before the age of two, is almost entirely confined to Jews from parts of Eastern Europe and their descendants elsewhere. Paget's disease, a bone disorder, is found most often among those of English descent. Impacted wisdom teeth are a common problem among Asians and Europeans but not among Africans. Children of all races are able to digest milk because their bodies make lactase, the enzyme that breaks down lactose, or milk sugar. But the ability to digest lactose in adulthood is a racially distributed trait.

About 90 percent of Orientals and blacks lose this ability by the time they reach adulthood and become quite sick when they drink milk.

Even African and Asian herders who keep cattle or goats rarely drink fresh milk. Instead, they first treat the milk with fermentation bacteria that break down lactose, in a sense predigesting it. They can then ingest the milk in the form of yogurt or cheese without any problem.

About 90 percent of Europeans and their American descendants, on the other hand, continue to produce the enzyme throughout their lives and can drink milk with no ill effects.

Even though Linnaeus's system of nomenclature survives, his classifications were discarded, especially after voyages of discovery revealed that there were many more kinds of people than could be pigeonholed into four categories. All over the world there are small populations that don't fit. Among the better known are:

- The so-called Bushmen of southern Africa, who look as much Mongoloid as Negroid.
- The Negritos of the South Pacific, who do look Negroid but are very far from Africa and have no known links to that continent.
- The Ainu of Japan, a hairy aboriginal people who look more Caucasoid than anything else.
- The Lapps of Scandinavia, who look as much like Eskimos as like Europeans.
- The aborigines of Australia, who often look Negroid but many of whom have straight or wavy hair and are often blond as children.
- The Polynesians, who seem to be a blend of many races, the proportions differing from island to island.

To accommodate such diversity, many different systems of classification have been proposed. Some set up two or three dozen races. None has ever satisfied all experts.

CLASSIFICATION SYSTEM

Perhaps the most sweeping effort to impose a classification upon all the peoples of the world was made by the American anthropologist Carleton Coon. He concluded there are five basic races, two of which have major subdivisions: Caucasoids; Mongoloids; full-size Australoids (Australian aborigines); dwarf Australoids (Negritos—Andaman Islanders and similar peoples); full-size Congoids (African Negroids); dwarf Congoids (African Pygmies); and Capoids (the so-called Bushmen and Hottentots).

In his 1965 classic, *The Living Races of Man*, Coon hypothesized that before A.D. 1500 there were five pure races—five centers of human population that were so isolated that there was almost no mixing.

Each of these races evolved independently, Coon believed, diverging from a pre-*Homo sapiens* stock that was essentially the same everywhere. He speculated that the common ancestor evolved into *Homo sapiens* in five separate regions at five different times, beginning about 35,000 years ago. The populations that have been *Homo sapiens* for the shortest periods of time, Coon said, are the world's "less civilized" races.

The five pure races remained distinct until A.D. 1500; then Europeans started sailing the world, leaving their genes—as sailors always have—in every port and planting distant colonies. At about the same time, thousands of Africans were captured and forcibly settled in many parts of the New World.

That meant the end of the five pure races. But Coon and other experts held that this did not necessarily rule out the idea of distinct races. In this view, there *are* such things as races; people just don't fit into them very well anymore.

The truth is that there is really no hard evidence to suggest that five or any particular number of races evolved independently. The preponderance of evidence today suggests that as traits typical of fully modern people arose in any one place, they spread quickly to all human populations. Advances in intelligence were almost certainly the fastest to spread. Most anthropologists and geneticists now believe that human beings have always been subject to migrating and mixing. In other words, there probably never were any such things as pure races.

Race mixing has not only been a fact of human history but is, in this day of unprecedented global mobility, taking place at a more rapid rate than ever. It is not farfetched to envision the day when, generations hence, the entire "complexion" of major population centers will be different. Meanwhile, we can see such changes taking place before our eyes, for they are a part of everyday reality.

HYBRID VIGOR

Oddly, those who assert scientific validity for their notions of pure and distinct races seem oblivious of a basic genetic principle that plant and animal breeders know well: too much inbreeding can lead to proliferation of inferior traits. Cross-breeding with different strains often produces superior combinations and "hybrid vigor."

The striking differences among people may very well be a result of constant genetic mixing. And as geneticists and ecologists know, in diversity lies strength and resilience.

To understand the origin and proliferation of human differences, one must first know how Darwinian evolution works.

Evolution is a two-step process. Step one is mutation: somehow a gene in the ovary or testes of an individual is altered, changing the molecular configuration that stores instructions for forming a new individual. The children who inherit that gene will be different in some way from their ancestors.

Step two is selection: for a racial difference, or any other evolutionary change to arise, it must survive and be passed through several generations. If the mutation confers some disadvantage, the individual dies, often during embryonic development. But if the change is beneficial in some way, the individual should have a better chance of thriving than relatives lacking the advantage.

NATURAL SELECTION

If a new trait is beneficial, it will bring reproductive success to its bearer. After several generations of multiplication, bearers of the new trait may begin to outnumber nonbearers. Darwin called this natural selection to distinguish it from the artificial selection exercised by animal breeders.

Skin color is the human racial trait most generally thought to confer an evolutionary advantage of this sort. It has long been obvious in the Old World that the farther south one goes, the darker the skin color. Southern Europeans are usually somewhat darker than northern Euro-

peans. In North Africa, skin colors are darker still, and, as one travels south, coloration reaches its maximum at the Equator. The same progressions holds in Asia, with the lightest skins to the north. Again, as one moves south, skin color darkens, reaching in southern India a "blackness" equal to that of equatorial Africans.

This north-south spectrum of skin color derives from varying intensities of the same dark brown pigment called melanin. Skin cells simply have more or less melanin granules to be seen against a background that is pinkish because of the underlying blood vessels. All races can increase their melanin concentration by exposure to the sun.

What is it about northerly latitudes in the Northern Hemisphere that favors less pigmentation and about southerly latitudes that favors more? Exposure to intense sunlight is not the only reason why people living in southerly latitudes are dark. A person's susceptibility to rickets and skin cancer, his ability to withstand cold and to see in the dark may also be related to skin color.

The best-known explanation says the body can tolerate only a narrow range of intensities of sunlight. Too much causes sunburn and cancer, while too little deprives the body of vitamin D, which is synthesized in the skin under the influence of sunlight. A dark complexion protects the skin from the harmful effects of intense sunlight. Thus, albinos born in equatorial regions have a high rate of skin cancer. On the other hand, dark skin in northerly latitudes screens out sunlight needed for the synthesis of vitamin D. Thus, dark-skinned children living in northern latitudes had high rates of rickets—a bone-deforming disease caused by a lack of vitamin D—before their milk was routinely fortified. In the sunny tropics, dark skin admits enough light to produce the vitamin.

Recently, there has been some evidence that skin colors are linked to differences in the ability to avoid injury from the cold. Army researchers found that during the Korean War blacks were more susceptible to frostbite than were whites. Even among Norwegian soldiers in World War II, brunettes had a slightly higher incidence of frostbite than did blonds.

EYE PIGMENTATION

A third link between color and latitude involves the sensitivity of the eye to various wavelengths of light. It is known that dark-skinned people have more pigmentation in the iris of the eye and at the back of the eye where the image falls. It has been found that the less pigmented the eye, the more sensitive it is to colors at the red end of the spectrum. In situations illuminated with reddish light, the northern European can see more than a dark African sees.

It has been suggested that Europeans developed lighter eyes to adapt to the longer twilights of the North and their greater reliance on firelight to illuminate caves.

Although the skin cancer-vitamin D hypothesis enjoys wide acceptance, it may well be that resistance to cold, possession of good night vision and other yet unknown factors all played roles in the evolution of skin colors.

Most anthropologists agree that the original human skin color was dark brown, since it is fairly well established that human beings evolved in the tropics of Africa. This does not, however, mean that the first people were Negroids, whose descendants, as they moved north, evolved into light-skinned Caucasoids. It is more likely that the skin color of various populations changed several times from dark to light and back as people moved from one region to another.

Consider, for example, that long before modern people evolved, *Homo erectus* had spread throughout Africa, Europe and Asia. The immediate ancestor of *Homo sapiens, Homo erectus*, was living in Africa 1.5 million years ago and in Eurasia 750,000 years ago. The earliest known forms of *Homo sapiens* do not make their appearance until somewhere between 250,000 and 500,000 years ago. Although there is no evidence of the skin color of any hominid fossil, it is probable that the *Homo erectus* population in Africa had dark skin. As subgroups spread into northern latitudes, mutations that reduced pigmentation conferred survival advantages on them and lighter skins came to predominate. In other words, there were probably black *Homo erectus* peoples in Africa and white ones in Europe and Asia.

Did the black *Homo erectus* populations evolve into today's Negroids and the white ones in Europe into today's Caucasoids? By all the best evidence, nothing like this happened. More likely, wherever *Homo sapiens* arose it proved so superior to the *Homo erectus* populations that it eventually replaced them everywhere.

If the first *Homo sapiens* evolved in Africa, they were probably dark-skinned; those who migrated northward into Eurasia lost their pigmentation. But it is just as possible that the first *Homo sapiens* appeared in northern climes, descendants of white-skinned *Homo erectus*. These could have migrated southward toward Africa, evolving darker skins. All modern races, incidentally, arose long after the brain had reached its present size in all parts of the world.

North-south variations in pigmentation are quite common among mammals and birds. The tropical races tend to be darker in fur and feather, the desert races tend to be brown, and those near the Arctic Circle are lighter colored.

There are exceptions among humans. The Indians of the Americas, from the Arctic to the southern regions of South America, do not conform to the north-south scheme of coloration. Though most think of Indians as being reddish-brown, most Indians tend to be relatively light skinned, much like their presumed Mongoloid ancestors in Asia. The ruddy complexion that lives in so many stereotypes of Indians is merely what years of heavy tanning can produce in almost any light-skinned person. Anthropologists explain the color consistency as a consequence of the relatively recent entry of people into the Americas—probably between 12,000 and 35,000 years ago. Perhaps they have not yet had time to change.

Only a few external physical differences other than color appear to have adaptive significance. The strongest cases can be made for nose shape and stature.

WHAT'S IN A NOSE

People native to colder or drier climates tend to have longer, more beak-shaped noses than those living in hot and humid regions. The nose's job is to warm and humidify air before it reaches sensitive lung tissues. The colder or drier the air is,

the more surface area is needed inside the nose to get it to the right temperature or humidity. Whites tend to have longer and beakier noses than blacks or Orientals. Nevertheless, there is great variation within races. Africans in the highlands of East Africa have longer noses than Africans from the hot, humid lowlands, for example.

Stature differences are reflected in the tendency for most northern peoples to have shorter arms, legs and torsos and to be stockier than people from the tropics. Again, this is an adaptation to heat or cold. One way of reducing heat loss is to have less body surface, in relation to weight or volume, from which heat can escape. To avoid overheating, the most desirable body is long limbed and lean. As a result, most Africans tend to be lankier than northern Europeans. Arctic peoples are the shortest limbed of all.

Hair forms may also have a practical role to play, but the evidence is weak. It has been suggested that the more tightly curled hair of Africans insulates the top of the head better than does straight or wavy hair. Contrary to expectation, black hair serves better in this role than white hair. Sunlight is absorbed and converted to heat at the outer surface of the hair blanket; it radiates directly into the air. White fur, common on Arctic animals that need to absorb solar heat, is actually transparent and transmits light into the hair blanket, allowing the heat to form within the insulating layer, where it is retained for warmth.

Aside from these examples, there is little evidence that any of the other visible differences among the world's people provide any advantage. Nobody knows, for example, why Orientals have epicanthic eye folds or flatter facial profiles. The thin lips of Caucasoids and most Mongoloids have no known advantages over the Negroid's full lips. Why should middle-aged and older Caucasoid men go bald so much more frequently than the men of other races? Why does the skin of Bushmen wrinkle so heavily in the middle and later years? Or why does the skin of Negroids resist wrinkling so well? Why do the Indian men in one part of South America have blue penises? Why do Hottentot women have such unusually large buttocks?

There are possible evolutionary explanations for why such apparently useless differences arise.

One is a phenomenon known as sexual selection. Environmentally adaptive traits arise, Darwin thought, through natural selection—the environment itself chooses who will thrive or decline. In sexual selection, which Darwin also suggested, the choice belongs to the prospective mate.

In simple terms, ugly individuals will be less likely to find mates and reproduce their genes than beautiful specimens will. Take the blue penis as an example. Women might find it unusually attractive or perhaps believe it to be endowed with special powers. If so, a man born with a blue penis will find many more opportunities to reproduce his genes than his ordinary brothers.

Sexual selection can also operate when males compete for females. The moose with the larger antlers or the lion with the more imposing mane will stand a better chance of discouraging less well-endowed males and gaining access to females. It is possible that such a process operated among Caucasoid males, causing them to become markedly hairy, especially around the face.

ATTRACTIVE TRAITS

Anthropologists consider it probable that traits such as the epicanthic fold or the many regional differences in facial features were selected this way.

Yet another method by which a trait can establish itself involves accidental selection. It results from what biologists call genetic drift.

Suppose that in a small nomadic band a person is born with perfectly parallel fingerprints instead of the usual loops, whorls or arches. That person's children would inherit parallel fingerprints, but they would confer no survival advantages. But if our family decides to strike out on its own, it will become the founder of a new band consisting of its own descendants, all with parallel fingerprints.

Events such as this, geneticists and anthropologists believe, must have occurred many times in the past to produce the great variety within the human species. Among the apparently neutral traits that differ among populations are:

Ear Wax

There are two types of ear wax. One is dry and crumbly and the other is wet and sticky. Both types can be found in every major population, but the frequencies differ. Among northern Chinese, for example, 98 percent have dry ear wax. Among American whites, only 16 percent have dry ear wax. Among American blacks the figure is 7 percent.

Scent Glands

As any bloodhound knows, every person has his or her own distinctive scent. People vary in the mixture of odoriferous compounds exuded through the skin—most of it coming from specialized glands called apocrine glands. Among whites, these are concentrated in the armpits and near the genitals and anus. Among blacks, they may also be found on the chest and abdomen. Orientals have hardly any apocrine glands at all. In the words of the Oxford biologist John R. Baker, "The Europids and Negrids are smelly, the Mongoloids scarcely or not at all." Smelliest of all are northern European, or so-called Nordic, whites. Body odor is rare in Japan. It was once thought to indicate a European in the ancestry and to be a disease requiring hospitalization.

Blood Groups

Some populations have a high percentage of members with a particular blood group. American Indians are overwhelmingly group O—100 percent in some regions. Group A is most common among Australian aborigines and the Indians in western Canada. Group B is frequent in northern India, other parts of Asia and western Africa.

Advocates of the pure-race theory once seized upon blood groups as possibly unique to the original pure races. The proportions of groups found today, they thought, would indicate the degree of mixing. It was subsequently found that chimpanzees, our closest living relatives, have the same blood groups as humans.

Taste

PTC (phenylthiocarbamide) is a synthetic compound that some people can taste and others cannot. The ability to taste it has no known survival value, but it is clearly an inherited trait. The proportion of persons who can taste PTC varies in different populations: 50 to 70 percent of Australian aborigines can taste it, as can 60 to 80 percent of all Europeans. Among East Asians, the percentage is 83 to 100 percent, and among Africans, 90 to 97 percent.

Urine

Another indicator of differences in body chemistry is the excretion of a compound known as BAIB (beta-amino-isobutyric acid) in urine. Europeans seldom excrete large quantities, but high levels of excretion are common among Asians and American Indians. It had been shown that the differences are not due to diet.

No major population has remained isolated long enough to prevent any unique genes from eventually mixing with those of neighboring groups. Indeed, a map showing the distribution of so-called traits would have no sharp boundaries, except for coastlines. The intensity of a trait such as skin color, which is controlled by six pairs of genes and can therefore exist in many shades, varies gradually from one population to another. With only a few exceptions, every known genetic possibility possessed by the species can be found to some degree in every sizable population.

EVER-CHANGING SPECIES

One can establish a system of racial classification simply by listing the features of populations at any given moment. Such a concept of race is, however, inappropriate to a highly mobile and ever-changing species such as *Homo sapiens*. In the short view, races may seem distinguishable, but in biology's long haul, races come and go. New ones arise and blend into neighboring groups to create new and racially stable populations. In time, genes from these groups flow into other neighbors, continuing the production of new permutations.

Some anthropologists contend that at the moment American blacks should be considered a race distinct from African blacks. They argue that American blacks are a hybrid of African blacks and European whites. Indeed, the degree of mixture can be calculated on the basis of a blood component known as the Duffy factor.

In West Africa, where most of the New World's slaves came from, the Duffy factor is virtually absent. It is present in 43 percent of American whites. From the number of American blacks who are now "Duffy positive" it can be calculated that whites contributed 21 percent of the genes in the American black population. The figure is higher for blacks in northern and western states and lower in the South. By the same token, there are whites who have black ancestors. The number is smaller because of the tendency to identify a person as black even if only a minor fraction of his ancestors were originally from Africa.

The unwieldiness of race designations is also evident in places such as Mexico where most of the people are, in effect, hybrids of Indians (Mongoloid by some classifications) and Spaniards (Caucasoid). Many South American populations are tri-hybrids—mixtures of Mongoloid, Caucasoid and Negroid. Brazil is a country where the mixture has been around long enough to constitute a racially stable population. Thus, in one sense, new races have been created in the United States, Mexico and Brazil. But in the long run, those races will again change.

Sherwood Washburn, a noted anthropologist, questions the usefulness of racial classification: "Since races are open systems which are intergrading, the number of races will depend on the purpose of the classification. I think we should require people who propose a classification of races to state in the first place why they wish to divide the human species."

The very notion of a pure race, then, makes no sense. But, as evolutionists know full well, a rich genetic diversity within the human species most assuredly *does*.

From *Science Digest*, January/February 1981. © 1981 by Boyce Rensberger. Reprinted by permission.

Commentary

The Tall and the Short of It

By Barry Bogin

BAFFLED BY YOUR FUTURE PROSPECTS? As a biological anthropologist, I have just one word of advice for you: plasticity. *Plasticity* refers to the ability of many organisms, including humans, to alter themselves—their behavior or even their biology—in response to changes in the environment. We tend to think that our bodies get locked into their final form by our genes, but in fact we alter our bodies as the conditions surrounding us shift, particularly as we grow during childhood. Plasticity is as much a product of evolution's fine-tuning as any particular gene, and it makes just as much evolutionary good sense. Rather than being able to adapt to a single environment, we can, thanks to plasticity, change our bodies to cope with a wide range of environments. Combined with the genes we inherit from our parents, plasticity accounts for what we are and what we can become.

Anthropologists began to think about human plasticity around the turn of the century, but the concept was first clearly defined in 1969 by Gabriel Lasker, a biological anthropologist at Wayne State University in Detroit. At that time scientists tended to consider only those adaptations that were built into the genetic makeup of a person and passed on automatically to the next generation. A classic example of this is the ability of adults in some human societies to drink milk. As children, we all produce an enzyme called lactase, which we need to break

down the sugar lactose in our mother's milk. In many of us, however, the lactase gene slows down dramatically as we approach adolescence—probably as the result of another gene that regulates its activity. When that regulating gene turns down the production of lactase, we can no longer digest milk.

Lactose intolerance—which causes intestinal gas and diarrhea—affects between 70 and 90 percent of African Americans, Native Americans, Asians, and people who come from around the Mediterranean. But others, such as people of central and western European descent and the Fulani of West Africa, typically have no problem drinking milk as adults. That's because they are descended from societies with long histories of raising goats and cattle. Among these people there was a clear benefit to being able to drink milk, so natural selection gradually changed the regulation of their lactase gene, keeping it functioning throughout life.

That kind of adaptation takes many centuries to become established, but Lasker pointed out that there are two other kinds of adaptation in humans that need far less time to kick in. If people have to face a cold winter with little or no heat, for example, their metabolic rates rise over the course of a few weeks and they produce more body heat. When summer returns, the rates sink again.

Lasker's other mode of adaptation concerned the irreversible, lifelong mod-

ification of people as they develop—that is, their plasticity. Because we humans take so many years to grow to adulthood, and because we live in so many different environments, from forests to cities and from deserts to the Arctic, we are among the world's most variable species in our physical form and behavior. Indeed, we are one of the most plastic of all species.

In an age when DNA is king, it's worth considering why Americans are no longer the world's tallest people, and some Guatemalans no longer pygmies.

One of the most obvious manifestations of human malleability is our great range of height, and it is a subject I've made a special study of for the last 25 years. Consider these statistics: in 1850 Americans were the tallest people in the world, with American men averaging 5'6". Almost 150 years later, American men now average 5'8", but we have fallen in the standings and are now only the third tallest people in the world. In first place are the Dutch. Back in 1850 they averaged only 5'4"—the shortest men in Europe—but today they are a towering 5'10". (In these two groups, and just about everywhere else, women average about five inches less than men at all times.)

So what happened? Did all the short Dutch sail over to the United States? Did the Dutch back in Europe get an infusion of "tall genes"? Neither. In both America and the Netherlands life got better, but more so for the Dutch, and height increased as a result. We know this is true thanks in part to studies on how height is determined. It's the product of plasticity in our childhood and in our mothers' childhood as well. If a girl is undernourished and suffers poor health, the growth of her body, including her reproductive system, is usually reduced. With a shortage of raw materials, she can't build more cells to construct a bigger body; at the same time, she has to invest what materials she can get into repairing already existing cells and tissues from the damage caused by disease. Her shorter stature as an adult is the result of a compromise her body makes while growing up.

Such a woman can pass on her short stature to her child, but genes have nothing to do with it for either of them. If she becomes pregnant, her small reproductive system probably won't be able to supply a normal level of nutrients and oxygen to her fetus. This harsh environment reprograms the fetus to grow more slowly than it would if the woman was healthier, so she is more likely to give birth to a smaller baby. Low-birth-weight babies (weighing less than 5.5 pounds) tend to continue their prenatal program of slow growth through childhood. By the time they are teenagers, they are usually significantly shorter than people of normal birth weight. Some particularly striking evidence of this reprogramming comes from studies on monozygotic twins, which develop from a single fertilized egg cell and are therefore identical genetically. But in certain cases, monozygotic twins end up being nourished by unequal portions of the placenta. The twin with the smaller fraction of the placenta is often born with low birth weight, while the other one is normal. Follow-up studies show that this difference between the twins can last throughout their lives.

As such research suggests, we can use the average height of any group of peo-

ple as a barometer of the health of their society. After the turn of the century both the United States and the Netherlands began to protect the health of their citizens by purifying drinking water, installing sewer systems, regulating the safety of food, and, most important, providing better health care and diets to children. The children responded to their changed environment by growing taller. But the differences in Dutch and American societies determined their differing heights today. The Dutch decided to provide public health benefits to all the public, including the poor. In the United States, meanwhile, improved health is enjoyed most by those who can afford it. The poor often lack adequate housing, sanitation, and health care. The difference in our two societies can be seen at birth: in 1990 only 4 percent of Dutch babies were born at low birth weight, compared with 7 percent in the United States. For white Americans the rate was 5.7 percent, and for black Americans the rate was a whopping 13.3 percent. The disparity between rich and poor in the United States carries through to adulthood: poor Americans are shorter than the better-off by about one inch. Thus, despite great affluence in the United States, our average height has fallen to third place.

People are often surprised when I tell them the Dutch are the tallest people in the world. Aren't they shrimps compared with the famously tall Tutsi (or "Watusi," as you probably first encountered them) of Central Africa? Actually, the supposed great height of the Tutsi is one of the most durable myths from the age of European exploration. Careful investigation reveals that today's Tutsi men average 5'7" and that they have maintained that average for more than 100 years. That means that back in the 1800s, when puny European men first met the Tutsi, the Europeans suffered strained necks from looking up all the time. The two-to-three-inch difference in average height back then could easily have turned into fantastic stories of African giants by European adventures and writers.

The Tutsi could be as tall or taller than the Dutch if equally good health care and diets were available in Rwanda and Bu-

rundi, where the Tutsi live. But poverty rules the lives of most African people, punctuated by warfare, which makes the conditions for growth during childhood even worse. And indeed, it turns out that the Tutsi and other Africans who migrate to Western Europe or North America at young ages end up taller than Africans remaining in Africa.

At the other end of the height spectrum, Pygmies tell a similar story. The shortest people in the world today are the Mbuti, the Efe, and other Pygmy peoples of Central Africa. Their average stature is almost 4'9" for adult men and 4'6" for women. Part of the reason Pygmies are short is indeed genetic: some evidently lack the genes for producing the growth-promoting hormones that course through other people's bodies, while others are genetically incapable of using these hormones to trigger the cascade of reactions that lead to growth. But another important reason for their small size is environmental. Pygmies living as hunter-gatherers in the forests of Central African countries appear to be undernourished, which further limits their growth. Pygmies who live on farms and ranches outside the forest are better fed than their hunter-gatherer relatives and are taller as well. Both genes and nutrition thus account for the size of Pygmies.

Peoples in other parts of the world have also been labeled pygmies, such as some groups in Southeast Asia and the Maya of Guatemala. Well-meaning explorers and scientists have often claimed that they are genetically short, but here we encounter another myth of height. A group of extremely short people in New Guinea, for example, turned out to eat a diet deficient in iodine and other essential nutrients. When they were supplied with cheap mineral and vitamin supplements, their supposedly genetic short stature vanished in their children, who grew to a more normal height.

ANOTHER WAY FOR THESE SO-CALLED pygmies to stop being pygmies is to immigrate to the United States. In my own research, I study the growth of two groups of Mayan children. One group lives in their homeland of Guatemala, and the other is a group of refugees living in the United States. The Maya in Guatemala live in the village of San Pedro, which has no safe source of drinking water. Most of the water is contaminated with fertilizers and pesticides used on nearby agricultural fields. Until recently, when a deep well was dug, the townspeople depended on an unreliable supply of water from rain-swollen streams. Most homes still lack running water and have only pit toilets. The parents of the Mayan children work mostly at clothing factories and are paid only a few dollars a day.

I began working with the schoolchildren in this village in 1979, and my research shows that most of them eat only 80 percent of the food they need. Other research shows that almost 30 percent of the girls and 20 percent of the boys are deficient in iodine, that most of the children suffer from intestinal parasites, and that many have persistent ear and eye infections. As a consequence, their health is poor and their height reflects it: they average about three inches shorter than better-fed Guatemalan children.

The Mayan refugees I work with in the United States live in Los Angeles and in the rural agricultural community of Indiantown in central Florida. Although the adults work mostly in minimum-wage jobs, the children in these communities are generally better off than their counterparts in Guatemala. Most Maya arrived in the 1980s as refugees escaping a civil war as well as a political system that threatened them and their children. In the United States they found security and started new lives, and before long their children began growing faster and bigger. My data show that the average increase in height among the first generation of these immigrants was 2.2 inches, which means that these so-called pygmies have undergone one of the largest single-generation increases in height ever recorded. When people such as my own grandparents migrated from the poverty of rural life in Eastern Europe to the cities of the United States just after World War I, the increase in height of the next generation was only about one inch.

One reason for the rapid increase in stature is that in the United States the

Maya have access to treated drinking water and to a reliable supply of food. Especially critical are school breakfast and lunch programs for children from low-income families, as well as public assistance programs such as the federal Woman, Infants, and Children (WIC) program and food stamps. That these programs improve health and growth is no secret. What is surprising is how fast they work. Mayan mothers in the United States tell me that even their babies are bigger and healthier than the babies they raised in Guatemala, and hospital statistics bear them out. These women must be enjoying a level of health so improved from that of their lives in Guatemala that their babies are growing faster in the womb. Of course, plasticity means that such changes are dependent on external conditions, and unfortunately the rising height—and health—of the Maya is in danger from political forces that are attempting to cut funding for food stamps and the WIC program. If that funding is cut, the negative impact on the lives of poor Americans, including the Mayan refugees, will be as dramatic as were the former positive effects.

Height is only the most obvious example of plasticity's power; there are others to be found everywhere you look. The Andes-dwelling Quechua people of Peru are well-adapted to their high-altitude homes. Their large, barrel-shaped chests house big lungs that inspire huge amounts of air with each breath, and they manage to survive on the lower pressure of oxygen they breathe with an unusually high level of red blood cells. Yet these secrets of mountain living are not hereditary. Instead the bodies of young Quechua adapt as they grow in their particular environment, just as those of European children do when they live at high altitudes.

One way for the so-called pygmies of Guatemala to stop being pygmies is to immigrate to the United States.

Plasticity may also have a hand in determining our risks for developing a number of diseases. For example, scientists have long been searching for a cause for Parkinson's disease. Because Parkinson's tends to run in families, it is natural to think there is a genetic cause. But while a genetic mutation linked to some types of Parkinson's disease was reported in mid-1997, the gene accounts for only a fraction of people with the disease. Many more people with Parkinson's do not have the gene, and not all people with the mutated gene develop the disease.

Ralph Garruto, a medical researcher and biological anthropologist at the National Institutes of Health, is investigating the role of the environment and human plasticity not only in Parkinson's but in Lou Gehrig's disease as well. Garruto and his team traveled to the islands of Guam and New Guinea, where rates of both diseases are 50 to 100 times higher than in the United States. Among the native Chamorro people of Guam these diseases kill one person out of every five over the age of 25. The scientists found that both diseases are linked to a shortage of calcium in the diet. This shortage sets off a cascade of events that result in the digestive system's absorbing too much of the aluminum present in the diet. The aluminum wreaks havoc on various parts of the body, including the brain, where it destroys neurons and eventually causes paralysis and death.

The most amazing discovery made by Garruto's team is that up to 70 percent of the people they studied in Guam had some brain damage, but only 20 percent progressed all the way to Parkinson's or Lou Gehrig's disease. Genes and plasticity seem to be working hand in hand to produce these lower-than-expected rates of disease. There is a certain amount of genetic variation in the ability that all people have in coping with calcium shortages—some can function better than others. But thanks to plasticity, it's also possible for people's bodies to gradually develop ways to protect themselves against aluminum poisoning. Some people develop biochemical barriers to the aluminum they eat, while others develop ways to prevent the aluminum from reaching the brain.

An appreciation of plasticity may temper some of our fears about these diseases and even offer some hope. For if Parkinson's and Lou Gehrig's diseases can be prevented among the Chamorro by plasticity, then maybe medical researchers can figure out a way to produce the same sort of plastic changes in you and me. Maybe Lou Gehrig's disease and Parkinson's disease—as well as many other, including some cancers—aren't our genetic doom but a product of our development, just like variations in human height. And maybe their danger will in time prove as illusory as the notion that the Tutsi are giants, or the Maya pygmies—or Americans still the tallest of the tall.

BARRY BOGIN is a professor of anthropology at the University of Michigan in Dearborn and the author of Patterns of Human Growth.

UNIT 7
Living With the Past

Unit Selections

Key Points to Consider

- What is "forensic anthropology"? How can it be applied to modern life?

- Is there any way to prevent epidemics in the human species? How?

- What social policy issues are involved in the nature versus nurture debate?

- What relevance does the concept of natural selection have to the treatment of disease?

- Is there any necessary conflict between science and religion with respect to explaining how we humans came to be as we are?

 **Links: www.dushkin.com/online/**
These sites are annotated in the World Wide Web pages.

Ancestral Passions
   http://www.canoe.ca/JamBooksReviewsA/ancestral_morell.html
Forensic Science Reference Page
   http://www.lab.fws.gov
Zeno's Forensic Page
   http://forensic.to/forensic.html

Anthropology continues to evolve as a discipline, not only in the tools and techniques of the trade, but also in the application of whatever knowledge we stand to gain about ourselves. It is in this context that Patrick Huyghe, in "Profile of an Anthropologist: No Bone Unturned," describes "forensic anthropology," a whole new field involving the use of physical similarities and differences between people in order to identify human remains. Sometimes an awareness of our biological and behavioral past may help us to better understand the present. In showing how our evolutionary past may make a difference in bodily health, Lori Oliwenstein (in "Dr. Darwin") talks about how the symptoms of disease must first be interpreted as to whether they represent part of the aggressive strategy of microbes or the defensive mechanisms of the patient before treatment can be applied.

One theme that ties the articles of this section together, then, is that they have as much to do with the present as they have to do with the past. Perhaps this is why "scientific creationists" (as described in "Kansas Recants") want to deny our evolutionary heritage, since it does not fit in with how they view the here-and-now.

As we reflect upon where we have been and how we came to be as we are in the evolutionary sense, the inevitable question arises as to what will happen next. This is the most difficult issue of all, since our biological future depends so much on long-range ecological trends that no one seems to be able to predict. There is no better example of this problem than the recent explosion of new diseases, as described in "The Viral Superhighway" by George Armelagos. Some wonder if we will even survive long enough as a species to experience any significant biological changes. Perhaps our capacity for knowledge is outstripping the wisdom to use it wisely, and the consequent destruction of our earthly environments and wildlife is placing us in ever greater danger of creating the circumstances of our own extinction.

Counterbalancing this pessimism is the view that because it has been our conscious decision making (and not the genetically predetermined behavior that characterizes some species) that has gotten us into this mess, then it will be the conscious will of our generation and future generations that will get us out. But, can we wait much longer for humanity to collectively come to its senses? Or is it already too late?

Profile of an Anthropologist

No Bone Unturned

Patrick Huyghe

The research of some physical anthropologists and archaeologists involves the discovery and analysis of old bones (as well as artifacts and other remains). Most often these bones represent only part of a skeleton or maybe the mixture of parts of several skeletons. Often these remains are smashed, burned, or partially destroyed. Over the years, physical anthropologists have developed a remarkable repertoire of skills and techniques for teasing the greatest possible amount of information out of sparse material remains.

Although originally developed for basic research, the methods of physical anthropology can be directly applied to contemporary human problems.... In this profile, we look briefly at the career of Clyde C. Snow, a physical anthropologist who has put these skills to work in a number of different settings....

As you read this selection, ask yourself the following questions:

- Given what you know of physical anthropology, what sort of work would a physical anthropologist do for the Federal Aviation Administration?
- What is anthropometry? *How might anthropometric surveys of pilots and passengers help in the design of aircraft equipment?*
- What is forensic anthropology? *How can a biological anthropologist be an expert witness in legal proceedings?*

Clyde Snow is never in a hurry. He knows he's late. He's always late. For Snow, being late is part of the job. In fact, he doesn't usually begin to work until death has stripped some poor individual to the bone, and no one—neither the local homicide detectives nor the pathologists—can figure out who once gave identity to the skeletonized remains. No one, that is, except a shrewd, laconic, 60-year-old forensic anthropologist.

Snow strolls into the Cook County Medical Examiner's Office in Chicago on this brisk October morning wearing a pair of Lucchese cowboy boots and a three-piece pin-striped suit. Waiting for him in autopsy room 160 are a bunch of naked skeletons found in Illinois, Wisconsin, and Minnesota since his last visit. Snow, a native Texan who now lives in rural Oklahoma, makes the trip up to Chicago some six times a year. The first case on his agenda is a pale brown skull found in the garbage of an abandoned building once occupied by a Chicago cosmetics company.

Snow turns the skull over slowly in his hands, a cigarette dangling from his fingers. One often does. Snow does not seem overly concerned about mortality, though its tragedy surrounds him daily.

"There's some trauma here," he says, examining a rough edge at the lower back of the skull. He points out the area to Jim Elliott, a homicide detective with the Chicago police. "This looks like a chopping blow by a heavy bladed instrument. Almost like a decapitation." In a place where the whining of bone saws drifts through hallways and the sweet-sour smell of death hangs in the air, the word surprises no one.

Snow begins thinking aloud. "I think what we're looking at here is a female, or maybe a small male, about thirty to forty years old. Probably Asian." He turns the skull upside down, pointing out the degree of wear on the teeth. "This was somebody who lived on a really rough diet. We don't normally find this kind of dental wear in a modern Western population."

"How long has it been around?" Elliott asks.

Snow raises the skull up to his nose. "It doesn't have any decompositional odors," he says. He pokes a finger in the skull's nooks and crannies. "There's no soft tissue left. It's good and dry. And it doesn't show signs of having been buried. I would say that this has been lying around in an attic or a box for years. It feels like a souvenir skull," says Snow.

Souvenir skulls, usually those of Japanese soldiers, were popular with U.S. troops serving in the Pacific during World War II; there was also a trade in skulls during the Vietnam War years. On closer inspection, though, Snow begins to wonder about the skull's Asian origins—the broad nasal aperture and the jutting forth of the upper-tooth-bearing part of the face suggest Melanesian features. Sifting through the objects found in the abandoned building with the skull, he finds several loose-leaf albums of 35-millimeter transparencies documenting life among the highland tribes of New Guinea. The slides, shot by an anthropologist, include graphic scenes of ritual warfare. The skull, Snow concludes, is more likely to be a trophy from one of these tribal battles than the result of a local Chicago homicide.

"So you'd treat it like found property?" Elliott asks finally. "Like somebody's garage-sale property?"

"Exactly," says Snow.

Clyde Snow is perhaps the world's most sought-after forensic anthropologist. People have been calling upon him to identify skeletons for more than a quarter of a century. Every year he's involved in some 75 cases of identification, most of them without fanfare. "He's an old scudder who doesn't have to blow his own whistle," says Walter Birkby, a forensic anthropologist at the University of Arizona. "He know's he's good."

Yet over the years Snow's work has turned him into something of an unlikely celebrity. He has been called upon to identify the remains of the Nazi war criminal Josef Mengele, reconstruct the face of the Egyptian boy-king Tutankhamen, confirm the authenticity of the body autopsied as that of President John F. Kennedy, and examine the skeletal remains of General Custer's men at the battlefield of the Little Bighorn. He has also been involved in the grim task of identifying the bodies in some of the United States' worst airline accidents.

Such is his legend that cases are sometimes attributed to him in which he played no part. He did not, as the *New York Times* reported, identify the remains of the crew of the *Challenger* disaster. But the man is often the equal of his myth. For the past four years, setting his personal safety aside, Snow has spent much of his time in Argentina, searching for the graves and identities of some of the thousands who "disappeared" between 1976 and 1983, during Argentina's military regime.

Snow did not set out to rescue the dead from oblivion. For almost two decades, until 1979, he was a physical anthropologist at the Civil Aeromedical Institute, part of the Federal Aviation Administration in Oklahoma City. Snow's job was to help engineers improve aircraft design and safety features by providing them with data on the human frame.

One study, he recalls, was initiated in response to complaints from a flight attendants' organization. An analysis of accident patterns had revealed that inadequate restraints on flight attendants'

jump seats were leading to deaths and injuries and that aircraft doors weighing several hundred pounds were impeding evacuation efforts. Snow points out that ensuring the survival of passengers in emergencies is largely the flight attendants' responsibility. "If they are injured or killed in a crash, you're going to find a lot of dead passengers."

Reasoning that equipment might be improved if engineers had more data on the size and strength of those who use it, Snow undertook a study that required meticulous measurement. When his report was issued in 1975, Senator William Proxmire was outraged that $57,800 of the taxpayers' money had been spent to caliper 423 airline stewardesses from head to toe. Yet the study, which received one of the senator's dubious Golden Fleece Awards, was firmly supported by both the FAA and the Association of Flight Attendants. "I can't imagine," says Snow with obvious delight, "how much coffee Proxmire got spilled on him in the next few months."

It was during his tenure at the FAA that he developed an interest in forensic work. Over the years the Oklahoma police frequently consulted the physical anthropologist for help in identifying crime victims. "The FAA figured it was a kind of community service to let me work on these cases," he says.

The experience also helped to prepare him for the grim task of identifying the victims of air disasters. In December 1972, when a United Airlines plane crashed outside Chicago, killing 43 of the 61 people aboard (including the wife of Watergate conspirator Howard Hunt, who was found with $10,000 in her purse), Snow was brought in to help examine the bodies. That same year, with Snow's help, forensic anthropology was recognized as a specialty by the American Academy of Forensic Sciences. "It got a lot of anthropologists interested in forensics," he says, "and it made a lot of pathologists out there aware that there were anthropologists who could help them."

Each nameless skeleton poses a unique mystery for Snow. But some, like the second case awaiting him back in the autopsy room at the Cook County morgue, are more challenging than oth-

ers. This one is a real chiller. In a large cardboard box lies a jumble of bones along with a tattered leg from a pair of blue jeans, a sock shrunk tightly around the bones of a foot, a pair of Nike running shoes without shoelaces, and, inside the hood of a blue windbreaker, a mass of stringy, blood-caked hair. The remains were discovered frozen in ice about 20 miles outside Milwaukee. A rusted bicycle was found lying close by. Paul Hibbard, chief deputy medical examiner for Waukesha County, who brought the skeleton to Chicago, says no one has been reported missing.

Snow lifts the bones out of the box and begins reconstructing the skeleton on an autopsy table. "There are two hundred six bones and thirty-two teeth in the human body," he says, "and each has a story to tell." Because bone is dynamic, living tissue, many of life's significant events—injuries, illness, childbearing—leave their mark on the body's internal framework. Put together the stories told by these bones, he says, and what you have is a person's "osteobiography."

Snow begins by determining the sex of the skeleton, which is not always obvious. He tells the story of a skeleton that was brought to his FAA office in the late 1970s. It had been found along with some women's clothes and a purse in a local back lot, and the police had assumed that it was female. But when Snow examined the bones, he realized that "at six foot three, she would have probably have been the tallest female in Oklahoma."

Then Snow recalled that six months earlier the custodian in his building had suddenly not shown up for work. The man's supervisor later mentioned to Snow, "You know, one of these days when they find Ronnie, he's going to be dressed as a woman." Ronnie, it turned out, was a weekend transvestite. A copy of his dental records later confirmed that the skeleton in women's clothing was indeed Snow's janitor.

The Wisconsin bike rider is also male. Snow picks out two large bones that look something like twisted oysters—the innominates, or hipbones, which along with the sacrum, or lower backbone, form the pelvis. This pelvis is narrow and steep-walled like a male's, not broad and shallow like a female's. And the sciatic notch (the V-shaped space where the sciatic nerve passes through the hipbone) is narrow, as is normal in a male. Snow can also determine a skeleton's sex by checking the size of the mastoid processes (the bony knobs at the base of the skull) and the prominence of the brow ridge, or by measuring the head of an available limb bone, which is typically broader in males.

From an examination of the skull he concludes that the bike rider is "predominantly Caucasoid." A score of bony traits help the forensic anthropologist assign a skeleton to one of the three major racial groups: Negroid, Caucasoid, or Mongoloid. Snow notes that the ridge of the boy's nose is high and salient, as it is in whites. In Negroids and Mongoloids (which include American Indians as well as most Asians) the nose tends to be broad in relation to its height. However, the boy's nasal margins are somewhat smoothed down, usually a Mongoloid feature. "Possibly a bit of American Indian admixture," says Snow. "Do you have Indians in your area?" Hibbard nods.

Age is next. Snow takes the skull and turns it upside down, pointing out the basilar joint, the junction between the two major bones that form the underside of the skull. In a child the joint would still be open to allow room for growth, but here the joint has fused—something that usually happens in the late teen years. On the other hand, he says, pointing to the zigzagging lines on the dome of the skull, the cranial sutures are open. The cranial sutures, which join the bones of the braincase, begin to fuse and disappear in the mid-twenties.

Next Snow picks up a femur and looks for signs of growth at the point where the shaft meets the knobbed end. The thin plates of cartilage—areas of incomplete calcification—that are visible at this point suggest that the boy hadn't yet attained his full height. Snow double-checks with an examination of the pubic symphysis, the joint where the two hipbones meet. The ridges in this area, which fill in and smooth over in adulthood, are still clearly marked. He concludes that the skeleton is that of a boy between 15 and 20 years old.

"One of the things you learn is to be pretty conservative," says Snow. "It's very impressive when you tell the police, 'This person is eighteen years old,' and he turns out to be eighteen. The problem is, if the person is fifteen you've blown it—you probably won't find him. Looking for a missing person is like trying to catch fish. Better get a big net and do your own sorting."

Snow then picks up a leg bone, measures it with a set of calipers, and enters the data into a portable computer. Using the known correlation between the height and length of the long limb bones, he quickly estimates the boy's height. "He's five foot six and a half to five foot eleven," says Snow. "Medium build, not excessively muscular, judging from the muscle attachments that we see." He points to the grainy ridges that appear where muscle attaches itself to the bone. The most prominent attachments show up on the teenager's right arm bone, indicating right-handedness.

Then Snow examines the ribs one by one for signs of injury. He finds no stab wounds, cuts, or bullet holes, here or elsewhere on the skeleton. He picks up the hyoid bone from the boy's throat and looks for the tell-tale fracture signs that would suggest the boy was strangled. But, to Snow's frustration, he can find no obvious cause of death. In hopes of identifying the missing teenager, he suggests sending the skull, hair, and boy's description to Betty Pat Gatliff, a medical illustrator and sculptor in Oklahoma who does facial reconstructions.

Six weeks later photographs of the boy's likeness appear in the *Milwaukee Sentinel*. "If you persist long enough," says Snow, "eighty-five to ninety percent of the cases eventually get positively identified, but it can take anywhere from a few weeks to a few years."

Snow and Gatliff have collaborated many times, but never with more glitz than in 1983, when Snow was commissioned by Patrick Barry, a Miami orthopedic surgeon and amateur Egyptologist, to reconstruct the face of the Egyptian boy-king Tutankhamen. Normally a facial reconstruction begins with a skull, but since Tutankhamen's 3,000-year-old remains were in Egypt, Snow had to

make do with the skull measurements from a 1925 postmortem and X-rays taken in 1975. A plaster model of the skull was made, and on the basis on Snow's report—"his skull is Caucasoid with some Negroid admixtures"—Gatliff put a face on it. What did Tutankhamen look like? Very much like the gold mask on his sarcophagus, says Snow, confirming that it was, indeed, his portrait.

Many cite Snow's use of facial reconstructions as one of his most important contributions to the field. Snow, typically self-effacing, says that Gatliff "does all the work." The identification of skeletal remains, he stresses, is often a collaboration between pathologists, odontologists, radiologists, and medical artists using a variety of forensic techniques.

One of Snow's last tasks at the FAA was to help identify the dead from the worst airline accident in U.S. history. On May 25, 1979, a DC-10 crashed shortly after takeoff from Chicago's O'Hare Airport, killing 273 people. The task facing Snow and more than a dozen forensic specialists was horrific. "No one ever sat down and counted," says Snow, "but we estimated ten thousand to twelve thousand pieces or parts of bodies." Nearly 80 percent of the victims were identified on the basis of dental evidence and fingerprints. Snow and forensic radiologist John Fitzpatrick later managed to identify two dozen others by comparing postmortem X-rays with X-rays taken during the victim's lifetime.

Next to dental records, such X-ray comparisons are the most common way of obtaining positive identifications. In 1978, when a congressional committee reviewed the evidence on John F. Kennedy's assassination, Snow used X-rays to show that the body autopsied at Bethesda Naval Hospital was indeed that of the late president and had not—as some conspiracy theorists believed—been switched.

The issue was resolved on the evidence of Kennedy's "sinus print," the scalloplike pattern on the upper margins of the sinuses that is visible in X-rays of the forehead. So characteristic is a person's sinus print that courts throughout the world accept the matching of antemortem and postmortem X-rays of the sinuses as positive identification.

Yet another technique in the forensic specialist's repertoire is photo superposition. Snow used it in 1977 to help identify the mummy of a famous Oklahoma outlaw named Elmer J. McCurdy, who was killed by a posse after holding up a train in 1911. For years the mummy had been exhibited as a "dummy" in a California funhouse—until it was found to have a real human skeleton inside it. Ownership of the mummy was eventually traced back to a funeral parlor in Oklahoma, where McCurdy had been embalmed and exhibited as "the bandit who wouldn't give up."

Using two video cameras and an image processor, Snow superposed the mummy's profile on a photograph of McCurdy that was taken shortly after his death. When displayed on a single monitor, the two coincided to a remarkable degree. Convinced by the evidence, Thomas Noguchi, then Los Angeles County corner, signed McCurdy's death certificate ("Last known occupation: Train robber") and allowed the outlaw's bones to be returned to Oklahoma for a decent burial.

It was this technique that also allowed forensic scientists to identify the remains of the Nazi "Angel of Death," Josef Mengele, in the summer of 1985. A team of investigators, including Snow and West German forensic anthropologist Richard Helmer, flew to Brazil after an Austrian couple claimed that Mengele lay buried in a grave on a São Paulo hillside. Tests revealed that the stature, age, and hair color of the unearthed skeleton were consistent with information in Mengele's SS files; yet without X-rays or dental records, the scientists still lacked conclusive evidence. When an image of the reconstructed skull was superposed on 1930s photographs of Mengele, however, the match was eerily compelling. All doubts were removed a few months later when Mengele's dental X-rays were tracked down.

In 1979 Snow retired from the FAA to the rolling hills of Norman, Oklahoma, where he and his wife, Jerry, live in a sprawling, early-1960s ranch house. Unlike his 50 or so fellow forensic anthropologists, most of whom are tied to

academic positions, Snow is free to pursue his consultancy work full-time. Judging from the number of miles that he logs in the average month, Snow is clearly not ready to retire for good.

His recent projects include a reexamination of the skeletal remains found at the site of the Battle of the Little Bighorn, where more than a century ago Custer and his 210 men were killed by Sioux and Cheyenne warriors. Although most of the enlisted men's remains were moved to a mass grave in 1881, an excavation of the battlefield in the past few years uncovered an additional 375 bones and 36 teeth. Snow, teaming up again with Fitzpatrick, determined that these remains belonged to 34 individuals.

The historical accounts of Custer's desperate last stand are vividly confirmed by their findings. Snow identified one skeleton as that of a soldier between the ages of 19 and 23 who weighed around 150 pounds and stood about five foot eight. He'd sustained gunshot wounds to his chest and left forearm. Heavy blows to his head had fractured his skull and sheared off his teeth. Gashed thigh bones indicated that his body was later dismembered with an ax or hatchet.

Given the condition and number of the bodies, Snow seriously questions the accuracy of the identifications made by the original nineteenth-century burial crews. He doubts, for example, that the skeleton buried at West Point is General Custer's.

For the last four years Snow has devoted much of his time to helping two countries come to terms with the horrors of a much more recent past. As part of a group sponsored by the American Association for the Advancement of Science, he has been helping the Argentinian National Commission on Disappeared Persons to determine the fate of some of those who vanished during their country's harsh military rule: between 1976 and 1983 at least 10,000 people were systematically swept off the streets by roving death squads to be tortured, killed, and buried in unmarked graves. In December 1986, at the invitation of the Aquino government's Human Rights Commission, Snow also spent several weeks training Philippine scientists to

investigate the disappearances that occurred under the Marcos regime.

But it is in Argentina where Snow has done the bulk of his human-rights work. He has spent more than 27 months in and around Buenos Aires, first training a small group of local medical and anthropology students in the techniques of forensic investigation, and later helping them carefully exhume and examine scores of the *desaparecidos*, or disappeared ones.

Only 25 victims have so far been positively identified. But the evidence has helped convict seven junta members and other high-ranking military and police officers. The idea is not necessarily to identify all 10,000 of the missing, says Snow. "If you have a colonel who ran a detention center where maybe five hundred people were killed, you don't have to nail them with five hundred deaths. Just one or two should be sufficient to get him convicted." Forensic evidence from Snow's team may be used to prosecute several other military officers, including General Suarez Mason. Mason is the former commander of the I Army Corps in Buenos Aires and is believed to be responsible for thousands of disappearances. He was recently extradited from San Francisco back to Argentina, where he is expected to stand trial this winter [1988].

The investigations have been hampered by a frustrating lack of antemortem information. In 1984, when commission lawyers took depositions from relatives and friends of the disappeared, they often failed to obtain such basic information as the victim's height, weight, or hair color. Nor did they ask for the missing person's X-rays (which in Argentina are given to the patient) or the address of the victim's dentist. The problem was compounded by the inexperience of those who carried out the first mass exhumations prior to Snow's arrival. Many of the skeletons were inadvertently destroyed by bulldozers as they were brought up.

Every unearthed skeleton that shows signs of gunfire, however, helps to erode the claim once made by many in the Argentinian military that most of the *desaparecidos* are alive and well and living in Mexico City, Madrid, or Paris. Snow recalls the case of a 17-year-old boy named Gabriel Dunayavich, who disappeared in the summer of 1976. He was walking home from a movie with his girlfriend when a Ford Falcon with no license plates snatched him off the street. The police later found his body and that of another boy and girl dumped by the roadside on the outskirts of Buenos Aires. The police went through the motions of an investigation, taking photographs and doing an autopsy, then buried the three teenagers in an unmarked grave.

A decade later Snow, with the help of the boy's family, traced the autopsy reports, the police photographs, and the grave of the three youngsters. Each of them had four or five closely spaced bul-let wounds in the upper chest—the signature, says Snow, of an automatic weapon. Two also had wounds on their arms from bullets that had entered behind the elbow and exited from the forearm.

"That means they were conscious when they were shot," says Snow. "When a gun was pointed at them, they naturally raised their arm." It's details like these that help to authenticate the last moments of the victims and bring a dimension of reality to the judges and jury.

Each time Snow returns from Argentina he says that this will be the last time. A few months later he is back in Buenos Aires. "There's always more work to do," he says. It is, he admits quietly, "terrible work."

"These were such brutal, cold-blooded crimes," he says. "The people who committed them not only murdered; they had a system to eliminate all trace that their victims even existed."

Snow will not let them obliterate their crimes so conveniently. "There are human-rights violations going on all around the world," he says. "But to me murder is murder, regardless of the motive. I hope that we are sending a message to governments who murder in the name of politics that they can be held to account."

The Viral Superhighway

Environmental disruptions and international travel have brought on a new era in human illness, one marked by diabolical new diseases

By George J. Armelagos

So the Lord sent a pestilence upon Israel from the morning until the appointed time; and there died of the people from Dan to Beer-sheba seventy thousand men.
—2 Sam. 24:15

SWARMS OF CROP-DESTROYING LO-custs, rivers fouled with blood, lion-headed horses breathing fire and sulfur: the Bible presents a lurid assortment of plagues, described as acts of retribution by a vengeful God. Indeed, real-life epidemics—such as the influenza outbreak of 1918, which killed 21 million people in a matter of months—can be so sudden and deadly that it is easy, even for non-believers, to view them as angry messages from the beyond.

How reassuring it was, then, when the march of technology began to give people some control over the scourges of the past. In the 1950s the Salk vaccine, and later, the Sabin vaccine, dramatically reduced the incidence of polio. And by 1980 a determined effort by health workers worldwide eradicated smallpox, a disease that had afflicted humankind since earliest times with blindness, disfigurement and death, killing nearly 300 million people in the twentieth century alone.

But those optimistic years in the second half of our century now seem, with hindsight, to have been an era of inflated expectations, even arrogance. In 1967 the surgeon general of the United States, William H. Stewart, announced that vic-tory over infectious diseases was immi-nent—a victory that would close the book on modern plagues. Sadly, we now know differently. Not only have deadly and previously unimagined new illnesses such as AIDS and Legionnaires' disease emerged in recent years, but historical diseases that just a few decades ago seemed to have been tamed are returning in virulent, drug-resistant varieties. Tuberculosis, the ancient lung disease that haunted nineteenth-century Europe, afflicting, among others, Chopin, Dostoyevski and Keats, is aggressively mutating into strains that defy the standard medicines; as a result, modern TB victims must undergo a daily drug regimen so elaborate that health-department workers often have to personally monitor patients to make sure they comply [see "A Plague Returns," by Mark Earnest and John A. Sbarbaro, September/October 1993]. Meanwhile, bacteria and viruses in foods from chicken to strawberries to alfalfa sprouts are sickening as many as 80 million Americans each year.

And those are only symptoms of a much more general threat. Deaths from infectious diseases in the United States rose 58 percent between 1980 and 1992. Twenty-nine new diseases have been reported in the past twenty-five years, a few of them so bloodcurdling and bizarre that descriptions of them bring to mind tacky horror movies. Ebola virus, for instance, can in just a few days reduce a healthy person to a bag of teeming flesh spilling blood and organ parts from every orifice. Creutzfeldt-Jakob disease, which killed the choreographer George Balanchine in 1983, eats away at its victims' brains until they resemble wet sponges. Never slow to fan mass hysteria, Hollywood has capitalized on the phenomenon with films such as *Outbreak*, in which a monkey carrying a deadly new virus from central Africa infects unwitting Californians and starts an epidemic that threatens to annihilate the human race.

The reality about infectious disease is less sensational but alarming nonetheless. Gruesome new pathogens such as Ebola are unlikely to cause a widespread epidemic because they sicken and kill so quickly that victims can be easily identified and isolated; on the other hand, the seemingly innocuous practice of overprescribing antibiotics for bad colds could ultimately lead to untold deaths, as familiar germs evolve to become untreatable. We are living in the twilight of the antibiotic era: within our lifetimes, scraped knees and cut fingers may return to the realm of fatal conditions.

Through international travel, global commerce and the accelerating destruction of ecosystems worldwide, people are inadvertently exposing themselves to a Pandora's box of emerging microbial threats. And the recent rumblings of biological terrorism from Iraq highlight the appalling potential of disease organisms for being manipulated to vile ends. But although it may appear that the apocalypse has arrived, the truth is that people today are not facing a unique predicament. Emerging diseases have long looted like a shadow over the human race.

PEOPLE AND PATHOGENS HAVE A LONG history together. Infections have been detected in the bones of human ancestors more than a million years old, and evidence from the mummy of the Egyptian pharaoh Ramses V suggests that he may have died from smallpox more than 3,000 years ago. Widespread outbreaks of disease are also well documented. Between 1347 and 1351 roughly a third of the population of medieval Europe was wiped out by bubonic plague, which is carried by fleas that live on rodents. In 1793, 10 percent of the population of Philadelphia succumbed to yellow fever, which is spread by mosquitoes. And in 1875 the son of a Fiji chief came down with measles after a ceremonial trip to Australia. Within four months more than 20,000 Fijians were dead from the imported disease, which spreads through the air when its victims cough or sneeze.

According to conventional wisdom in biology, people and invading microorganisms evolve together: people gradually become more resistant, and the microorganisms become less virulent. The result is either mutualism, in which the relation benefits both species, or commensalism, in which one species benefits without harming the other. Chicken pox and measles, once fatal afflictions, now exist in more benign forms. Logic would suggest, after all, that the best interests of an organism are not served if it kills its host; doing so would be like picking a fight with the person who signs your paycheck.

But recently it has become clear to epidemiologists that the reverse of that cooperative paradigm of illness can also be true: microorganisms and their hosts sometimes exhaust their energies devising increasingly powerful weaponry and defenses. For example, several variants of human immunodeficiency virus (HIV) may compete for dominance within a person's body, placing the immune system under ever-greater siege. As long as a virus has an effective mechanism for jumping from one person to another, it can afford to kill its victims

[see "The Deadliest Virus," by Cynthia Mills, January/February 1997].

If the competition were merely a question of size, humans would surely win: the average person is 10^{17} times the size of the average bacterium. But human beings, after all, constitute only one species, which must compete with 5,000 kinds of viruses and more than 300,000 species of bacteria. Moreover, in the twenty years it takes humans to produce a new generation, bacteria can reproduce a half-million times. That disparity enables pathogens to evolve ever more virulent adaptations that quickly outstrip human responses to them. The scenario is governed by what the English zoologist Richard Dawkins of the University of Oxford and a colleague have called the "Red Queen Principle." In Lewis Carroll's *Through the Looking Glass* the Red Queen tells Alice she will need to run faster and faster just to stay in the same place. Staving off illness can be equally elusive.

THE CENTERS FOR DISEASE CONTROL and Prevention (CDC) in Atlanta, Georgia, has compiled a list of the most recent emerging pathogens. They include:

- *Campylobacter*, a bacterium widely found in chickens because of the commercial practice of raising them in cramped, unhealthy conditions. It causes between two million and eight million cases of food poisoning a year in the United States and between 200 and 800 deaths.

- *Escherichia coli* 0157:H7, a dangerously mutated version of an often harmless bacterium. Hamburger meat from Jack in the Box fast-food restaurants that was contaminated with this bug led to the deaths of at least four people in 1993.

- Hantaviruses, a genus of fast-acting, lethal viruses, often carried by rodents, that kill by causing the capillaries to leak blood. A new hantavirus known as *sin nombre* (Spanish for "nameless") surfaced in 1993 in the southwestern United States, causing the sudden and mysterious deaths of thirty-two people.

- HIV, the deadly virus that causes AIDS (acquired immunodeficiency syndrome). Although it was first observed in people as recently as 1981, it has spread like wildfire and is now a global scourge, affecting more than 30 million people worldwide.

- The strange new infectious agent that causes bovine spongiform encephalopathy, or mad cow disease, which recently threw the British meat industry and consumers into a panic. This bizarre agent, known as a prion, or "proteinaceous infectious particle," is also responsible for Creutzfeldt-Jakob disease, the brain-eater I mentioned earlier. A Nobel Prize was awarded last year to the biochemist Stanley B. Prusiner of the University of California, San Francisco, for his discovery of the prion.

- *Legionella pneumophila*, the bacterium that causes Legionnaires' disease. The microorganism thrives in wet environments; when it lodges in air-conditioning systems or the mist machines in supermarket produce sections, it can be expelled into the air, reaching people's lungs. In 1976 thirty-four participants at an American Legion convention in Philadelphia died—the incident that led to the discovery and naming of the disease.

- *Borrelia burgdorferi*, the bacterium that causes Lyme disease. It is carried by ticks that live on deer and white-footed mice. Left untreated, it can cause crippling, chronic problems in the nerves, joints and internal organs.

HOW IRONIC, GIVEN SUCH A ROGUES' gallery of nasty characters, that just a quarter-century ago the Egyptian demographer Abdel R. Omran could observe that in many modern industrial nations the major killers were no longer infectious diseases. Death, he noted, now came not from outside but rather from within the body, the result of gradual deterioration. Omran traced the change to the middle of the nineteenth century, when the industrial revolution took hold in the United States and parts of Europe. Thanks to better nutrition, improved public-health measures and medical advances such as mass immunization and the introduction of antibiotics, microorganisms were brought under control. As people began living longer, their aging bodies succumbed to "diseases of civilization": cancer, clogged arteries, diabetes, obesity and osteoporosis. Omran was the first to formally recognize that shift in the disease environment. He called it an "epidemiological transition."

Like other anthropologists of my generation, I learned of Omran's theory early in my career, and it soon became a basic tenet—a comforting one, too, implying as it did an end to the supremacy of microorganisms. Then, three years ago, I began working with the anthropologist Kathleen C. Barnes of Johns Hopkins University in Baltimore, Maryland, to formulate an expansion of Omran's ideas. It occurred to us that his epidemiological transition had not been a unique event. Throughout history human populations have undergone shifts in their relations with disease—shifts, we noted, that are always linked to major changes in the way people interact with the environment. Barnes and I, along with James Lin, a master's student at Johns Hopkins University School of Hygiene and Public Health, have since developed a new theory: that there have been not one but three major epidemiological transitions; that each one has been sparked by human activities; and that we are living through the third one right now.

The first epidemiological transition took place some 10,000 years ago, when people abandoned their nomadic existence and began farming. That profoundly new way of life disrupted ecosystems and created denser living conditions that led, as I will soon detail, to new diseases. The second epidemiological transition was the salutary one Omran singled out in 1971, when the war against infectious diseases seemed to have been won. And in the past two decades the emergence of illnesses such as hepatitis C, cat scratch disease (caused by the bacterium *Bartonella henselae*), Ebola and others on CDC's list has created a third epidemiological transition, a disheartening set of changes that in many

ways have reversed the effects of the second transition and coincide with the shift to globalism. Burgeoning population growth and urbanization, widespread environmental degradation, including global warming and tropical deforestation, and radically improved methods of transportation have given rise to new ways of contracting and spreading disease.

We are, quite literally, making ourselves sick.

WHEN EARLY HUMAN ANCESTORS moved from African forests onto the savanna millions of years ago, a few diseases came along for the ride. Those "heirloom" species—thus designated by the Australian parasitologist J. F. A. Sprent because they had afflicted earlier primates—included head and body lice; parasitic worms such as pinworms, tapeworms and liver flukes; and possibly herpes virus and malaria.

Global Warming could allow the mosquitoes that carry dengue fever to survive as far north as New York City.

For 99.8 percent of the five million years of human existence, hunting and gathering was the primary mode of subsistence. Our ancestors lived in small groups and relied on wild animals and plants for their survival. In their foraging rounds, early humans would occasionally have contracted new kinds of illnesses through insect bites or by butchering and eating disease-ridden animals. Such events would not have led to widespread epidemics, however, because groups of people were so sparse and widely dispersed.

About 10,000 years ago, at the end of the last ice age, many groups began to abandon their nomadic lifestyles for a more efficient and secure way of life. The agricultural revolution first appeared in the Middle East; later, farming centers developed independently in China and Central America. Permanent

villages grew up, and people turned their attention to crafts such as toolmaking and pottery. Thus when people took to cultivating wheat and barley, they planted the seeds of civilization as well.

With the new ways, however, came certain costs. As wild habitats were transformed into urban settings, the farmers who brought in the harvest with their flint-bladed sickles were assailed by grim new ailments. Among the most common was scrub typhus, which is carried by mites that live in tall grasses, and causes a potentially lethal fever. Clearing vegetation to create arable fields brought farmers frequently into mite-infested terrain.

Irrigation brought further hazards. Standing thigh-deep in watery canals, farm workers were prey to the worms that cause schistosomiasis. After living within aquatic snails during their larval stage, those worms emerge in a free-swimming form that can penetrate human skin, lodge in the intestine or urinary tract, and cause bloody urine and other serious maladies. Schistosomiasis was well known in ancient Egypt, where outlying fields were irrigated with water from the Nile River; descriptions of its symptoms and remedies are preserved in contemporary medical papyruses.

The domestication of sheep, goats and other animals cleared another pathway for microorganisms. With pigs in their yards and chickens roaming the streets, people in agricultural societies were constantly vulnerable to pathogens that could cross interspecies barriers. Many such organisms had long since reached commensalism with their animal hosts, but they were highly dangerous to humans. Milk from infected cattle could transmit tuberculosis, a slow killer that eats away at the lungs and causes its victims to cough blood and pus. Wool and skins were loaded with anthrax, which can be fatal when inhaled and, in modern times, has been developed by several nations as a potential agent of biological warfare. Blood from infected cattle, injected into people by biting insects such as the tsetse fly, spread sleeping sickness, an often-fatal disease marked by tremors and protracted lethargy.

A SECOND MAJOR EFFECT OF AGRI-culture was to spur population growth and, perhaps more important, density. Cities with populations as high as 50,000 had developed in the Near East by 3000 B.C. Scavenger species such as rats, mice and sparrows, which congregate wherever large groups of people live, exposed city dwellers to bubonic plague, typhus and rabies. And now that people were crowded together, a new pathogen could quickly start an epidemic. Larger populations also enabled diseases such as measles, mumps, chicken pox and smallpox to persist in an endemic form—always present, afflicting part of the population while sparing those with acquired immunity.

Thus the birth of agriculture launched humanity on a trajectory that has again and again brought people into contact with new pathogens. Tilling soil and raising livestock led to more energy-intensive ways of extracting resources from the earth—to lumbering, coal mining, oil drilling. New resources led to increasingly complex social organization, and to new and more frequent contacts between various societies. Loggers today who venture into the rain forest disturb previously untouched creatures and give them, for the first time, the chance to attack humans. But there is nothing new about this drama; only the players have changed. Some 2,000 years ago the introduction of iron tools to sub-Saharan Africa led to a slash-and-burn style of agriculture that brought people into contact with *Anopheles gambiae*, a mosquito that transmits malaria.

Improved transportation methods also help diseases extend their reach: microorganisms cannot travel far on their own, but they are expert hitchhikers. When the Spanish invaded Mexico in the early 1500s, for instance, they brought with them diseases that quickly raged through Tenochtitlán, the stately, temple-filled capital of the Aztec Empire. Smallpox, measles and influenza wiped out millions of Central America's original inhabitants, becoming the invisible weapon in the European conquest.

I N THE PAST THREE DECADES PEOPLE AND their inventions have drilled, polluted, engineered, paved, planted and deforested at soaring rates, changing the biosphere faster than ever before. The combined effects can, without hyperbole, be called a global revolution. After all, many of them have worldwide repercussions: the widespread chemical contamination of waterways, the thinning of the ozone layer, the loss of species diversity. And such global human actions have put people at risk for infectious diseases in newly complex and devastating ways. Global warming, for instance, could expose millions of people for the first time to malaria, sleeping sickness and other insect-borne illnesses; in the United States, a slight overall temperature increase would allow the mosquitoes that carry dengue fever to survive as far north as New York City.

Major changes to the landscape that have become possible in the past quarter-century have also triggered new diseases. After the construction of the Aswan Dam in 1970, for instance, Rift Valley fever infected 200,000 people in Egypt, killing 600. The disease had been known to affect livestock, but it was not a major problem in people until the vast quantities of dammed water became a breeding ground for mosquitoes. The insects bit both cattle and humans, helping the virus jump the interspecies barrier.

In the eastern United States, suburbanization, another relatively recent phenomenon, is a dominant factor in the emergence of Lyme disease—10,000 cases of which are reported annually. Thanks to modern earth-moving equipment, a soaring economy and population pressures, many Americans have built homes in formerly remote, wooded areas. Nourished by lawns and gardens and unchecked by wolves, which were exterminated by settlers long ago, the deer population has exploded, exposing people to the ticks that carry Lyme disease.

Meanwhile, widespread pollution has made the oceans a breeding ground for microorganisms. Epidemiologists have suggested that toxic algal blooms—fed by the sewage, fertilizers and other contaminants that wash into the oceans—harbor countless viruses and bacteria. Thrown together into what amounts to a dirty genetic soup, those pathogens can undergo gene-swapping and mutations, engendering newly antibiotic-resistant strains. Nautical traffic can carry ocean pathogens far and wide: a devastating outbreak of cholera hit Latin America in 1991 after a ship from Asia unloaded its contaminated ballast water into the harbor of Callao, Peru. Cholera causes diarrhea so severe its victims can die in a few days from dehydration; in that outbreak more than 300,000 people became ill, and more than 3,000 died.

The modern world is becoming—to paraphrase the words of the microbiologist Stephen S. Morse of Columbia University—a viral superhighway. Everyone is at risk.

Our newly global society is characterized by huge increases in population, international travel and international trade—factors that enable diseases to spread much more readily than ever before from person to person and from continent to continent. By 2020 the world population will have surpassed seven billion, and half those people will be living in urban centers. Beleaguered third-world nations are already hard-pressed to provide sewers, plumbing and other infrastructure; in the future, clean water and adequate sanitation could become increasingly rare. Meanwhile, political upheavals regularly cause millions of people to flee their homelands and gather in refugee camps, which become petri dishes for germs.

More than 500 million people cross international borders each year on commercial flights. Not only does that traffic volume dramatically increase the chance a sick person will infect the inhabitants of a distant area when she reaches her destination; it also exposes the sick person's fellow passengers to the disease, because of poor air circulation on planes. Many of those passengers can, in turn, pass the disease on to others when they disembark.

T HE GLOBAL ECONOMY THAT HAS arisen in the past two decades has established a myriad of connections between far-flung places. Not too long ago bananas and oranges were rare treats in northern climes. Now you can walk into your neighborhood market and find food that has been flown and trucked in from all over the world: oranges from Israel, apples from New Zealand, avocados from California. Consumers in affluent nations expect to be able to buy whatever they want whenever they want it. What people do not generally realize, however, is that this global network of food production and delivery provides countless pathways for pathogens. Raspberries from Guatemala, carrots from Peru and coconut milk from Thailand have been responsible for recent outbreaks of food poisoning in the United States. And the problem cuts both ways: contaminated radish seeds and frozen beef from the United States have ended up in Japan and South Korea.

Finally, the widespread and often indiscriminate use of antibiotics has played a key role in spurring disease. Forty million pounds of antibiotics are manufactured annually in the United States, an eightyfold increase since 1954. Dangerous microorganisms have evolved accordingly, often developing antibiotic-resistant strains. Physicians are now faced with penicillin-resistant gonorrhea, multiple-drug-resistant tuberculosis and E. coli variants such as 0157:H7. And frighteningly, some enterococcus bacteria have become resistant to all known antibiotics. Enterococcus infections are rare, but staphylococcus infections are not, and many strains of staph bacteria now respond to just one antibiotic, vancomycin. How long will it be before run-of-the-mill staph infections—in a boil, for instance, or in a surgical incision—become untreatable?

ALTHOUGH CIVILIZATION CAN EXPOSE people to new pathogens, cultural progress also has an obvious countervailing effect: it can provide tools—medicines, sensible city planning, educational campaigns about sexually transmitted diseases—to fight the encroachments of disease. Moreover, since biology seems to side with microorganisms anyway, people have little choice but to depend on protective cultural practices to keep pace: vaccinations, for instance, to confer immunity, combined with practices such as handwashing by physicians between patient visits, to limit contact between people and pathogens.

All too often, though, obvious protective measures such as using only clean hypodermic needles or treating urban drinking water with chlorine are neglected, whether out of ignorance or a wrongheaded emphasis on the short-term financial costs. The worldwide disparity in wealth is also to blame: not surprisingly, the advances made during the second epidemiological transition were limited largely to the affluent of the industrial world.

Such lapses are now beginning to teach the bitter lesson that the delicate balance between humans and invasive microorganisms can tip the other way again. Overconfidence—the legacy of the second epidemiological transition—has made us especially vulnerable to emerging and reemerging diseases. Evolutionary principles can provide this useful corrective: in spite of all our medical and technological hubris, there is no quick fix. If human beings are to overcome the current crisis, it will be through sensible changes in behavior, such as increased condom use and improved sanitation, combined with a commitment to stop disturbing the ecological balance of the planet.

The Bible, in short, was not far from wrong: We do bring plagues upon ourselves—not by sinning, but by refusing to heed our own alarms, our own best judgment. The price of peace—or at least peaceful coexistence—with the microorganisms on this planet is eternal vigilance.

George J. Armelagos is a professor of anthropology at Emory University in Atlanta, Georgia. He has coedited two books on the evolution of human disease: PALEOPATHOLOGY AT THE ORIGINS OF AGRICULTURE, *which deals with prehistoric populations, and* DISEASE IN POPULATIONS IN TRANSITION, *which focuses on contemporary societies.*

This article is reprinted by permission of *The Sciences* and is from the January/February 1998 issue, pp. 24–29. Individual subscriptions are $28 per year. Write to: The Sciences, 2 East 63rd Street, New York, NY 10021.

Dr. Darwin

***With a nod to evolution's god, physicians are looking at illness
through the lens of natural selection to find out why we get sick
and what we can do about it.***

Lori Oliwenstein

PAUL EWALD KNEW FROM THE BEGINNING
that the Ebola virus outbreak in Zaire
would fizzle out. On May 26, after eight
days in which only six new cases were
reported, that fizzle became official. The
World Health Organization announced it
would no longer need to update the
Ebola figures daily (though sporadic
cases continued to be reported until June
20).

The virus had held Zaire's Bandundu
Province in its deadly grip for weeks, in-
fecting some 300 people and killing 80
percent of them. Most of those infected
hailed from the town of Kikwit. It was all
just as Ewald predicted. "When the
Ebola outbreak occurred," he recalls, "I
said, as I have before, these things are
going to pop up, they're going to smol-
der, you'll have a bad outbreak of maybe
100 or 200 people in a hospital, maybe
you'll have the outbreak slip into another
isolated community, but then it will peter
out on its own."

> *"If you look at it from an
> evolutionary point of view,
> you can sort out the 95
> percent of disease
> organisms that aren't a
> major threat from the 5
> percent that are."*

Ewald is no soothsayer. He's an evolutionary biologist at Amherst College in

Massachusetts and perhaps the world's
leading expert on how infectious diseases—and the organisms that cause
them—evolve. He's also a force behind
what some are touting as the next great
medical revolution: the application of
Darwin's theory of natural selection to
the understanding of human diseases.

A Darwinian view can shed some
light on how Ebola moves from human
to human once it has entered the population. (Between human outbreaks, the virus resides in some as yet unknown
living reservoir.) A pathogen can survive
in a population, explains Ewald, only if it
can easily transmit its progeny from one
host to another. One way to do this is to
take a long time to disable a host, giving
him plenty of time to come into contact
with other potential victims. Ebola, however, kills quickly, usually in less than a
week. Another way is to survive for a
long time outside the human body, so
that the pathogen can wait for new hosts
to find it. But the Ebola strains encountered thus far are destroyed almost at
once by sunlight, and even if no rays
reach them, they tend to lose their infec-
tiousness outside the human body within
a day. "If you look at it from an evolutionary point of view, you can sort out
the 95 percent of disease organisms that
aren't a major threat from the 5 percent
that are," says Ewald. "Ebola really isn't
one of those 5 percent."

The earliest suggestion of a Darwinian approach to medicine came in 1980,
when George Williams, an evolutionary

biologist at the State University of New
York at Stony Brook, read an article in
which Ewald discussed using Darwinian
theory to illuminate the origins of certain
symptoms of infectious disease—things
like fever, low iron counts, diarrhea.
Ewald's approach struck a chord in Williams. Twenty-three years earlier he had
written a paper proposing an evolutionary framework for senescence, or aging.
"Way back in the 1950s I didn't worry
about the practical aspects of senescence, the medical aspects," Williams
notes. "I was pretty young then." Now,
however, he sat up and took notice.

While Williams was discovering
Ewald's work, Randolph Nesse was discovering Williams's. Nesse, a psychia-
trist and a founder of the University of
Michigan Evolution and Human Behavior Program, was exploring his own interest in the aging process, and he and
Williams soon got together. "He had
wanted to find a physician to work with
on medical problems," says Nesse, "and
I had long wanted to find an evolutionary
biologist, so it was a very natural match
for us." Their collaboration led to a 1991
article that most researchers say signaled
the real birth of the field.

NESSE AND WILLIAMS DEFINE
Darwinian medicine as the hunt for evolutionary explanations of vulnerabilities
to disease. It can, as Ewald noted, be a
way to interpret the body's defenses, to
try to figure out, say, the reasons we feel

pain or get runny noses when we have a cold, and to determine what we should—or shouldn't—be doing about those defenses. For instance, Darwinian researchers like physiologist Matthew Kluger of the Lovelace Institute in Albuquerque now say that a moderate rise in body temperature is more than just a symptom of disease; it's an evolutionary adaptation the body uses to fight infection by making itself inhospitable to invading microbes. It would seem, then, that if you lower the fever, you may prolong the infection. Yet no one is ready to say whether we should toss out our aspirin bottles. "I would love to see a dozen proper studies of whether it's wise to bring fever down when someone has influenza," says Nesse. "It's never been done, and it's just astounding that it's never been done."

Diarrhea is another common symptom of disease, one that's sometimes the result of a pathogen's manipulating your body for its own good purposes, but it may also be a defense mechanism mounted by your body. Cholera bacteria, for example, once they invade the human body, induce diarrhea by producing toxins that make the intestine's cells leaky. The resultant diarrhea then both flushes competing beneficial bacteria from the gut and gives the cholera bacteria a ride into the world, so that they can find another hapless victim. In the case of cholera, then, it seems clear that stopping the diarrhea can only do good.

But the diarrhea that results from an invasion of shigella bacteria—which cause various forms of dysentery—seems to be more an intestinal defense than a bacterial offense. The infection causes the muscles surrounding the gut to contract more frequently, apparently in an attempt to flush out the bacteria as quickly as possible. Studies done more than a decade ago showed that using drugs like Lomotil to decrease the gut's contractions and cut down the diarrheal output actually prolong infection. On the other hand, the ingredients in over-the-counter preparations like Pepto Bismol, which don't affect how frequently the gut contracts, can be used to stem the diarrheal flow without prolonging infection.

Seattle biologist Margie Profet points to menstruation as another "symptom" that may be more properly viewed as an evolutionary defense. As Profet points out, there must be a good reason for the body to engage in such costly activities as shedding the uterine lining and letting blood flow away. That reason, she claims, is to rid the uterus of any organisms that might arrive with sperm in the seminal fluid. If an egg is fertilized, infection may be worth risking. But if there is no fertilized egg, says Profet, the body defends itself by ejecting the uterine cells, which might have been infected. Similarly, Profet has theorized that morning sickness during pregnancy causes the mother to avoid foods that might contain chemicals harmful to a developing fetus. If she's right, blocking that nausea with drugs could result in higher miscarriage rates or more birth defects.

Darwinian medicine isn't simply about which symptoms to treat and which to ignore. It's a way to understand microbes—which, because they evolve so much more quickly than we do, will probably always beat us unless we figure out how to harness their evolutionary power for our own benefit. It's also a way to realize how disease-causing genes that persist in the population are often selected for, not against, in the long run.

Sickle-cell anemia is a classic case of how evolution tallies costs and benefits. Some years ago, researchers discovered that people with one copy of the sickle-cell gene are better able to resist the protozoans that cause malaria than are people with no copies of the gene. People with two copies of the gene may die, but in malaria-plagued regions such as tropical Africa, their numbers will be more than made up for by the offspring left by the disease-resistant kin.

Cystic fibrosis may also persist through such genetic logic. Animal studies indicate that individuals with just one copy of the cystic fibrosis gene may be more resistant to the effects of the cholera bacterium. As is the case with malaria and sickle-cell, cholera is much more prevalent than cystic fibrosis; since there are many more people with a single, resistance-conferring copy of the gene than with a disease-causing double dose, the gene is stably passed from generation to generation.

"I used to hunt saber-toothed tigers all the time, thousands of years ago. I got lots of exercise and all that sort of stuff. Now I sit in front of a computer and don't get exercise, so I've changed my body chemistry."

"With our power to do gene manipulations, there will be temptations to find genes that do things like cause aging, and get rid of them," says Nesse. "If we're sure about everything a gene does, that's fine. But an evolutionary approach cautions us not to go too fast, and to expect that every gene might well have some benefit as well as costs, and maybe some quite unrelated benefit."

Darwinian medicine can also help us understand the problems encountered in the New Age by a body designed for the Stone Age. As evolutionary psychologist Charles Crawford of Simon Fraser University in Burnaby, British Columbia, put it: "I used to hunt saber-toothed tigers all the time, thousands of years ago. I got lots of exercise and all that sort of stuff. Now I sit in front of a computer, and all I do is play with a mouse, and I don't get exercise. So I've changed my body biochemistry in all sorts of unknown ways, and it could affect me in all sorts of ways, and we have no idea what they are."

Radiologist Boyd Eaton of Emory University and his colleagues believe such biochemical changes are behind today's breast cancer epidemic. While it's impossible to study a Stone Ager's biochemistry, there are still groups of hunter-gatherers around—such as the San of Africa—who make admirable stand-ins. A foraging life-style, notes Eaton, also means a life-style in which menstruation begins later, the first child is born earlier, there are more children altogether, they are breast-fed for years rather than months, and menopause comes somewhat earlier. Overall, he says, American women today probably experience 3.5 times more menstrual cycles than our ancestors did 10,000 years ago. During each cycle a woman's body is flooded with the hormone estrogen, and breast cancer, as research has found, is very much estrogen related. The more frequently the breasts are exposed to the hormone, the greater the chance that a tumor will take seed.

Depending on which data you choose, women today are somewhere between 10 and 100 times more likely to be stricken with breast cancer than our ancestors were. Eaton's proposed solutions are pretty radical, but he hopes people will at least entertain them; they include delaying puberty with hormones and using hormones to create pseudopregnancies, which offer a woman the biochemical advantages of pregnancy at an early age without requiring her to bear a child.

In general, Darwinian medicine tells us that the organs and systems that make up our bodies result not from the pursuit of perfection but from millions of years of evolutionary compromises designed to get the greatest reproductive benefit at the lowest cost. We walk upright with a spine that evolved while we scampered on four limbs; balancing on two legs leaves our hands free, but we'll probably always suffer some back pain as well.

"What's really different is that up to now people have used evolutionary theory to try to explain why things work, why they're normal," explains Nesse. "The twist—and I don't know if it's simple or profound—is to say we're trying to understand the abnormal, the vulnerability to disease. We're trying to understand why natural selection has not made the body better, why natural selection has left the body with vulnerabilities. For every single disease, there is an answer to that question. And for very few of them is the answer very clear yet."

One reason those answers aren't yet clear is that few physicians or medical researchers have done much serious surveying from Darwin's viewpoint. In many cases, that's because evolutionary theories are hard to test. There's no way to watch human evolution in progress—

at best it works on a time scale involving hundreds of thousands of years. "Darwinian medicine is mostly a guessing game about how we think evolution worked in the past on humans, what it designed for us," say evolutionary biologist James Bull of the University of Texas at Austin. "It's almost impossible to test ideas that we evolved to respond to this or that kind of environment. You can make educated guesses, but no one's going to go out and do an experiment to show that yes, in fact humans will evolve this way under these environmental conditions."

Yet some say that these experiments can, should, and will be done. Howard Howland, a sensory physiologist at Cornell, is setting up just such an evolutionary experiment, hoping to interfere with the myopia, or nearsightedness, that afflicts a full quarter of all Americans. Myopia is thought to be the result of a delicate feedback loop that tries to keep images focused on the eye's retina. There's not much room for error: if the length of your eyeball is off by just a tenth of a millimeter, your vision will be blurry. Research has shown that when the eye perceives an image as fuzzy, it compensates by altering its length.

This loop obviously has a genetic component, notes Howland, but what drives it is the environment. During the Stone Age, when we were chasing buffalo in the field, the images we saw were usually sharp and clear. But with modern civilization came a lot of close work. When your eye focuses on something nearby, the lens has to bend, and since bending that lens is hard work, you do as little bending as you can get away with. That's why, whether you're conscious of it or not, near objects tend to be a bit blurry. "Blurry image?" says the eye. "Time to grow." And the more it grows, the fuzzier those buffalo get. Myopia seems to be a disease of industrial society.

To prevent that disease, Howland suggests going back to the Stone Age— or at least convincing people's eyes that that's where they are. If you give folks with normal vision glasses that make their eyes think they're looking at an object in the distance when they're really looking at one nearby, he says, you'll

avoid the whole feedback loop in the first place. "The military academies induct young men and women with twenty-twenty vision who then go through four years of college and are trained to fly an airplane or do some difficult visual task. But because they do so much reading, they come out the other end nearsighted, no longer eligible to do what they were hired to do," Howland notes. "I think these folks would very much like not to become nearsighted in the course of their studies." He hopes to be putting glasses on them within a year.

THE NUMBING PACE OF EVOlution is a much smaller problem for researchers interested in how the bugs that plague us do their dirty work. Bacteria are present in such large numbers (one person can carry around more pathogens than there are people on the planet) and evolve so quickly (a single bacterium can reproduce a million times in one human lifetime) that experiments we couldn't imagine in humans can be carried out in microbes in mere weeks. We might even, says Ewald, be able to use evolutionary theory to tame the human immunodeficiency virus.

"HIV is mutating so quickly that surely we're going to have plenty of sources of mutants that are mild as well as severe," he notes. "So now the question is, which of the variants will win?" As in the case of Ebola, he says, it will all come down to how well the virus manages to get from one person to another.

"If there's a great potential for sexual transmission to new partners, then the viruses that reproduce quickly will spread," Ewald says. "And since they're reproducing in a cell type that's critical for the well-being of the host—the helper T cell—then that cell type will be decimated, and the host is likely to suffer from it." On the other hand, if you lower the rate of transmission—through abstinence, monogamy, condom use—then the more severe strains might well die out before they have a chance to be passed very far. "The real question," says Ewald, "is, exactly how mild can you make this virus as a result of reducing the rate at which it could be transmitted to new partners, and how long will it take for this change to occur?" There are already strains of HIV in Senegal with such low virulence, he points out, that most people infected will die of old age. "We don't have all the answers. But I think we're going to be living with this virus for a long time, and if we have to live with it, let's live with a really mild virus instead of a severe virus."

Though condoms and monogamy are not a particularly radical treatment, that they might be used not only to stave off the virus but to tame it is a radical notion—and one that some researchers find suspect. "If it becomes too virulent, it will end up cutting off its own transmission by killing its host too quickly," notes James Bull. "But the speculation is that people transmit HIV primarily within one to five months of infection, when they spike a high level of virus in the blood. So with HIV, the main period of transmission occurs a few months into the infection, and yet the virulence—the death from it—occurs years later. The major stage of transmission is decoupled from the virulence." So unless the protective measures are carried out by everyone, all the time, we won't stop most instances of transmission; after all, most people don't even know they're infected when they pass the virus on.

But Ewald thinks these protective measures are worth a shot. After all, he says, pathogen taming has occurred in the past. The forms of dysentery we encounter in the United States are quite mild because our purified water supplies have cut off the main route of transmission for virulent strains of the bacteria.

Not only did hygienic changes reduce the number of cases, they selected for the milder shigella organisms, those that leave their victim well enough to get out and about. Diphtheria is another case in point. When the diphtheria vaccine was invented, it targeted only the most severe form of diphtheria toxin, though for economic rather than evolutionary reasons. Over the years, however, that choice has weeded out the most virulent strains of diphtheria, selecting for the ones that cause few or no symptoms. Today those weaker strains act like another level of vaccine to protect us against new, virulent strains.

"We did with diphtheria what we did with wolves. We took an organism that caused harm, and unknowingly, we domesticated it into an organism that protects us."

"You're doing to these organisms what we did to wolves," says Ewald. "Wolves were dangerous to us, we domesticated them into dogs, and then they helped us, they warned us against the wolves that were out there ready to take our babies. And by doing that, we've essentially turned what was a harmful organism into a helpful organism. That's the same thing we did with diphtheria; we took an organism that was causing harm, and without knowing it, we do-

mesticated it into an organism that is protecting us against harmful ones."

Putting together a new scientific discipline—and getting it recognized—is in itself an evolutionary process. Though Williams and Neese say there are hundreds of researchers working (whether they know it or not) within this newly built framework, they realize the field is still in its infancy. It may take some time before *Darwinian medicine* is a household term. Nesse tells how the editor of a prominent medical journal, when asked about the field, replied, "Darwinian medicine? I haven't heard of it, so it can't be very important."

But Darwinian medicine's critics don't deny the field's legitimacy; they point mostly to its lack of hard-and-fast answers, its lack of clear clinical guidelines. "I think this idea will eventually establish itself as a basic science for medicine, " answers Nesse. "What did people say, for instance, to the biochemists back in 1900 as they were playing out the Krebs cycle? People would say, 'So what does biochemistry really have to do with medicine? What can you cure now that you couldn't before you knew about the Krebs cycle?' And the biochemists could only say, 'Well, gee, we're not sure, but we know what we're doing is answering important scientific questions, and eventually this will be useful.' And I think exactly the same applies here."

Lori Oliwenstein, a former DISCOVER senior editor, is now a freelance journalist based in Los Angeles.

Kansas Recants

By Leon Albert

As the Kansas Board of Education has just reversed its ban on the teaching of evolution, and mandated that the teachers of the state expose their students to a theory which scientists virtually universally consider to be the back-bone idea underlying all of biology and its diverse branches, from anatomy through microbiology to zoology, we are confronted with an apparent basic paradox in American culture. The paradox is also reflected in the comment of the leader of the creationist bloc on the Board who explained that they, the creationists, "want to teach the controversy. That evolution may not be the be-all and end-all."

This comment indicates both a deep lack of awareness of the nature of science and a correspondingly deep fear of the threat presented to popular religion by science. Ignorance of science is nowhere more evident than in the popularity of the belief in biblical creationism. Polls show that nearly 40% of Americans say they believe in strict biblical creationism. This widespread belief inspired not only the Kansas Board's original outlawing of the teaching of evolution, it is also behind similar efforts to, at least, undermine the scientific legitimacy of evolution in the schools of a number of other states.

The underlying paradox is that, while we pride ourselves on our advanced, scientifically based technology (indeed our lives would be unimaginably altered without it), the vast majority of the citizenry remains abysmally ignorant of not only basic scientific knowledge, but also, more importantly, the very ABC's of the scientific approach to understanding the world. One end result of this ignorance is that as science has increasingly described a reality that conflicts

with the emotionally comforting certainties of popular religious mythology, we have seen the development of an American love-hate relationship with science.

This "schizoid" view (I here intentionally use the term in the mistaken popular sense of a combination of opposites) of science is dramatically and symbolically reflected in the very name of the most vocal, and most organized of the various anti-evolutionist movements. It is located in Southern California (those living elsewhere in the world may now give vent to the obligatory, "Where Else?"), and likes to consider itself the "think-tank" of what has become known as the "young earth creationism" movement. This is the Institute for Creation Research (ICR), affiliated with Christian Heritage College, which is an outgrowth from fundamentalist Christianity. They identify their movement with the oxymoron, "Scientific Creationism," which is a name change that came about with their realization that a little document called the Constitution would prevent them from getting their religious doctrine taught in public schools as long as they called it by its original designation, "biblical creationism." I call the revised name, "scientific" creationism, an oxymoron because one of the defining characteristics of the scientific approach to understanding the world is that scientific explanations cannot use any appeal to supernatural beings, as the existence and actions of such beings are beyond the capacity of science to disprove. A divine creator is the ultimate supernatural being, Thus, the phrase, "scientific creationism" is an obvious contradiction in terms.

Unfortunately for them, this name-changing tactic has not worked as hoped,

at least in the courts, which have regularly recognized that laws mandating the teaching of "scientific" creationism are in fact based in a sectarian religious doctrine. Thus the shift in tactics to pushing their thinly disguised religious ideology/ "science" through state and local school boards rather than through the passing of laws. School boards, being made up of ordinary citizens, rather than judges who must consider such "technicalities" as the U.S. Constitution, are more easily swayed by popular prejudices. Indeed, if fundamentalists themselves can gain a majority on a school board, they will even eagerly use public funds to finance the expensive legal defense of their religiously motivated decisions regarding the teaching of evolution and the advocacy of creationism. Such school board decisions on behalf of creationism do regularly suffer legal reversals, at least in the higher courts. But, as conservatives generally undergo a dramatic change in their principled opposition to judicial social engineering when they are in power, it remains to be seen whether the current trend of judges reversing religiously based school board decisions will continue.

The thinness of the semantic façade of the designation, "scientific creationism" is so embarrassingly obvious that more intellectually aware creationists have, in recent years, undergone a further metamorphosis in terms of their self-designation. They now euphemistically refer to themselves as advocates of "intelligent design." The apparently unconscious hope is that such an exercise in "word-magic" will prevent anyone, including scientists, from noticing that Intelligent Designer=Creator, and that thus, their version of creationist "theory" may thereby claim scientific legitimacy. Failing this, intelligent design advocates are pushing to redefine science in such a way that supernatural-based explanations are acceptable within science. Here, the implicit hope, apparently, is that nobody will notice that by means of this Orwellian newspeak, the new "science" will no longer be science.

As is evident from the preceding, when emotions are aroused, reason rapidly becomes their servant, and for many, the subject of our origins has become the focal point of a variety of deeply felt social and personal concerns. The more extreme biblical creationists and their legally sanitized clones, the "scientific" creationists, argue that if we think we came from animals, we will behave like animals. They trace an army of what they see as modern evils to the influence of satanically inspired evolutionary thinking. This is, of course utter nonsense. Evil existed in the world long before the concept of evolution was even a glimmer in the mind of Darwin. And Darwin himself, the very architect of the theory, was virtually the ideal of the proper, staid, English gentleman.

If reason were the driving force of biblical creationism, then, when Steve Abrams, the above referred-to leader of the Kansas creation-bloc, contended that they were only concerned with teaching the controversial idea that evolution may not be the be-all and end-all, the obvious inference would be that he and his fellow creationists consider it a basic educational principle to teach such "controversy" regarding core knowledge in virtually every educational field.

But creationists do not advocate the teaching of controversial ideas that question basic core knowledge in fields *other than biology*. They don't advocate introducing controversial astrological concepts, or the controversial idea of geocentrism, in astronomy classes. They don't suggest that psychology students should be exposed to the controversial idea that mental disturbances may be due to hexes or witchcraft (although witches are mentioned in the Bible and belief in them was central to Christianity in the past). And do any creationists give even a passing thought to the idea that in their own fundamentalist schools it would be

good educational policy to require all students to have extensive exposure to the controversial idea that the Bible is simply nothing more than the mythology of Western culture with no more basis in reality than any of a thousand other mythologies? Of course not. This is not to say that creationists are engaged in a massive exercise in hypocrisy, at least not conscious hypocrisy. Abba Eban once said something to the effect that while man is the only creature capable of reason, he appears to resort to it only when all else fails. Let's be kind, and simply say that the creationists have suffered a failure of reason in the service of what they believe to be a good cause.

Science also sees itself as advocating a good cause. It is a way of explaining reality, at least the reality that we can observe. It is an approach that is in some ways simply an extension of ordinary reasoning. But, in other ways it is dramatically unlike the way most people try to understand things. A major problem, that is an outgrowth of general lack of knowledge about the nature of science, is that there are various conflicts between the popular image of what science is, and what science actually is.

Probably one of the most widespread misconceptions about science, one that is also most relevant to the current issue of the theory of evolution, concerns the relationship between facts and theories. Many, especially creationists, mistakenly think that facts and theories are in some basic way opposed to each other in science. For example, people commonly speak of facts "versus" theories, and they say, "Evolution is only a theory." While in popular language the word, "theory" often denotes a fuzzy kind of guess or hunch, with little relationship to reality, let alone to the "facts," in science, theories and facts are actually practically inseparable from one another. Facts are used to test theories, and theories are created to explain facts by interrelating them to one another in terms of theoretical forces and entities.

In sharp contrast to modern science, creationist thought, and indeed much of popular thought, is mired in a conception of science that can be traced back to the thinking of the early seventeenth century philosopher, Francis Bacon. Writing be-

fore even the term "science" had been coined, when what we now call scientists were known as "natural philosophers," Bacon frowned on the creation of hypotheses and theories, and restricted natural philosophy/science to just the observation of facts. By the time of Darwin, it had long been realized that the mere collection of observable facts was an empty enterprise. One could endlessly describe every grain of sand on a beach but it would explain nothing. Darwin himself made a comment in one of his notebooks to the effect that he could not understand how anyone could make observations without a theory in mind. Modern science is grounded in the construction of, and the testing of theories.

Testing is thus also a key element in the scientific enterprise. It is so key that science will not even consider a theory that is not, at least in principle, testable. To test a theory is to subject it to possible disproof or, to use the scientific term, falsification. This reflects another important difference between the popular misconception of science and science as it actually is. Scientists do not devote their time primarily to *proving* their theories. The concept of proof is more at home in the non-empirical science of math. No theory in the empirical sciences can be proven in the absolute sense of a mathematical certainty. Rather than proving their theories, scientists seek evidence that supports them. And, rather than proving their theories, scientists devote great energy to *disproving* them. When an individual scientist comes up with a new theory, his/her first obligation is to try to falsify it in every possible conceivable way. Only after failing to disprove the theory, does he/she submit it to the relevant scientific journal. Why?... So that all the other scientists in that specialty can exercise their critical-skeptical thinking skills to tear it apart, to falsify it. This is one of the primary functions of scientific journals.

The theory of evolution has survived such a firestorm of critical attacks for over a century and a half now. The theory of biblical creation has *not* survived scientific criticism for two reasons, a minor one and a major one. The minor reason relates to the testing of the major observable implications of that theory, that is, a relatively young age for the earth (10,000 years or so at most, as determined by estimations of the ages of the biblical patriarchs in the so-called "begats"), and the occurrence of a worldwide flood (Noah and the Ark). The evidence overwhelmingly points to a 4 to 4.5 billion year old earth. A world-wide flood of only slightly less than 10,000 years ago would leave massive evidence. Not the slightest evidence of such a flood has been found (this is not to say that there's no evidence of strictly local floods at diverse times and places). Creationists try to argue against this virtually universal rejection of a young earth and a flood through various forms of special pleading and appeals to ambiguous isolated alleged "anomalies."

The *major* reason why the theory of biblical creation has not survived any firestorm of scientific scrutiny is simply because it is impossible to submit it to such critical testing. Its sole causative agent, a supernatural being, is beyond testing, beyond disproof, beyond falsification. Whenever a scientist points to one of the many, many problems in the biblical creationist "explanation," *e.g.*, how did all those pairs of creatures on the Ark manage to disperse to their current locations, the creationist can simply invoke one un-testable supernatural intervention after another Biblical creationism and its various euphemistic reincarnations, "scientific" creationism, and intelligent design theory simply don't qualify as legitimate scientific theories. They cannot be taught in any class that purports to be a biological science

class. They could be offered in classes in comparative religion, or possibly in a class on comparative philosophy, or maybe even in a class on current social issues, but not in a biological science class.

Another recent tactical maneuver utilized by creationists to get creationism through the back door of the science class room is to sneak it in under yet another euphemistic title, "Evidences Against Evolution." The content remains the same. Here we see the same logic that drives most creationist argumentation: if we can demonstrate that evolution is false, creationism wins by default, because it's the only alternative. This logic ignores the fact that the creationists' standard armory of arguments against evolution have repeatedly been shown to be fallacious. Also ignored in this logic is the fact that, despite their co-opting of the term "creationism," there are in fact hundreds of different creationists mythologies in a wide diversity of religious traditions. Most importantly, this logic ignores the fact that even in the unlikely event that evolution were to be falsified, this would not justify the acceptance of *any* supernatural theory as its replacement. Science, when confronted with unexplained phenomena is permitted to say, "We don't know how or why, at least for now. We anticipate and hope that an explanation in terms of the operation of natural forces and process will eventually be formulated. Meantime, we humbly confess our ignorance."

Such willingness to admit ignorance, especially about issues considered im-

portant, is yet another important difference between science and the average person's mode of reasoning. The average person is perfectly willing, indeed eager, to fill in such gaps in knowledge with supernaturally based "explanations." This results in a "God of the gaps" form of simplistic folk theology that more sophisticated religious thinkers reject because it puts religion in a state of perpetual retreat as each advance in naturalistic scientific knowledge and understanding fills in yet another gap, discrediting the supernatural explanations. Thus natural forces such as gravity replaced the angels pushing the planets about. Microbes replaced demons to explain sickness. The diversity of life forms, their adaptations to their environments, their extinctions, their fossil record, and even their geographic distribution, as well as a seeming infinity of various other aspects of biology, previously not even addressed, let alone "explained," as the result of God's direct actions, are now understood in terms of the theory of evolution through natural selection. Phenomena such as the apparently designed nature of the way in which life forms were adapted to their environments were cited as major evidence of a grand designer in one of the classic arguments for the existence of God. Darwin's removal of God from the explanation of a diversity of phenomena also removed the existence of those phenomena as evidence of God's existence. Is it any wonder that this has triggered ongoing, religiously-based, deep emotional resistance to the theory of evolution?

An original document written by Leon Albert and published by McGraw-Hill/Dushkin for Annual Editions: Physical Anthropology 2002/2003. Reprinted by permission.

Index

Index

Folsom people, of North America, 182, 185
forensic anthropology, 202–206
Fossey, Dian, 37–40
fossils, controversy over Kennewick Man and, 179–186; dating of, 135–136, 159–163; evolution and, 3, 5, 9; of hominids, 124–127, 128–131
founder effect, 17
France, cave art in, 149–151, 152–153
friendship, among East Africa baboons, 32–36

G

Gabunia, Leo, 140, 142, 143
Galileo, 2, 3
Gardner, Allen, 43–44
Gardner, Trixie, 43–44
Gatliff, Betty Pat, 204
Gaucher's disease, 19
genetic drift, 10, 17
giant hyenas, 146–147, 148
gibbons, 89–90
G[&subscript]M2[&stop] ganglioside, Tay-Sachs disease and, 17, 18
Goodall, Jane, 29, 46, 47, 53, 55, 57, 108; on minds of chimpanzees, 41–45
gorillas, 89; Dian Fossey and, 37–40
Gould, John, 5
grandmothers, 101–103
gravity, 3
great chain of being, 2, 3
Grim, Clarence, 24, 25
Guinier, Lani, 188–189

H

Hadza people, 101
Haile-Selassie, Yohannes, 118, 119, 122
hair, race and, 194
Haldane, J. B. S., 9
hanta virus, 208
Haraway, Donna, 81
Hawkes, Kristen, 84, 101
height, plasticity and, 196–199
hexosaminidase, 17, 18
HIV, 41, 56, 207, 208; natural selection and, 214
hominids: dating fossils and, 159–163; language of, 154–158; as scavengers, 128–131
Homo erectus, 123, 134–137, 140–143, 144–148, 160, 193–194
Homo ergaster, 136–138, 140
Homo habilis, 130, 136, 138, 160
homozygotes, 16–20
Hooker, Joseph, 6
horse jumps, 150–151
Howell, Clark F., 124
Hrdy, Sarah Blaffer, 78–81, 106
Hubbard, Ruth, 79
Humphrey, Nicholas, 29–31
hunter-gatherers, 128–131, 209
hunting, cooperative, by chimpanzees, 53–56, 57–59
Hutton, James, 3
hyenas, 146–147, 148
hypertension, blacks and, 21–25

"hypothetico-deductive" method, 8

I

imitation, great apes and, 50
inbreeding depression, 77
infants, adult males and primate, 34–35
Institute for Creation Research (ICR), 216
intelligence, of chimpanzees, 28–31, 68–70
intelligent design, 216–217
isolation, evolution and, 10
Ivey, Paula, 82

J

Jantz, Richard, L., 181, 182–183
Java Man. *See Homo erectus*
jealousy, among baboons, 35–36
Jelderks, John, 182, 186
Jews, Tay-Sachs disease and, 16–20, 192
Johanson, Donald C., 114
Johnson, Floyd, 179, 180
Jones, Nicholas Blurton, 84, 101
Jones, Rhys, 161–162
Justus, Antje, 140, 142, 143

K

Kachigan, Sam Kash, 78, 81
Kansas Board of Education, biblical creationism and, 216–218
Kanzi, 65, 66
Kennedy, John F., 204
Kennewick Man, 179–187
killer whales, 90–91
Klein, Richard, 138
!Kung san, 84

L

laboratories, chimpanzees and, 67
language, chimpanzees and, 65–67
language training, development of chimpanzees and, 41–45
larynx, 155
Laslar, Gabriel, 196
laws, theory of evolution and, 13
Leakey, Louis, 42, 43
Leakey, Mary, 113
Leakey, Meave, 120–122; on evolution of human bipedalism, 113–117
Legionnaire's disease, 207, 208
Leroi-Gourhan, André, 149–150
Lieberman, Philip, 155
life expectancy, child care sex roles and, 91–94
Linneaus, 188–189, 191
Lordkipanidze, David, 140, 143
Lou Gehrig's disease, 198, 207, 208
Lovejoy, C. Owen, 118, 119–120, 122, 126
Lucy, 69, 114, 124–125, 137
Lyell, Charles, 4, 6, 8
Lyme disease, 208
lysosome, 17

M

mad cow disease, 208
malaria, 21, 192
Malthus, Thomas, 5, 7
Man-Eating Myth, The (Arens), 174
manipulation hypothesis of Hrdy, 80
marmosets, 83, 93
Mayans, height and, 197–198
Mayr, Ernst, 10
McCurdy, Elmer J., 205
Mediterranean race, 189
Mendel, Gregor, 9
Mengele, Josef, 205
menopause, 99–103
menstruation: natural selection and, 213; as women's curse, among Dogon people, 95–98
Millennium Man, 119, 122
Milton, Katherine, 75, 76
Minthorn, Armand, 181, 182, 185
miscegenation laws, 188
missing link, 134
Mittermeier, Russell, 73, 74, 77
Mongoloid race, 191, 192, 194, 195
monkeys: cooperative hunting of colobus, by chimpanzees, 57–59; sexual behavior of muriqui, 73–77. *See also* primates
Morgan, Thomas Hunt, 9, 10
mothers, cooperative breeding and, 82–87
muriqui monkeys, sexual behavior of, 73–77
mutations, 9–10
mythograms, cave art as, 149–150

N

National Institute of Child Health and Human Development (NICHD), study of day care by, 85–86
Native American Graves Protection and Repatriation Act (NAGPRA), Kennewick Man and, 179–187
natural selection, 2–11, 14; genetic diseases and, 16–20, 21–25, 212–215; race and, 193. *See also* evolution
natural theology, 3
natural-fertility population, 95, 97
Neanderthals: cannibalism of, 163–165; interbreeding between humans and, 164–172
Negroid race, 192, 194, 195
Nesse, Randolph, 212–213, 215
Niemann-Pick disease, 19
Nishida, Toshisada, 30
Nordic race, 189
noses, race and, 194

O

O'Connell, James, 84, 101
Olsen, Sandra, 150–151
Omran, Abdel R., 208–209
orangutans, 89
Origin of Species, The (Darwin), 2–11
Orrorin tugenensis, 119, 122
Owen, Richard, 9
Owsley, Douglas, 180, 181, 182–183, 186
owl monkeys, 90, 92

We Want Your Advice

ANNUAL EDITIONS revisions depend on two major opinion sources: one is our Advisory Board, listed in the front of this volume, which works with us in scanning the thousands of articles published in the public press each year; the other is you—the person actually using the book. Please help us and the users of the next edition by completing the prepaid article rating form on this page and returning it to us. Thank you for your help!

ANNUAL EDITIONS: Physical Anthropology 02/03

ARTICLE RATING FORM

Here is an opportunity for you to have direct input into the next revision of this volume.
We would like you to rate each of the articles listed below, using the following scale:

1. **Excellent: should definitely be retained**
2. **Above average: should probably be retained**
3. **Below average: should probably be deleted**
4. **Poor: should definitely be deleted**

Your ratings will play a vital part in the next revision.
Please mail this prepaid form to us as soon as possible.
Thanks for your help!

RATING	ARTICLE	RATING	ARTICLE
	1. The Growth of Evolutionary Science		40. Profile of an Anthropologist: No Bone Unturned
	2. Darwin's Influence on Modern Thought		41. The Viral Superhighway
	3. Curse and Blessing of the Ghetto		42. Dr. Darwin
	4. The Saltshaker's Curse		43. Kansas Recants
	5. Machiavellian Monkeys		
	6. What Are Friends For?		
	7. Fossey in the Mist		
	8. The Mind of the Chimpanzee		
	9. The Cultures of Chimpanzees		
	10. Dim Forest, Bright Chimps		
	11. To Catch a Colobus		
	12. Coping With Crowding		
	13. Aping Language		
	14. Are We in Anthropodenial?		
	15. These Are Real Swinging Primates		
	16. The Myth of the Coy Female		
	17. Mothers and Others		
	18. Big Brains and Parenting		
	19. A Woman's Curse?		
	20. Why Women Change		
	21. What's Love Got to Do With It?		
	22. Apes of Wrath		
	23. Early Hominid Fossils From Africa		
	24. One Giant Step for Mankind		
	25. A New Human Ancestor?		
	26. Scavenger Hunt		
	27. Erectus Rising		
	28. Doubting Dmanisi		
	29. The Scavenging of "Peking Man"		
	30. Old Masters		
	31. Secrets of the Cave's Art		
	32. The Gift of Gab		
	33. The Dating Game		
	34. Who Were the Neandertals?		
	35. Archaeologists Rediscover Cannibals		
	36. The Lost Man		
	37. Black, White, Other		
	38. Racial Odyssey		
	39. The Tall and the Short of It		

(Continued on next page)

BUSINESS REPLY MAIL
FIRST-CLASS MAIL PERMIT NO. 84 GUILFORD CT

POSTAGE WILL BE PAID BY ADDRESSEE

McGraw-Hill/Dushkin
530 Old Whitfield Street
Guilford, Ct 06437-9989

ABOUT YOU

Name   Date

Are you a teacher? ☐   A student? ☐
Your school's name

Department

Address   City   State   Zip

School telephone #

YOUR COMMENTS ARE IMPORTANT TO US!

Please fill in the following information:
For which course did you use this book?

Did you use a text with this ANNUAL EDITION?   ☐ yes ☐ no
What was the title of the text?

What are your general reactions to the *Annual Editions* concept?

Have you read any pertinent articles recently that you think should be included in the next edition? Explain.

Are there any articles that you feel should be replaced in the next edition? Why?

Are there any World Wide Web sites that you feel should be included in the next edition? Please annotate.

May we contact you for editorial input?   ☐ yes ☐ no
May we quote your comments? ☐ yes ☐ no